The History of the H.I.S.
1885–1985

THE HISTORY OF THE H.I.S.

1885-1985

100 years of the Hunters'
Improvement and National Light Horse
Breeding Society

Pamela Macgregor-Morris

THE TREMATON PRESS

Acknowledgements

The author and publishers are pleased to acknowledge the generous support of ICI Agricultural Division in the production of this book.

Grateful thanks are due to Gerald Evans and the H.I.S. office staff who were so helpful. Thanks, too, to *Horse & Hound* for assistance in obtaining photographs.

Photographic credits are as follows:

Sport & General, London (Seaward II, Burrough Hills, Viscount Knutsford); Monty (Topnotch, State Visit, Solon Morn, Maj.-Gen. Fanshawe, Maj. Sir R. Macdonald Buchanan, Lord Margadale, H.M. Queen Mother and Mr Manning); Kit Houghton Photography (Periglen, Oxford Blue, Seabrook, Beagle Bay, St James, Tony Murray-Smith); Photofinish, Sue Stevens (Blazaway); Independent Newspapers Ltd, Dublin (Lady Violet Vernon and Mrs Gibson); courtesy of the H.I.S. (Orville, Peppermill, Huguenot, Eglamor, Scarlet Rambler, Handley Cross, Game Rights, Saunter, Formula, Arch Guard, Boothby, Prince's Grace, Aldaniti); W. W. Rouch (Sporting Rights); Carol Gilson (Cuillin Hills, Elite); Godfrey New Photographics (H.I.S. bronze).

Published by

Trematon Press
Trematon Hall
Saltash
Cornwall
PL12 4RU

British Library Cataloguing in Publication Data

Macgregor-Morris, Pamela
    The history of the H.I.S., 1885–1985:
    100 years of the Hunters' Improvement &
    National Light Horse Breeding Society.
    1. Hunters Improvement Society——History
    636.1′08′86   SF293.H8

ISBN 0 9509663 1 2

Designed by David Way

Typeset in 10 on 11 point Baskerville

Printed in Great Britain by
Butler & Tanner Ltd, Frome and London

CONTENTS

---※---

Part I: The history of the Society

1   The origins of the Society   *1*
2   The problems of hunter breeding   *11*
3   The second decade's consolidation   *21*
4   The Spring Show progresses   *37*
5   Report of the Horse Supply Committee   *45*
6   Report of the Advisory Council   *63*
7   The Society in the war years   *87*
8   Between the wars   *121*

Part II: The people who made the Society

9   The Viscount Knutsford   *145*
10   The Judges   *160*
11   The stallion owners — a special breed   *182*
12   The breeders   *191*
13   The owners   *198*
14   The lady judges   *208*
15   The dealers   *213*
16   The officials of the Society   *220*
17   The professionals   *230*
18   Champion hunters since 1945   *239*
19   The 'competition horse'   *254*

Appendix I: Presidents of the Society   *259*

Appendix II: Winners of the King George V
Champion Challenge Cup   *261*

Appendix III: Winners of the Edward, Prince of Wales's
Cup for Champion Young Stock   *264*

Appendix IV: The responsibilities of judges and stewards   *266*

Index   *271*

Part I

The history of the Society

CHAPTER 1

The origins of the Society

MORE THAN 100 years later, it scarcely seems credible that, during the decade from 1863 until 1872, no fewer than 79,131 horses were imported into England. Worse still was to come, for in the next ten years, from 1873 until 1882, the figure had reached the astronomical total of 197,022. Not surprisingly, considerable concern was occasioned by these unsatisfactory, uneconomic circumstances. The estimated cost of importing the horses was between £6–7 million (or the equivalent, according to Lloyds Bank in July 1983, of £218 million today).

This was the situation when the Hunters' Improvement and National Light Horse Breeding Society came into being in 1885, with the following stated objectives:

(1) To improve and encourage the breeding of horses for hunting, riding, driving and military purposes.

(2) to give premiums at spring shows to owners of thoroughbred stallions, and thus obtain for breeders the use of sound stud horses at service fees not to exceed 50 shillings for each mare.

(3) To publish Prize Books, and use means to induce the various Agricultural societies to offer prizes for mares (and later for young stock) at their shows.

(4) To endeavour to attract public attention to a subject so important to the nation, and to spread knowledge of the principles upon which better horses may be bred.

(5) The question of horse-breeding may be regarded as of great importance, the supply of good, sizeable horses being altogether unequal to the demand. The preceding figures from the Government returns show the enormous increase in horses imported during the last twenty years.

The first show of the Society was held in conjunction with the Hackney Horse Society's show at the Royal Agricultural Hall in Islington, North London, in 1885. The judges were the Earl of Coventry, Colonel Luttrell and Mr J. Sawrey Cookson, who handled a total of 35 stallions in two classes. Class 'A' was restricted to horses not previously used at stud, while Class 'B' was for those who had. In 1887, Cassells the publishers produced, at La Belle Sauvage in London, E.C., the first Record for the Society of 141 Prize Mares that had gained honours at shows in the United Kingdom, and Thoroughbred Stallions to gain prizes, premiums and honours at the Society's shows held in London in the years 1885 and 1886.

The first class for what is now the Macdonald-Buchanan Trophy, for stallions new to the premium scheme, was won with a £50 premium by Lord Tredegar's Chevronel, a 10-year-old by Cathedral out of Cognisaunce by Stockwell. He won his first race at two, ran 10 or 12 times yearly over various distances with varying success, and when taken out of training after eight seasons his legs were as fresh and sound, it was said, as an unbroken 2-year-old. In 1885 he won prizes as a stallion at Cardiff, Cheltenham and Newport, but his career at stud was brief and ended in 1886, when he died following an accident.

Twelve stallions turned out for this class, which Vero Shaw, displaying a degree of knowledge and courage sadly denied to many of his modern equivalents, roundly declared to leave considerable room for improvement:

'At the same time', he added by way of extenuation, 'There is every reason to hope that another year, with more extended notice, the owners of this class of sire will be able to do themselves and their horses greater justice. Lord Hastings' Prince Maurice, a 5-year-old chesnut brother to Dutch Oven, by Dutch Skater out of Cantiniere, was by far the best looking. He is a grandly-topped horse, with great substance and plenty of quality.

The one-eyed chesnut, Chevronel was, however, selected for the premier honour. He is a very short-legged Thoroughbred, with great quarters and an intelligent head, but the dip of his back will not recommend him to every breeder of hunters. . . .

. . . Class 'B', for stallions that have already served mares, produced an entry of 23. Two of the best-looking horses in the class were Scot Guard and Polardine, the former the *beau ideal* of the sire for getting hunters. Eventually Mulatto, a dark bay, low, muscular type, was placed first, but subsequently disqualified as ineligible through not complying with the conditions for entry in the General Stud Book, due to the duplicity of his dam, who is said to have received equal attentions from a racehorse and a cart-horse.

Victory therefore went to the horse placed second, Mr (later Sir) Walter Gilbey's Pedometer, another of the same type though not so good in the shoulders as Mulatto despite being very well bred, by King Tom, dam Miss Peddie by Poynton.

Knight of the Laund, who was second, and is by Knight of the Garter ex May Queen by Kettledrum, is said to look common despite his breeding, while Troll, by Doncaster out of a mare by Hermit, is considered "hardly likely to get a good hunter. A very showy and bright-coloured horse, he is heavily-topped and his round, gummy forelegs are quite sufficient in themselves to account for his failure on the Turf".'

Charles Armstrong, a considerable scribe thereafter, contributed the official report on the second HIS show, at Islington on 2 and 3 March 1886:

The pleasure and advantage of sitting upon or behind a good horse are so universally recognised that the breeder has no difficulty in obtaining a long price for him; but the disappointment and disgust to the use of a bad horse are so well marked as to recoil with heavy loss upon the ignorant or luckless producer of this unprofitable class of animal. Why then, it may be asked, breed bad or commonplace animals? The answer is that the knowledge and capital necessary to breed good ones are not generally in the possession of such persons as have the occupation of the land upon which horses should be reared. Somewhat similar difficulties have long been recognised on the Continent, and large sums of public money have been annually voted for the support of what are known as Government Studs.

The HIS proposes, by various means, to produce for the United Kingdom effects somewhat similar, but superior to those in France, which result from the breeding establishments supported by Government. The extent of the good done will be regulated by the amount of support accorded by the public. With the exception of a small minority of the people, it may safely be stated that the whole world is still in profound ignorance on the subject of breeding and management of horses for pleasure. But centuries of racing have, in England and Ireland, so sharply and continuously attracted the attention of a few as to result in such an accumulation of knowledge and energy as is shown in the creation of the finest breed in the world — the Thoroughbred Horse.

To this magnificent breed all nations wisely resort; but, although horses generally may be as good as ever, and possibly better, the whole of this particular breed is not now so well adapted as it was for the especial purpose of improving the breed of hunters and harness horses. The reasons are quite plain. Our ancestors patronised long races under such heavy weights as required horses of great power and mature age to compete successfully in them. This class of racing is so much akin to carrying a gentleman in the first flight in the hunting field, or drawing his carriage a long journey at a quick pace, that the breeders of old-fashioned racehorses produced a highly beneficial effect upon the breed of all horses used for riding and driving; but since racing has been given up to the gratification of those who delight to see abused two-year-olds go for their lives in a half-mile scurry, the good effects of racing upon the breed of hunters has been seriously minimised, if it has not disappeared altogether.

To meet modern turf requirements, racehorses have been bred not for the strength and soundness required in the hunter, but for the speed alone required on the turf, regardless alike of the constitutional weakness and hereditary unsoundness which so often accompany this turn of speed. When these roarers and broken-down racehorses are no longer able to compete on the turf, they find their way into the country districts to solicit the mares of farmers at low fees, and thus naturally propagate constitutional lameness, roaring and other derangements. It is true that there are in the country some good blood stallions, but often the distance, and always the fees, are far beyond the reach of the majority of farmers. In these adverse circumstances, the farmers have as a rule been unable to breed good, paying animals and many have, through disappointment and disgust, given up breeding horses altogether, allowing the increasing demand to be met by the unsatisfactory expediency of a largely increased importation.

Mr Walter Gilbey produced a pamphlet setting forth the situation. Citing the figures for imports of horses in the 20 years from 1863 until 1882 as 276,225, he stressed that since 1882 the figures continued to show an increase. The loss of over £7 million was surely calculated to arouse the energy of home breeders, who could hardly be gratified to know that so vast a sum was being paid annually to foreigners for what they themselves might easily produce in this country. It was also an accepted fact that a very large proportion of these imported horses were of an inferior stamp; flashy, soft substitutes, not of a kind that would find a ready or profitable sale in this country, if only a sufficiency of good, typical English horses were produced to supply the demand.

In view of the enormous existing import trade, the encouragement of the breeding of horses assumed great national importance, not only for the pleasure which a good horse afforded, but from the additional security assured by the possession of a suitable supply of sound, sizeable, well-bred horses always available for military purposes.

This, then, was the situation which called into existence the Hunters' Improvement Society, determined to obtain for the use of farmers and others

3

an adequate supply of good, sound Thoroughbred stallions at a moderate fee. Those with sound, high-class mares would then have the opportunity of producing very valuable animals, while those with more commonplace mares might expect to breed sound, useful riding or driving horses, free from the mortification of spavin or roaring, or other serious, ruinous hereditary derangements.

The early liaison between the Hackney Horse Society and the HIS, which led to the holding of an annual show conjointly, was a boon to the new enterprise. The two societies did not clash in any way, and their second show, where expenses were divided equally between them, was another source of strength. So, too, was the fact that another very useful and wealthy society, the Shire Horse, held its annual show at the same venue in February, which lessened expenses when the same stalls and fittings were used by all three.

At the second show of the Hunter and Hackney Societies, under Lord Combermere, the Hon Thomas Wentworth Fitzwilliam and General Thornhill, Class 'A' (by now confined to established stallions already used at stud) was won by the Compton Stud Company's 8-year-old chestnut, Huguenot, by Lowlander out of Eurydice, by Orpheus. Charles Armstrong describes him as having a good back and loin as were ever seen, the remaining essentials of body, bone and breeding being also of the highest order. His sloping shoulders and 'general good frontage' were of similar calibre, and though some considered him to be short of muscle in his second thighs, he was generally regarded as the overall outstanding hunter in the show, well able to carry 15 stone to hounds. He won on the flat, over hurdles and fences both in England and Ireland, five times in seven starts, and would have been favourite for the 1883 Grand National but for an injury.

The most remarkable horse in the show was said to be the Duke of Hamilton's Scot Guard, by Strathconan, dam Reveillee by Rataplan. Bred by Lord Scarborough in 1877, tracing back on his dam's side to Touchstone and Birdcatcher, he was disqualified at the first show for supposed unsoundness. His owner persisted and sent him for exhibition the following year, when a panel of three veterinary surgeons could discern no hereditary unsoundness and declared him a sound horse for stud purposes.

By way of compensation, perhaps, an engraving of Scot Guard was reproduced to provide the frontispiece to the second edition of the HIS *Record*, published in 1888. He won the HIS medal on his second visit to Islington and also won at the Royal Show at Norwich. The highlight of his career on the Flat was winning the sweepstake as a 3-year-old at the Newmarket Craven meeting, but it was as a jumper that he excelled, winning the Grand Handicap at Kempton Park in 1881 and the Grand Handicap Hurdle at Sandown Park in 1882.

Pedometer, the winner by default the previous year, stood previously at Althorp when owned by Lord Spencer, and acquired a considerable reputation as a sire of hunters, prior to which he was a fair performer on the Turf; but before a panel of three died-in-the-wool fox-hunters this son of Baron Rothschild's King Tom was relegated to the silver medal of second place, the jury opining that his size, bone, knee action and colour (dark brown) rendered him more suitable for getting carriage or barouche horses than hunters. The

4

same criticism applied to Knight of the Laund, said to move like a carriage horse.

A premium horse by a Derby winner out of an Oaks winner is a *rara avis*, but such was Polardine, by Beadsman out of Regalia by Stockwell. Though getting on in years (15) and rather small, this is the sum total of criticism advanced concerning him by Mr Armstrong, who regarded the latter contingency as no obstacle to his getting big stock. The fact that his sire won the Derby is cited as no mean qualification for hunting, as no horse can win a big, long, rich race without undergoing a severity of training which may fairly be compared to the 'violence and smash' of a hunter's life. Lord Middleton's Peppermint was 'as strong as a castle, altogether a beautiful, broad-backed, short-legged blood hunter, but too small to have the reach and stride sought by first flight men'. Others were dismissed as coachy.

In one of the mare classes, 'a distinct murmur of disapproval ran through certain experts round the ring when Lorna, who had the appearance of being broken down in the suspensory ligament, resulting probably from inherent weakness', was put second. Obviously the aristocratic owners of those days took criticism of their horses like the men they were, unlike some of those who have taken their place in this commercial age. Certainly they would have known whether the criticism was justified, which is by no means always the case today.

This second show was 'a great success throughout, and a well-attended, enthusiastic meeting of the Society at the Hall became the occasion for a large accession of members to that already popular institution, the HIS'. By June, 1887, membership stood at 459.

The frontispiece to the first volume of the *Record* is an engraving of Orville, a muscular, compact stallion with excellent chest and forearms, on short legs, with a great middle piece and good back ribs, a fine, sloping shoulder and muscular neck, not too long and inclined to arch. Bred in 1799 by Lord Fitzwilliam, standing 15.2 hands high, he was by Beningborough out of Evelina, by Highflier out of Termagant by Tantrum, dam by Regulus out of the dam of Marske. Beningborough, who won the St Leger for Mr Hutchinson in 1794, was by King Fergus (by Eclipse) out of a mare foaled in 1780 by Herod out of Pyrrha by Matchem. Orville won the Doncaster St Leger for Lord Fitzwilliam in 1802. Of his descendants, Ebor won the St Leger for Mr Petre in 1817, Octavius won the Derby for Mr Ladbrooke in 1812, and Emilius for Mr Udny in 1823.

The Druid (Henry Hall Dixon, son of a cotton manufacturer, a product of Dr Arnold's Rugby and of Cambridge who contributed copiously to the sporting magazines in the middle of the last century) wrote of Orville that William Edwards declared him to be the best horse for all distances he ever rode. His lungs and courage were inexhaustible. All his stock, including half-breds, were highly thought of. His son Don Juan, put to Cleveland mares near Catterick Bridge, got some of the best coaching stock that ever went into a Yorkshire fair. Emilius, his best son, was the most successful at stud. Looking as much a hunter as a blood horse, he got some excellent hunters at Riddlesworth, where he served half-bred mares at a nominal fee and Thoroughbreds at 50 guineas. His daughters likewise were very successful at stud.

When the second *Record* was published in 1888 it was more than a hundred pages thicker than its predecessor. The number of mares registered had grown from 141 to 284; brood mares at the show were classified according to weight-carrying capacity and included classes for fillies likely to make matrons; and the stallions were classified in District classes, according to the area in which they were to travel or were based, as they are today. Not only were the results of the HIS show catalogued, but also the Royal Agricultural Society of England's Spring Show at Newcastle-on-Tyne. Thoroughbred stallion results are listed for 1887 and the 1888 Spring Show at Nottingham, in addition to the Queen's premiums offered by the Royal Commission on Horse Breeding.

It is strange to modern eyes to find listed the premiums awarded at the Royal Dublin Society Show in 1887 — sixteen of £200 each, to serve in Ireland at a fee of £1.10s. Southern Ireland was still part of the United Kingdom, many Irish members of the Society are listed and by 1903 the Earl of Dunraven was a member of the Council.

In his official report of 1887, Charles Armstrong remarked that the young Society was already recognised as a very necessary and highly useful institution, not only in respect of its attractive shows, handsome premiums and instructive prize record but more especially as the means of impressing the public with the advantages of energetic action on the part of breeders of light-legged horses. The RASE, ever ready to render great services to the public, had taken up the cue to giving £1,000 in premiums of £200 each to Thoroughbred stallions best adapted for getting hunters. Under its auspices, a grand show of some 40 stallions was held in January 1887, at Newcastle, awakening such an interest among Northern breeders as was sure to result in an immediate improvement in the young stock of that enthusiastic district.

Also in pursuance of a wholesome public opinion, created mainly by the HIS, the Government of the day proposed an annual grant of £5,000 for the purpose of improving the breed of horses in Ireland, and a further £5,000 for a similar purpose in Great Britain. The thanks of the entire community were due to Lord Ribblesdale for the trouble he had taken to collect information and keep the subject before Parliament, and to Mr Walter Gilbey for his active and permanent interest in the cause, publishing statements which proved conclusively that the importation of horses was increasing rapidly, whereas the value of general productions of home-bred horses had for years been on the decline. Inevitably, the economic conclusion was that more horses of the best type should be bred in the kingdom, and certain drafts be bought for Army purposes.

When hereditary unsoundness was eliminated from our studs, and ordinary horses superseded by those of a higher class, it was argued, there would no longer be any reluctance on the part of farmers to embark upon an enterprise which had been hazardous because of unsoundness and other remedial failures. Was it not impolitic for a leading nation to rely upon precarious importations of remounts when large tracts of land, suited to breeding horses, were making but a small return in the production of beef, mutton and grain? Every Englishman of position, who valued the security of his country, should support the HIS or otherwise assist in the great and important work of bringing about a permanent improvement in the breed of our noblest domesticated animal.

In 1887 at the third annual show, increased support brought the introduction of four classes for mares and the stallion classes were re-arranged. Five premiums worth £50 each, and a medal, were awarded; no prizes were given until every horse had been thoroughly examined by veterinary surgeons and at the time of entry each exhibitor was required to guaranteee to tenant farmers the service of 20 mares at the nominal fee of 50 shillings each.

By 1888, three short years after its inception, the HIS was firmly established. The year marked a decided advance in an extended and natural production of horses suitable for hunting, riding, driving and military purposes. The society had already done much for breeders and the public generally. Already premiums were given for mares as well as stallions.

Among the principal errors in horse breeding of the past, the Society considered the use of unsound and unsymmetrical stallions to be the most deplorable and most inevitably fatal to the success of the exercise, though it was the most controllable and remediable. No society, or even a government department, could handle all the brood mares in the kingdom, but the stallions were more readily influenced and more easily and cheaply improved.

As opinions among breeders were about equally divided as to whether the sire or the dam has the greater influence or prepotency upon the progeny, the probability was that the influence was about equally divided. Hence, if means were taken to improve one stallion, the effect would be as great as if 50 mares were improved to a similar degree; but if the male exercises the greater influence, then the improvement of the stallion was of infinitely more importance. (It is now believed that conformation, generally speaking, is passed on by the sire, and the constitution by the dam.)

The practically equal division of the influence of each parent holds good, of course, only through youth and the prime of life, but not necessarily during declining years. A very old or decrepit mare may breed a foal to a vigorous young horse, but that effort, lasting for 11 months, may be the last constitutional struggle of her life and she may not be able to meet the requisite supplement of sustenance to the foal. As it grows older it is far more like the mare than the horse, not because of her greater influence before birth but because of her shortcomings afterwards. This principle, which might apply more or less to all mammals, applies most to horses, because their work is hard beyond conception, showing itself in shortening of life and the perpetuation of diseases which would disappear with the abolition of hardship and overwork.

The RASE and the government grants made it possible to subsidise 27 sound Thoroughbred stallions, and spread them all over Great Britain to supply the requirements of farmers, at a fee as low as that of the bad or unsound stallions, which alone were available to farmers before the HIS pioneered this splendid national provision.

The Royal Show at Nottingham in 1888 may have been somewhat marred by an unusually large proportion of animals being found unsound by the Veterinary Board, but Charles Armstrong declared it to be 'The finest show of Thoroughbred stallions ever held on the face of the earth'.

In March 1888, the HIS formulated a new veterinary rule. Two years earlier, the Society asked a professor of the Royal Veterinary College to send the names of four veterinary surgeons, from which the Horse Show Committee

7

selected two to act with the professor in the examination of all animals selected by the judges for further consideration. No animal could be condemned without the signature of the professor and one other veterinary inspector.

In 1887 and 1888, however, the Society appointed each of its veterinary surgeons independently. On 8 March the President of the Royal Veterinary College wrote to the Society as follows:

Dear Sir,

I beg to submit to you the desirability of appointing a small committee to consider the question of a conference of members of the horse show societies, of exhibitors at horse shows and of veterinary surgeons.

I have very little doubt that such a body could lay down some general rules as to what deviation from natural formation, action or function shall disqualify horses from taking prizes at horse shows.

I need hardly tell you that differences of opinion between veterinary boards are not as a rule on matters of fact, but as to whether certain deviations from natural formation, action or function, especially in stallions, are to be regarded as unsoundness or not.

The time has now arrived when it is desirable to attempt a settlement of this important question.

Believe me, dear Sir, yours very faithfully,
HENRY SIMPSON

President of the Royal College of Veterinary Surgeons. To the President, Hunters' Improvement Society, Agricultural Hall, Islington, N.

The council, after discussing this letter, decided that in future their new rule should come into force, bringing with it a material change of procedure. No veterinary surgeon would be able to condemn a horse as unsound and thereby disqualify it from taking a prize, which would be beyond his jurisdiction. He would confine himself to pointing out an unsoundness, in whatever part of the body, to the judges, who alone would decide whether the horse had a prize or not.

A form had to be filled in by the examiners and handed by the stewards to the judges. It followed the lines opposite.

Great advantages, averred Mr Armstrong, would accrue from this system of reporting examinations. If 40 horses in a class present themselves before the judges, who are requested by the stewards to select the eight best sound ones, the 20 best would then be consigned to the veterinary department. If six were found to be unsound, only 14 would then, under the old system, return to the judges for final judging. Under the new code, however, all 20 would return to the judges, together with their veterinary sheets, so that the judges, guided by veterinary opinion, would be the final arbiters.

Another innovation recommended at this time, when the duties of judges were becoming more and more arduous, was for three judges to be appointed but only two called upon to work at one time, the third serving as referee in the case of disagreement. Under this system, no exhibitor would know who his judges were to be, nor judges any exhibitor.

REPORT OF THE VETERINARY INSPECTORS TO THE JUDGES.

Thoroughbred Horse No. _____

Eyes _____

Wind _____

Fore Legs _____

Hind Legs _____

Feet _____

Remarks, if any _____

_____

_____

_____

Date _____ 188

Certain influential members wished the Society to promote the breeding of high-stepping carriage horses for fashionable use in London. There was no doubt that such a move would be financially successful, but being local rather than national it could hardly claim a position of primary importance in the programme, although perhaps one or two premiums for upstanding Thoroughbred stallions showing knee action and aristocratic appearance would create a little spirit in the breeding of high-class carriage horses for town, parade and park purposes.

It was to be clearly understood that a high-class London carriage horse was *not* the best animal for long, wearying country journeys, which were fully dealt with in the promotion of hunter breeding. A well-bred hunter made the best coach horse that goes on the road, as well as the best hack for long distances, the best military horse, the best general purpose utility horse and a useful carriage horse; at the same time, he was nothing like a showy, high-stepping London carriage horse.

In the encouragement of superior Thoroughbred stallions, the HIS claimed to have an influence upon the breeds of Hackneys and Yorkshire Coach horses, both Societies admitting stock sired by Thoroughbred stallions to their stud books; while there was a growing demand for upstanding carriage horses with some of the breeding and character of the blood horse.

The same conditions prevail today, except that for carriage horses one may substitute 'competition horse', for which non-hunting people are continually clamouring in suburban areas and in the area loosely termed South of London, demanding that German stallions should be made available in order to breed dressage horses and show jumpers who will hopefully overlook their lack of expertise in these considerable arts. The hunter of quality and substance is the best 'competition horse' of them all, as the Germans among others have proved in the 3-day-event, but they require sympathetic riding, as half of a partnership, and will not tolerate a master-and-slave relationship. Indeed, the quality hunter can also excel as a show jumper (*vide* Foxhunter, Sunsalve, Video), 3-day-event horse (Starlight, Cornishman V, Laurien, Be Fair, Goodwill, George, etc) or indeed Grand National horse (Freddie, Merryman II, Specify), as has been proved abundantly right through this century and is still demonstrably true today.

At the fourth show of the HIS, which created more interest and attracted a more numerous and fashionable attendance than had any of its predecessors, Aerides was considered to be the perfect model of a hunter stallion. Though only standing 15 hands 3 ins., he was said to be more powerful than most tall horses, with his great depth and width, standing over a lot of ground on very short legs, up to 14 stone or more over any country. Bred by Mr Leopold de Rothschild in 1883, he sustained an accident as a yearling which precluded his going into training. Tried and found to be exceptionally good by Lord Marcus Beresford, he was bought by him and sold on to the Compton Stud to stand near Gillingham in Dorset.

As 103 stallions had already contested the Queen's premiums at Nottingham, the entries dropped in 1888 from 49 to 29, but the quality was unsurpassed. The judges were Lord Combermere of Combermere Abbey, Whitchurch, Thomas Ellerby of Melton-on-the-Hill, Doncaster, and Major C. M. Studdert from Corofin, Co. Clare.

The hunter brood mare class attracted an entry of 38 of the finest matrons ever seen together in England. Only three failed to pass the vet, and most of them had made their reputation in the hunting field before retiring to stud. Two were bought by the Prince of Wales, who with the Duke of Connaught was a patron of the Society.

CHAPTER 2

The problems of hunter breeding

IN THE *Prize Record* of 1888, Charles Armstrong (whose words provide the text for most of this chapter) stated that it might not be so difficult to breed a good hunter as a good racehorse, but it is far more difficult to breed hunters than carthorses. The Shire Horse Society could be congratulated on having surmounted most, if not all, of the difficulties that confronted them in 1879, when they commenced such operations as have already resulted in the elimination of side-bones and other unsoundnesses peculiar to the heavy and hairy breeds. Successes of symmetry, power and activity had also been achieved, and consequently an increasing demand for Shire horses was making itself felt in every part of the world. The Hackney Horse Society was also doing good work in putting style and knee action within the reach of its numerous admirers.

Hunter breeding, however, was confronted with difficulties of a nature nowhere else to be found in horse breeding, nor in the production of any animal under domestication. The racehorse was extremely difficult to breed because the speed was so very killing, and its maintenance, even for one solitary minute, makes demands not only upon the limbs but upon the organs of respiration and circulation quite out of all comparison with the demands of slow work, however heavy and prolonged. Hence a racehorse should not only be sound and true-built in bone and muscle, but the mechanism of the interior must also be as near perfect as possible in every part and particular.

The breeder of the racehorse, the Shire horse, the hackney and many others enjoys the immense advantage of having both sire and dam of absolutely one and the same type, but the bewildered hunter-breeder must wander through the mental mazes of mixing two opposites to produce the happy mean. Most people agreed that at present there was no possible hunter stallion except the Thoroughbred (nor, for most people, is there yet, 95 years later): and a large majority preferred a hunter with a stain in the pedigree of his dam. Very few Thoroughbreds were sufficiently strong to carry an upstanding Englishmen through the slough of February, so consequently strength was sought either in the active and handsome cart mare, whose quick step and prick-ears would indicate that one must not crack the whip over her: or in the light draught mare, who earns her daily keep on the farm and also breeds a horse of general utility: or else, according to the third school, the hunter must be bred from a mare who was herself qualified by being regularly in the first flight, following hounds over a fast and formidable country.

This very difference of opinion was an additional difficulty in the policy and programme of the HIS, and of other bodies no less anxious to do something to improve the general run of riding, driving and military horses.

Another important and relevant fact should not be overlooked. Had the shire stallion been put to heavy work as a gelding, he would have done it neither better nor worse than his parents or progeny or other relatives. Could the same be said of the hunter sire, bred for speed rather than strength, from parents which had shown their excellence on the turf, but never proved themselves capable of withstanding long journeys or long days in deep going? The Thoroughbred is a horse to admire, and there was at present no other hunter stallion, but the fact that he was bred for racing, and not necessarily adapted for hunting, was an important factor in hunter breeding and consequently another difficulty in the rugged path of the Hunters' Improvement Society.

Charles Armstrong then uttered the great truth about the HIS which still holds good today, and which places it apart from every other horse society (largely because of the calibre of its members of Council, most of whom are landowners and gentry). 'It cannot be too often repeated,' he said, 'that this Society came into existence not with any view of direct profit to anybody, but simply to assist in the production of sounder and better horses for hunting, riding, driving and military purposes; and success herein must necessarily result in considerable profit and advantage to the entire community, and eventually to every part of the world.'

Five annual shows had now been held since the formation of the Society, of which that of 1889 was quite the grandest, with no fewer than 94 Thoroughbred stallions. Since the abolition in 1886 of the races known as Queen's Plates, certain moneys were set free, which with a small Governmental grant, enabled the Royal Commission to dispense £5,000 a year in direct assistance to breeders. The RASE, following the initiative, also gave £650 for the same object, so the stallion owners were attracted by 25 premiums of £200 each, £4,400 given by the Royal Commission and £600 by the RASE.

The stallions having been handsomely provided for, the HIS now devoted itself to brood mares by distributing £345 in 20 premiums of £15 and 20 silver medals for a record entry of 71. It was considered most important that the farmer should recognise the desirability of securing good brood mares. A really good mare that bred good stock consistently was worth more than some of the country stallions, and often proved an important source of income to the farmer.

To become the owner of good brood mares, good hunters, or in fact anything good, the two requisite conditions were judgement and money. The Show system might not be all that could be desired, but it could not be denied that it was a valuable educational medium in a subject in which further knowledge was sorely needed; and the full attainment of that knowledge would ultimately result in the provision of very large numbers of such good horses as had hitherto been seen only in very small numbers.

What would the present important Shire Horse interest have been without the educational influences connected with its annual show? Would 10 years of existence, without shows, have enabled it to eliminate sidebones and to have become, as it now was, the exporter of the best, soundest and heaviest draught horse? The Show system was the best yet devised, a natural and logical extension of the movements of our ancestors in the improved breeding of horses.

In his *Book of the Horse*, Mr S. Sidney wrote: 'It is abundantly clear that, without any assistance from the State beyond the exportation of Charles the Second's Royal mares, and a trifling sum expended annually in King's Plates, the noblemen, country gentlemen and yeomen of England succeeded between the years of 1618 and 1700 in founding on the stock of the best British mares, by the aid of Oriental sires — Barb, Turkish, Arab, Persian — and a few Oriental mares, a breed of horses superior to either.'

Then, as now, there were writers who deplored the decline of our breed of horses, and implored the restrictive interference of the state. Even as recently as 1826, George IV recommended that the exportation of horses should be forbidden — a cry which was sometimes nowadays ignorantly repeated. Nothing but immediate national danger would justify such an unfair interference with the liberty of breeders and traders. Were it enacted tomorrow it would not increase or improve the supply for the home market, inasmuch that such curtailment of demand would immediately bring about a lessened supply.

In the reign of James II, when Turkey was a great European as well as Oriental power, the sultan obtained, by conquest or tribute, the finest Oriental horses in his armies, and certain of these found their way to England, to the great advantage and improvement of the breeds then prevailing here. Further records prove that throughout the eighteenth century the landed gentry encouraged their tenantry to improve their native stock by the use of the then well-established racing blood. Then, as now, improvements were sought in size, strength, quality and soundness.

Admiral Rous was in the habit of saying that the average height of racehorses had been raised at the rate of four inches per century; but this could hardly be substantiated, seeing that the beautiful, long, low and powerful skeleton of Eclipse, the unconquered and unconquerable, who lived in 1764, may now be measured to prove that he stood 15 hands 2 ins. He is, however, reported to be a biggish horse for that day; the average height for racehorses now (in 1899) may be about 15 hands 3 ins.

Size is a great advantage when it is accompanied by strength, quality, and soundness; but those who breed for size at the sacrifice of other good qualities will repent when it is too late.

The generality of small hunters are at a discount in the open market, and do not pay for breeding; whereas there is a large margin of profit for the breeder who is fortunate enough to combine size and power with quality. How, in the face of this well-established fact, anyone can breed from ordinary small stock seems unaccountable. There are in England many hunter stallions standing the full height of 16 to 16 hands 1 in, that also possess as much quality as the smaller horse can boast. As a model I may mention Lord Fitzwilliam's Xenophon, who stands 16 hands 1 in., and yet is built on the same short-legged lines as the beautiful little cobby Peppermint, who walks under 15 hands 2 ins.

Some like a small stallion to mate with a big, coarse mare, with a hope of getting quality from the former and size from the latter. A long and careful experience of breeding horses brings me to the conclusion that the above desiderata would not be realised more often than once in 10 foals so bred; and the natural tendency being always towards deterioration — or, more correctly, towards the unimproved jungle or prairie stock — the foal so hopefully bred from the small blood horse of quality and the coarse, sour mare of size is most likely to inherit the small limbs and other weaknesses of the horse without his quality, together with the coarse, unseemly head and other undesirable parts of the mare without her size. The successful small stallions are those descended from big stock, and there is no serious objection to the use of such horses, though I fail to see how they are better than a horse belonging to a family whose members all grow to a full 16-hand standard.

Although the importation of Arabs and other Eastern horses has played such an important part in the formation of the English Thoroughbred, that is no reason whatever for resorting again to the Arab. Having spent two centuries in a well-sustained effort to obtain size, let us not for a moment entertain the idea of a retrograde movement to a pony breed, however otherwise attractive. The idea is too preposterous to need further comment.

Let us persevere on the lines of the more recent improvements of the blood horse, the principle of which is the selection and propagation of the best performers. If sire and dam alike were asked to qualify with hounds in a quick country, there would be a ghastly weeding out, but the successful animals would form the nucleus of a great national stud that would supply the world with good hunters and other fashionable horses of general utility.

The closing years of the nineteenth century were destined to mark another revival in breeding superior horses for both fast and slow work, and for general purposes. Every pure breed, and good half-breds, received marked attention, to meet not only a growing demand but also an increasing and soundly established export trade. Upstanding horses with substance, activity and quality were sought all over the world. In 1868 4,000 English horses went for export, to the value of £200,000, in 1885 there were 6,300 worth £400,000, and in 1888 it was 13,500 to the value of £874,000. It took 17 years to double the value of horses exported, but only three years to double the value of horses exported in 1885.

In the records of the English exchequer there is an entry to the effect that on 20 December 1616 the sum of £154 was paid to Master Markham for an Arabian horse for His Majesty's own use. It is highly improbable that Markham was the first of his breed to be imported, as many Oriental horses were brought to Europe by the Crusaders, but this was the first to go on record.

From this time until 1791, when Mr Weatherby published the first edition of the General Stud Book, many Barbs, Arabians and Turkish horses had contributed in varying degrees to the creation of the British racehorse, which is now used to improve all the world's general utility horses.

During the three hundred years to which the history of the horse then appeared to be confined, the efforts of breeders had been spasmodic, accidental, unscientific, unsatisfactory and inefficient; and there was great danger that the same might be written of the current generation of breeders by the truthful historian of the 1890s. Even the great Godolphin Arabian (without whose blood no horse could then win a good race) was only allowed to cover his first mare, Roxana, because the much-vaunted stallion Hobgoblin refused to look at her.

Every breeder could recall similar incidents of accidents and chance that have produced good results. A generation earlier, Sesostris improved the hacks and hunters of Cambridgeshire, and Lancastrian those of Bedfordshire, yet they were thought nothing of at the time. Instances could be given of one solitary mare, bought cheaply and casually, breeding a superior and valuable family and laying the foundation of her owner's fortune.

That unsatisfactory element of chance is not to be found in anything like the same degree in the breeding of Shorthorns, or Southdowns, or Shires, and as disappointment is more frequent than success, the time had come for chance to yield to science in the production of the hunter, the carriage horse, the charger and the general purpose horse.

The class of horse that was then greatly in demand was the 16-hand blood hunter up to about 14 stone. He needed to be thick and strong of back and loin, with long, powerful quarters and muscular thighs, the sudden and repeated contraction of which would strain the hocks and hind legs at fast paces, long continued in heavy going, unless the hocks were well made and correctly shaped, big-boned and clean, and the hind legs good, measuring not less than about $9\frac{1}{2}$ inches around their smallest part.

Just as a large mill grinds more material than a small one, so a big-bodied horse eats and digests more food than a horse with a narrow waist, and is therefore enabled, in defiance of severe work, to maintain the thickness of his muscle, without which both strength and courage soon fail him. A horse or any other animal without a good constitution is by no means the servant of mankind, but is rather a pauper invalid on his hands, and no such horse or mare should ever be used for stud purposes. The scapula, or shoulder-blade, should be sloping, and the lower bone of the shoulder, or humerus, is all the better for being placed in a position as near the perpendicular as is possible to breed it. The neck should not be long, but the rider should sit a long way from the horse's ears and require long reins from hand to bit. The length of the frontage should be in the shoulders rather than in the neck. The crest should be firm and muscular, with the head hanging at such medium height and angle as will enable the horse to bridle well, and go firmly up to the bit. The head should be long, lean and blood-like; but the fulness of the eye, the playfulness of the ear, and the general cast and expression of countenance are more important than any particular or exact shape of the head. A small head often accompanies a small heart, and unless the latter, together with all blood vessels, be large and efficient, the horse may do hacking or harness work but he cannot be a first-flight hunter.

The forearms should be full of muscle — the elbows turning neither in nor out — the knees strong and big, and the shank clear and hard as polished ivory, and measure from 8 to $8\frac{1}{2}$ inches. If less than 8 inches the horse may break down, if more than $8\frac{1}{2}$ inches he will be slow and cumbrous. The feet should be neither too brittle nor too 'fleshy', neither too small nor too big, neither too flat nor too perpendicular. They must hold a shoe during three weeks of much exercise, including four days' hunting; and above all, they must swing clear of opposite fetlocks and all other parts. A horse that 'cuts' is at a serious disadvantage in work, and depreciation of value in the open market.

It matters little whether he be Thoroughbred or nearly so, if he can gallop on without tiring in deep going, and after his exertions drink his gruel, eat his digestible supper of hay and mash, and run out with clean, free limbs in the morning. All this list of qualifications is hereditary to a marked degree, and yet how rarely do we see a horse that comes fully up to the standard!

Manners are also hereditary, and so is every form of temper, so-called. A mare sold because she habitually ran away, bred for me a colt that also ran away with my men, and broke down in so doing; but the breaking down would be exceptional, and I should consider a restive or runaway animal very good for stud purposes. I do not, however, expect nervous riders to agree with me on this point. We now know how to civilise a wild colt in 20 minutes, whereas formerly a month was not considered too long.

Colour is an important matter. Mahogany brown is as good as any, then bay or chesnut; but greys and roans are not so saleable, and should not generally be produced.

Why has the horse exceeding 300 guineas in value not habitually been produced throughout the ninety years of the present century?

The reasons are numerous and cumulative:

(1) In the early part of the century there was no demand, and the price of such good imitations as then obtained were very low.

(2) The wars, and rumours and fears of wars absorbed the minds of all.

(3) The agricultural depression, which succeeded the peace of 1815, was severe enough to shrivel up every enterprise and to cool down every enthusiast.

(4) Later on, the supercession of coaching by the railways established the popular belief that horses would no longer be wanted.

(5) About the middle of the present century, the ambition was to grow wheat to the greatest possible extent, and grass land, woods, coppices and double-hedgerows were converted into virgin arable for the production of wheat and other grain. How many owners and occupiers have more recently regretted the loss of their green fields and pleasant and useful groves?

(6) Then the Crimean War of 1855 disturbed the balance, and wheat was for years at a high and profitable price; and the seasons were favourable to its production, and therefore encouraged farmers to plant it extensively.

(7) About 1860, beef and mutton had become very dear, and the production thereof paid better than breeding horses.

(8) The Thoroughbred stallions that have travelled the country have been often unsound, and generally unsatisfactory, yet there are no hunters worth riding but such as have derived most of their good qualities from them. But for racing, the horses of England would be as bad as they are in certain other parts of the world.

More recently, meat has become cheaper, and for various causes horses have become dearer, so that now the judicious breeder of horses can obtain more profit than the breeder of ordinary sheep or cattle.

During the last quarter of a century, every hunter worth over £50 has gradually become more difficult to find and more costly to buy. They were never so dear as in the autumn of 1889, when the trade of some dealers was much restricted, not for want of customers but because they could not find the animals. Farming has apparently seen its worst, and the general trade of the country was rapidly improving; therefore nothing could prevent a further rise in the value of good, upstanding, well-bred hunters, high-class carriage horses and officers' chargers.

The HIS had shown the way to help the farmers to the use of good sound stallions at moderate fees, and the RASE and the Royal Commissioners on horse-breeding had wisely pursued the same sound and hopeful policy. The races known as the Queen's Guineas had been abolished, and the money devoted to the more useful purposes of Queen's Premiums. (The King's prize started as a bell, was afterwards a bowl and still later a purse of one hundred guineas.) The £5,000 devoted to the placing of 22 good sound and powerful stallions in different counties, to cover fifty mares each at the low fee of £2.2s.6d., by no means supplied the national requirements but was very good, as far as it went.

It now remained for the various hunts of England, especially in the fashionable countries, to supplement the work of the Royal Commissioners by hiring or buying a good hunter stallion for the use of the farmers to whom they were indebted for the privilege of riding over their land. Hunting men would then reap the twofold advantage of conciliating the farmers and of getting better horses to ride. In unfashionable countries, where cash was short, similar duties might with great advantage devolve upon the local agricultural societies.

Assuming that ultimately a good national supply of Thoroughbred hunter stallions would be provided for the cheap use of farmers and breeders, the remaining question concerned what sort of mare should be sent to them, with a view to the breeding of a valuable class of animal? Some considered a cart mare to be ideal, and certainly Mr Walter Gilbey's commended half-bred mare, Half-a-Crown, was a good specimen of a powerful, symmetrical and useful animal; but few would imagine that either she or her progeny by a blood horse would be at all likely to be fast enough for present fashions in flying countries, where good prices were habitually given for hunters. Even supposing the three-quarters Thoroughbred and one-quarter cart mare should perform better than one might predict, one would not recommend the pursuit of cart blood for hunter breeding. Few men would have cart mares so good or so suitable as Mr Gilbey's, and his possible but improbable success might be followed by many glaring failures, bringing in their wake discouragement and loss.

Another class of brood mare was the common ride-and-drive animal of the small or old-fashioned farmer. This is no doubt the same class of animal as the Compton Stud Company refer to in the catalogue of their sale under the heading 'Selection of Brood Mares for Breeding Hunters'. They say that a mare to suit Thoroughbred stallions should be 'bony and thick, on short legs'. There is not a word about the mare's performances and ancestry, but bone and substance are evidently to come from the dam and quality from the blood horse. This style of breeding might produce a horse for the farmer's own use, but lower down the same page of the Compton Stud's catalogue is to be found the following very good advice: 'It is a great mistake for a farmer to breed a horse with no other object than that of its being adapted for his own common use only. If he breeds horses he should aim at breeding the best for the market, and if he miss that mark, the animal is then useful for common general purposes.'

The class of mare represented above is not herself a fast, good hunter and cannot gallop on through the deep, but the theory is that her foal is to get all his galloping and staying powers from his sire. It is just possible that in one case among twenty the mare might find the bone, and the horse provide heart and lungs, style and agility; but such a happy combination of the good qualities of both, with the absence and exclusion of their many shortcomings, will occur very rarely, and certainly not often enough to pay the breeder as he ought to be paid. Therefore I do not recommend breeding from this class of mare.

It is useless to breed from little light hacks, as unless of very high quality, such animals are a drug on the market, and will not pay the cost of raising. The general small animal or pony cannot be profitably bred on good enclosed rent-paying land, though the mountains of Wales and the wilds of Exmoor could not, perhaps, be better used than by producing good hardy cobs and ponies.

Having thus tried to show what not to breed from, I will give my own idea of the class of animal likely to become a profitable and successful hunter brood mare. She should be a good hunter herself, with constitution, limbs and breeding. Her height should be between 15.3 and 16.1, and below the knee she should tape not less than $8\frac{1}{4}$ inches in the smallest part. Any fault or defect she has must be expected to show itself in her stock, because her influence is certainly not less than that of the sire. My own experience is that the mare has the greater influence, but I do not wish to press this view upon others. This mare is assumed to be well-bred, but not thoroughbred, and though carrying 14 stone in a quick thing with hounds, she can hold her own against all comers. A long, slow hunting run is no test of a horse; an underbred mare can stay out all day without galloping, and go home a long journey cheerfully, but she cannot gallop even twenty minutes in mud at the pace of the modern foxhound on a good scent.

Breed from the mare that gallops in mud, stays through the run, goes home cheerfully and takes her turn regularly, and finishes the season a happy, healthy, robust, and practically sound horse; then you will rarely suffer disappointment, and may often get very valuable young animals.

During their hunting career, big mares should not be summered at grass, as they are liable to take cold and make a noise, but smaller animals may go to grass without that danger. A mare defective nowhere except in the feet is far better at grass than anywhere, but space does not permit setting out the reasons.

The last, and in many respects the best class of mare I will introduce is the strong Thoroughbred. She may not be quick enough to race, but she will be all the better hunter and brood mare. I wonder why societies and companies and wealthy sportsmen do not breed hunters wholesale from mares of this description. They can always carry the weight — indeed, the weight is not the main difficulty with hunters generally. 'It is the speed which kills the steed'; and a careful and reasonable 16-stone man on what is called a 14-stone hunter is much kinder and fairer to a horse than a wild or ignorant 12-stone rider.

Mr Herbert Spencer says that the English nation is 'uncomfortably placed in an intermediate position between two eras; and that we consequently get our practice from an age of war, and our inspiration from a newer century of commerce'.

Certain it is that as a nation we are not horsey. The real racing or steeplechasing man, the trainer, the jockey, the groom and some few owners are very smart amongst horses; so is the first-flight hunting man and, possibly, his stud groom; but these are only a few, and the large remainder of the nation may claim the inspiration of commerce, but know little about the breeding, selection and management of a hunter. Probably Hungary, and certainly Ireland are in advance of England in its knowledge of horses for quick work.

It may, therefore, be premature to suggest to commercial England the following method of breeding what will eventually be called pure-bred hunters:—

Select 14-stone, blood-like hunting mares — I care not whether Thoroughbred or nearly so — put them to horses like Silver Crown, Truefit, Blue Grass, Blue Blood, Ruddigore, Suleiman, Roswal, Knight Templar or other strong horses I could name, and then select the best of the resulting fillies and colts, and put unrelated ones together to breed hunters. Again select in like manner from the youngsters and you will gradually get a stronger and sounder animal than the racehorse, but not quite so speedy. Even the comparative failures will pay the cost, and the successes will pay a good profit.

A thousand guineas each would not be too much to give for such mares as Messrs Tattersall sold at Christmas, 1889, for the executors of the late Lord Falmouth. Not, of course, to breed hunters from the first generation, but to start a stud farm with a new pure breed on a new idea, though founded on ancient principles.

I conclude with a remark to the ordinary breeder upon the rearing of foals. Most bloodstock breeders try to get their foals to fall as early in the year as possible, so that their early competitors shall be younger, or at any rate not a month older than themselves. Hunter breeders have no such object, and the best time for an ordinary hunter foal to fall is about April, soon after which time a bite of new grass will stimulate the mare's milk, and also supplementally feed the foal at about the age when he is disposed to nibble it; and when, also, his very short neck has grown long enough to reach the ground.

As a rule, the foal gets on very well till the autumnal grazing fails both himself and his dam. Then is the time to hold out the sympathetic handful of corn and bran and other nice digestible foods, maintaining or increasing the supply throughout the first winter. The cost is very little, say a shilling a day, and on the first of May you will turn out to grass such a robust yearling as will take care of himself and do well during the next three winters at small cost, and be a far better 4-year-old than the foal that is debilitated by starvation during his first, coldest and most cruel winter.

The 1890 show, the sixth in the series, attracted a record entry of 103 Thoroughbred stallions and 109 brood mares. It was remarked that one of the drawbacks of the show system was overfeeding — as it still is today. All breeding stock should be shown rather light of flesh than otherwise. If fat they should, in Charles Parsons's private opinion, be disqualified, and he would offer more prizes for the best mares in poor condition. Fattening up for the show will cause more barrenness and abortion than any travelling, hunting or outside causes.

The same thing still prevails today. It was not long ago that I heard it said despairingly in Dublin: 'It's no good showing a horse to the English judges unless it's seventeen hands high and pig fat!'

In his report on the show in 1891, G. S. Lowe declares that the HIS may be said to have arrived at its third stage. Having started the movement to promote the breeding of riding, driving and military horses it had then handed over some of its powers to the Royal Commission on horse-breeding, and has now been working to advance the results achieved over the last seven years. The stallions are safe under the jurisdiction of the Royal Commission, but the mares and young stock are better under the auspices of the HIS, whose efforts to improve the class of brood mares had been of considerable importance, as had their efforts to induce their breeders to keep their young mares, rather than selling them off at three and four years to agents of foreign countries. This practice had been draining the country of its best blood for years.

The best type of brood mare, a Thoroughbred with more substance, had now been established and their worth appreciated. One there was whose produce in seven years had made £1,900, and though she was unique at this juncture, encouragement would bring others to the fore.

Mr Lowe concluded that the HIS had much to be proud of in the general results of the show, which was visited by Her Gracious Majesty the Queen and the Empress Frederick of Germany, while HRH the Prince of Wales made the presentation of a testimonial to Mr Walter Gilbey in token of his work towards horse-breeding generally.

The quality of the mares had now become a very marked feature and breeders had learned what a hunter brood mare should look like, for they were becoming more typical. In the young stock classes the best-conformed, and most likely to grow into money, were out of these typical mares.

The hunter must be the type of horse to breed, as if he was good enough to carry weight over a country he was worth a great deal of money, and if he failed to reach the highest echelons he may still be worth £100 as an ordinary hunter, from £50 to £60 as a harness horse or £45 as a cavalry horse.

CHAPTER 3

The second decade's consolidation

THE TENTH Spring Show of the Hunters' Improvement Society, held in conjunction with the Royal Commission on Horse-Breeding from Tuesday 6 to Thursday 8 March 1894 at the Royal Agricultural Hall, marked an important epoch in the history of its exhibitions. Since its inception in 1885, the Society had allied itself with the Hackney Horse Society in the promotion of an annual joint show, at which specimens of each breed were exhibited for prizes provided by the respective associations. In 1889 the Royal Commission on Horse-Breeding joined the show and increased the prize list by their offer of Queen's Premiums for Thoroughbred stallions.

The results can best be appreciated by the rise in entries which immediately resulted, growing from 236 in 1888 to 389 in 1889, which growth continued steadily in each succeeding year until they had reached the unwieldy total of 609 in 1893, taxing the accommodation in stalls and boxes to its utmost limits and throwing the whole programme out of gear. Membership of each Society was also increasing, with the final result that the seating became inadequate, the Hall inconveniently crowded and the Stewards and other officials impeded in the performance of the duties concomitant with the exhibition and parading of the horses in their charge.

After consideration, it was decided at the conclusion of the 1893 show to part company, the HIS and the Royal Commission holding a third week's show. It was fraught with danger, for there was no real evidence that there was sufficient interest in breeding to secure a public for the third show, after two successive weeks of Shires and Hackneys; but the 1894 proved beyond all doubt that there was indeed ample support for the experiment and that the two Societies were now in a position to develop fully their respective shows.

Large and liberal prizes were offered to every class of young stock up to five years old, each age group being divided into colts and geldings and mares and fillies, with four prizes allotted to the value of £60 for colts (£30, £15, £10 and £5) and a further £30 in the female classes, with a handsome £40 first prize. A new and much appreciated feature was the riding classes for 4- and 5-year-olds — 4-year-old mares, 4-year-old geldings, 5-year-old mares and geldings under 14 stone and over 14 stone. Sir Walter Gilbey presented two £50 challenge cups for the best young hunter and the best mare or gelding in these classes.

The total prizes offered by the HIS amounted to £830, and, with the addition of 29 Queen's Premiums offered by the Royal Commission, came to an aggregate of £5,180. Forty-six stallions (15 of them Premium stallions) accounted for the 58 prize winners. Ruddigore, with 11 entries, had the largest number of produce at the show. By Thurio out of Blood Red, by Lord Lyon — Rouge Rose (dam of the Duke of Westminster's celebrated Derby winner, Bend 'Or) Ruddigore, own brother to Royal Red, was later bought by Sir Gilbert Greenall (subsequently Lord Daresbury) and stood in the Belvoir country when he had these hounds, for the farmers to use at a nominal fee.

The judges, Mr Maxwell Angus and Mr Henry Boden, were invited to give a short report of the exhibits which came before them. They were of the opinion that the young classes were far superior to the ones for older horses, probably due to the fact that the hunting season had not yet finished, and that the better horses had been sold.

The 1895 show was judged by the Rev. Cecil Legard, who founded the *Foxhound Kennel Stud Book*, and Mr J. C. Straker of The Leases, Hexham, Master for many years of the Tynedale in Northumberland, his family pack. The entry was increased by 65, comprising 127 stallions, 36 hunter sires and colts, 99 hunter geldings and 78 mares and fillies. Havoc, a stallion by Thunderbolt out of Hubbub by Commotion. The largest number of winners (six) were bred in Ireland — as indeed is still so often the case. The judges presented the following report:

We beg to express our satisfaction at the general excellence of the exhibits.

As regards condition, the young colts and fillies, more especially the yearlings, showed unmistakable signs of the unusual severity of the winter, prolonged up to within almost a fortnight of the show.

The class for three-year-old fillies was undoubtedly the best among the young stock, showing plenty of quality combined with substance; indeed, speaking generally, this may be said all through.

We would call special attention to the fact that of the many animals sent to the Veterinary Surgeons for examination, only two cases of unsoundness, we believe, were discovered, and when we consider how many were by Queen's Premium Stallions it must prove the great advantages breeders are reaping from having the use of these *sound* sires.

The Hunters' Improvement Society may be congratulated also on the number and excellence of the horses shown in the four riding classes.

Cecil Legard
John C. Straker

Membership had now risen to 995 and the future, in ten short years, was assured.

In 1896 a section for 108 Irish mares was included, and in consequence the pedigrees and particulars of seven Old Irish sires, ranging from 1730 to 1822. The details were reproduced from service cards placed at the disposal of the editing committee by Mr J. Harold Barry of Ballyvonare, Buttevant, Co. Cork, who produced that of Merry Andrew, owned first by Sir Edward O'Brien, Bt., and secondly by George Clonchy of Cratloe, Co. Clare.

'It was from these, and such horses as these, that our old Irish mares were descended,' he told the Irish horse-breeding Commission. All details have been tabulated and the quaint phraseology of each card as far as possible retained. Bred by the Duke of Bolton, by Fox out of Bonny Lass (own sister to Lord

Godolphin's Whitefoot) by Bay Bolton. His grand-dam was by Darley's Arabian, great-grand-dam by Byerly Turk, great-great grand-dam by Taffolet Barb, her dam being by Mr Place's White Arabian, who was out of a Thoroughbred mare owned by Mr Treganvellsi. Confirmation of this pedigree is to be found on page 27, Vol. I of the *General Stud Book*.

In 1735 he won the Seven Hundred Guinea Stakes at Newmarket in April and the Thousand Guinea Stakes from twelve others in October.

In 1736 he won King's Plates at Lewes and Canterbury, after which he was brought to Ireland by Sir Edward O'Brien, Bart., and won the Subscription Plate at the Curragh in 1739.

In 1739 on May 1st. he beat Mr. Peggot's 'Infant' in a match over the Curragh for 100 Guinea Plate, and the following October won a £50 Plate at Loughrea.

In 1740 June and July, two £60 Plates at Tralee and Kilfinny, and in September, 1741 and 1742, King's Plates at the Curragh.

In 1742 April, walked over in his clothes for the Subscription Plate at the Curragh, 'nothing daring to start against him'.

Foaled in 1730, Merry Andrew stood at Assollas, Co. Clare, at a fee of Two Guineas, and 'a crown to the Groom' from 20 March to 10 August.

Then there was Cato, owned by Henry Hunt, a 16-hand bay brown horse whose card was dated 25 March 1789. Bred by Sampson Stawell of Kilbrittain, Co. Cork, he stood at Saffron Heart, near Doneraile, Buttevant, Co. Cork, at a fee of One Guinea and 2/6 each mare. By Strongbow, by Old England (son of the Godolphin Arabian) out of a mare by Forester (sire of Gustavus, Blameless, Music etc) his dam, imported from England, was bred by Mr Panton (full sister to Crab) by Sheppard's Crab, granddam Miss Partner by Old Partner. G.g. dam by Makeless (son of the Oglethorpe Arabian, G.g.g. dam by Brimmer, by the Yellow Turk. G.g.g.g. dam, Trumpet's dam, by Place's White Turk (son of Commoner), G.g.g.g.g. dam by Dodsworth (Natural Barb, foaled in England, dam importer in the time of Charles II). G.g.g.g.g.g. dam, Layton Barb Mare. Ran once at the Curragh, when he beat Governor and others.

High Flier, brown, foaled in 1784, standing 16 hands, was owned by Mr Harris and his card was dated 1 March 1784. He stood at Will's Fort, near Cork, at Five guineas Bred Mares; all others at Three Guineas, or at Ten Guineas and engage a Foal, and a Crown to the Groom. In 1791 he covered forty mares.

By Old High-Flier out of a mare by Matchem, his G. dam was by Alcides and his G.g. dam was own sister to the Duke of Cumberland's Crab, by Crab. The G.g.g. dam Fox mare, (sister to Slipby), G.g.g.g. dam Gypsy, by Bay Bolton, G.g.g.g.g. dam by Duke of Newcastle's Turk, G.g.g.g.g.g. dam by Byerl Turk, G.g.g.g.g.g.g. by Taffolet Bark, G.g.g.g.g.g.g.g. dam, by Place's White Turk, G.g.g.g.g.g.g.g. dam, Natural Barb mare. (Confirmation of above particulars will be found on pages 76 and 354 of Vol. I of *General Stud Book*.)

Performances

1789 July, 12-stone Hunters' Plate (£50) at Limerick, beating five others. August, Hunters' Plate at Ennis, beating Hazard.
October £50 race at Mallow.
Hunters' Stakes (£252) carrying 12 stone 7 lbs. at the Curragh, beating Queensberry, Mad Tom, Honest Paddy and four others.

1790 July The Six-and-Aged Plate (£50) four mile heats, beating Eliza, Scourge and Fairy Queen.
The Weight-for-Age plate (£50) four miles, beating Lovemore, Coolin and others. Both races at Cork.
The Six-and-Aged Plate, four mile heats, at Kilkenny, beating Rutland etc.
August The Six-and-Aged Plate (£50), four mile heats, £50 Plate for all ages, at Rathkeale.
September 8th, King's Plate, 12 stone, four mile heats, at the Curragh.
September 11th., Lord Lieutenant's Plate (£105), Cup Articles, four miles.

1792 July Won at Kilkenny his first heat, though broke down before he had run two miles.

Dash, Thomas Scanlan's 15-hand brown horse, foaled in 1796, card dated March 1802, stood at Manister, Limerick, at a fee of Three Guineas and a Crown for Bred Mares; all others, Two Guineas and a Crown. By Xenophon, by Turf (son of Matchem), his dam was by Smallhopes, by Scaramouch (son of Snap, out of the Godolphin Arabian mare); G. dam by Old Traveller, G.g. dam by Ancaster Starling, G.g.g. dam, Sister to Bajazet's dam, by Whitefoot, G.g.g.g. dam by Leedes, G.g.g.g.g. dam Moonah Barb Mare. (Confirmation of these details in *General Stud Book*, Vol. 1, pages 104 and 221.)

Performances

1799 King's Plate at the Curragh. He also won two '50's at Loughrea and three 50's at Rathkeale, the first day carrying 13 stone, free for any horse, four mile heats; next day 8 stone; and the third day walked over the course, no horses daring to start against hin at 10 stone. The above being certified by Mr. P. Sharky, 'sworn Judge of the Curragh.'

Merry Andrew, date of card 20 April 1804. Location: Mallow.

Fee: One Guinea and Half and Half-a-Crown to Gentlemen, and One Guinea and Half-a-Crown to Farmers.
Sire: Young Andrew, by Carpenter's Andrew, by Barry's Old Andrew.
Dam: Brown weight-carrying huntress, belonging to Mr. John Barry of Ballyvonare, by Mr. Phil Barry's Old Andrew. The latter got on a Cumberland Mare by Beavan's Original Old Andrew. Unites two crosses of Old Andrew blood.

Mr Coulthurst's Challenger, described as a 'racing Hunter', date of card 7 March 1811, was Blood-bay, with black legs, foaled 1805, height 16 hands. He stood at Dripsey Castle at Three Guineas for Half-bred mares; Blood Mares 'Five Guineas each and a Crown to the Groom'. By Diamond, his dam (bred by the late Colonel Quin, of Adare), was by Bumbrusher. G. dam, Sister to Toys.

His record was formidable. In August, 1809, at Clonakilty, he won the Weight-for-Age Hunters' Plate, and the next day but one the 12-Stone Hunters' Plate, distancing (the first heat both races) all the horses that ran against him. Soon after, Mr Coulthurst challenged the whole county of Cork to run over Mallow course, four mile heats, and across country, 12 stone each, for 100 guineas. Challenge not accepted. In July, 1810, Challenger (then but five years old) won the Heavy Stake 12-stone Hunters' Plate at Mallow, for which eleven of the highest bred and best racing hunters in Ireland were entered, beating in most superior style, without receiving a single stroke of the whip, Colonel Vandaleur's Hawthorn, by Ebony and Alaric, by Maximin, Mr Reed's Regent, by Diamond, Captain Wattle by Diamond, Walkover by Master Bagot; and Mr Croker's Richardson, by Champion. The horses Whisko, Harkaway, Orville and Orlando paid him forfeit (Calendar). This race was considered the best trial of speed and stoutness a young horse could have sustained, as all the above horses for two heats ran at him alternately, but could not for a moment distress him, so that there is every reason to suppose Challenger would have won his race at Limerick, but that he was amiss at starting (Calendar), from a relaxation of the sinews received a fortnight before, which prevented his getting proper exercise. In this state, however, he won the first heat; after the second he was quite lame, and broke down entirely, running the third a desperate race with Captain Wattle. Able to carry 14 stone with any hounds.

What a sort he must have been, and how legendary a figure with the Co. Limerick Hounds — too good, one might think, to be raced!

Last is another Merry Andrew, owned by Edmund G. Barry, a bay, foaled in 1818, card dated 22 March 1822. He stood at 'Ballyellis, near the Fair Field of Cahirmee', at 'Two Guineas and a Crown each Mare'. He was by Merry Andrew (Hunter Sire), his dam A. Beavan's Old Andrew Mare.

For the show at Islington in 1896, the Council introduced several amendments to the schedule which met with general approval, extending as they did the scope and influence of the show and particularly holding out encouragement to breeders, who then as now receive little enough. There were four innovations:

(1) The introduction of breeders' prizes in all young hunter classes.
(2) The reduction of entry fees throughout the young stock classes.
(3) An increase in all the fourth prizes.
(4) The institution of two new classes: (a) for young horses likely to make Officers' Chargers, and (b) for Officers' Chargers — horses the property of officers in the army or auxiliary forced, which had been ridden with troops, and were their accredited chargers.

Thus, exclusive of the reduction in entry fees, the Council thereby added £175 to the 1896 schedule, bringing the total amount of money in the HIS classes to £1,000. With the Royal Commission adding 29 Queen's Premiums of £150, the total value of prizes, cups and medals came to £5,350. The average entry was 307 over the previous three years.

In 1896 the weight division for the two 5-year-old classes was altered from 'under 14 stone' and 'over 14 stone' to a 15 stone line of demarcation. Havoc was again the most successful sire, his seven entries including two first prize winners, one of whom was reserve champion. The second most consistent sire was Southampton, by Hermit out of a mare by Stockwell, grand-sire to Havoc too through his sire, Thunderbolt.

Another innovation at the 1896 show was the abolition of the rule accepting a veterinary certificate, obtained privately, sent in with the entry. Now entries were all sent out by the judges for examination by the veterinary inspectors before returning for the award of prizes to those passed sound. Four horses did not pass—two for wind afflictions, one for spavin and one for cataract. Sir Henry Simpson, the senior veterinary surgeon, wrote: 'It must be a matter for congratulation by the Council that an exhibit affected with hereditary unsoundness is becoming so rare.'

Among the most successful exhibitors was a name that was to become very famous indeed—that of Bert Drage, who with his brother John had so successful a dealing business in Chapel Brampton, Northamptonshire. His 2-year-old Thoroughbred colt The Weaver finished second in its class, while Thomas Bradley's Sultan, led champion a year earlier, headed the 4-year-olds for his Lincolnshire owner.

In 1897 the most notable new departure, with the purpose of ensuring that breeders receive due credit, was a stipulation that entries would not be accepted without full pedigrees, in an effort to dispense with the description: 'Name and pedigree unknown.'

In 1899 a new regulation, of which eighteen months' notice had been given, required that all yearlings should be exhibited undocked. A new class, which still continues today under the title of Produce Groups, was introduced for three young animals in a family group, the progeny of the same premium or registered hunter sire. The In-Foal class and the class for Officers' Chargers was omitted from the schedule. Mr J. Maunsell Richardson, who won the Grand National in both 1869 and 1870 on Captain Machell's Disturbance and Reugny respectively, and was married to the widow of the third Earl of Yarborough, judged the ridden hunters and reported: 'I consider the riding classes over four years old were decidedly good, but the four-year-old fillies very moderate and backward in condition. Four-year-old colts were far better in every detail. I know the show must be held early in the Spring, on account of locating the stallions, but in my opinion this early period for young horses rather curtails the number shown.'

Concerning the 1899 show, Mr E. H. Barlow and the Rev. Cecil Legard commended the show of young stock as distinctly above average in general and individual merit. Of 69 young animals sent for veterinary examination, only four were rejected as unsound, one of them having been pricked in shoeing. The yearlings shown undocked were generally a well-grown lot, an especially good colt and filly winning their respective classes; while the five equal premium winners in both colt and filly classes were all promising animals. Two-year-old colts were 23 in number, the winner and premium takers were all of good size and substance. The winner of the filly class was an extremely nice mare by Yard Arm, with limbs, depth and quality of an exceptional character.

The first prize in the 3-year-old class was awarded to a very beautiful chesnut colt by Sir Hugh, bred in Ireland, and was an easy winner among a particularly good lot. Another chesnut was also bred in Ireland, a strong horse with excellent limbs and a fine mover. Three-year old fillies also well up to the average, the winner by Belville was a charming brown mare of a nice size and excellent quality. Her dam was the well-known Snowstorm. The other young mares to whom premiums were awarded made up a very satisfactory class.

The special prize given by Mr Leopold de Rothschild for the best colt likely to make a hunter sire was not a success, four animals only competing. It may be mentioned that a fair proportion of the winners of prizes and premiums in the above classes were sired by Queen's Premium Stallions. Only three sires were represented in the produce class for the best group of three animals.

Taking into consideration the large number of exhibits that came from Devonshire, Yorkshire, and distant counties, the organisers felt satisfied that the present plan of giving a first prize and five equal premiums caused the classes to fill so well. 'Thanks to the most able management of the stewards, so little delay occurred that we were able to complete our duties within ten minutes of the time allotted to us (from 9 to 1.30). Having regard to the fact that only four out of 69 were rejected as unsound, it seems superfluous for the yearlings and 2-year-olds to be subjected at all to the process of a veterinary examination. If the inspector were in attendance at the ringside for consultation in case of doubt, each class could have the prizes awarded without any of the exhibits leaving the ring; this would greatly expedite the judging, and be of infinitely more interest to the spectators.'

The riding classes of 1899 were assessed by Mr Gerald H. Hardy from Atherstone and the Earl of Orkney, who likewise reviewed their classes with specific reference to their winners and runners-up; an intriguing custom which it would be interesting to see resuscitated, though in this commercial age the repercussions of criticism might rebound on their perpetrators.

Thus, the winner of Class IX for 4-year-olds mares 'was a nice mare with very good back and quarters, but not quite scope enough. She rode well. Class X for 4-year-old geldings: the winner was a beautiful horse and the second and also very nice, and a fine mover. Class XI, 5-year-olds not exceeding 13 st. 7 lbs: the winner was a nice quick horse and gave one a very good feel, but was perhaps a little short of bone. The second was also a nice horse who galloped well. Class XII, over 13 st. 7 lbs. and not exceeding 15 stone was small, but very good. The winner was a very nice horse with beautiful shoulders. The second was a stronger horse but did not ride so well. Class XIII (over 15 st.) likewise was a very good class. The winner was a fine big horse with immense bone and good shoulders. Though such a big horse he rode like a pony. The second was a smaller horse but again, a beautiful ride.

The Society's Challenge Cup, value one hundred guineas, went to the winner of Class X, a chesnut gelding with four white heels. He is a beautifully balanced horse with the best of shoulders, good back and quarters and plenty of bone. Though only four, he rode like an older horse and gave one a rare feel. If anything might be said against him, it would be perhaps that he slightly lacks quality, but that, in his case, is certain to come with age. Mr T. D. John from St Fagans, Cardiff, was winning his third consecutive ridden championship, with Raby, led champion at Islington the previous year. The in-hand title for Sir Walter Gilbey's cup went to the Irish-bred Shannon View, a son of one of the stallions registered by the Royal Dublin Society, exhibited by James S. Darrell from Yorkshire. Shannon View was bred in Co. Limerick by Michael O'Brien. Raby was bred by James Ingledew of Bedale, Yorkshire, by Knight of Ruby out of the registered mare Jess.'

In the Royal Dublin Society returns for 1898 it is stipulated that stallion owners had the right to require hobbles to be used when necessary and to refuse mares suffering from contagious disease. There were already 55 registered stallions in Ireland as compared with only 29 in England. In 1899 applications were received by the RDS for the registration of 275 stallions, of which 206 were accepted. Each County Committee was given the option of adopting or modifying the nomination or Premium systems.

By 1898 HIS membership had increased to 1399. At the annual general meeting it was announced in 1898 that the Irish entries were included in the *Record* as the outcome of a pledge given by the Council to their affiliated Societies in Ireland to offer special facilities for registration, provided sufficient support was forthcoming. Their anticipations were more than justified by the results, which would form the basis of an extensive scheme for the registration of Irish hunters, in a joint *Record* which would give Irish animals equal prominence and setting as English breeders enjoyed. The advantages offered to Irish breeders by a book published outside Ireland were obvious, bringing to the immediate attention of hunting men and breeders in the United Kingdom and the representatives of foreign governments, the pedigrees and performances of their registered hunting stock.

By 1899 the membership had risen to 1463. The weights laid down for ridden classes underwent their first change — '13 stone', 'over 13 stone' and 'under 15 stone', and 'over 15 stone'. Suffice it to say that they still provoke controversy, as most notably at the Royal Show in 1983, and they probably always will! Expediency causes exhibitors to enter borderline middleweights in the lower division, and inevitably and rightly, some judges insist on moving them up, which is only fair to the genuine lightweight.

In 1904 the *Prize Record* was discontinued and its place was taken by the first volume of the *Hunter Stud Book* and *Supplement*, printed for the Society by the ecclesiastical publishers William Clowes & Sons and distributed by the Secretary, A. B. Charlton, from 12 Hanover Square. In January 1904, the membership had risen to 1688. This first volume contained 525 entries, comprising 18 stallions, 229 mares and fillies, with a supplement of 278 mares and fillies. The frontispiece was a painting of three champion hunters at the three London shows of 1901, 1902 and 1903 — Royal Flush, Tennis Ball and Red Cloud, all of them owned by Mr J. H. Stokes of Market Harborough, the well-known dealer, who thus won the Gold Cup, valued at one hundred guineas, outright.

Mention is made of the fact that young stock sired by the premium stallions had secured a large percentage of the prizes and medals given at the shows affiliated to the HIS, and Red Cloud in particular had two such crosses, Red Eagle and Prescription. The 340 premium stallions are tabulated, with their 1200 progeny.

The 1902 and 1903 shows produced little in the way of change, other than that in 1903 the Produce class was withdrawn, owing to the great difficulty experienced in getting the entries properly grouped, the result of exhibitors not sending their animals into the ring, thereby debarring the stallion they represented from competition. The revived charger classes were reduced from four to two, and two Jumping classes were introduced for the first time, and an entry of 46 competed for prize money of £84. In four years' time, the International Horse Show was to start at Olympia.

Lt-Colonel G. C. Ricardo reported on the young stock classes on behalf of the judges. The championship went to the 3-year-old filly Waterglass, by Waterford out of Maid of Coventry by Ambergris, bred at Malton in Yorkshire by William L'Anson and shown by John Lett from Rillington in the same county. Breeding honours throughout the show were divided equally between Yorkshire and Ireland.

The Judges of the riding classes, the Hon. E. S. Douglas-Pennant from Towcester, Master of the Grafton, and Mr George Evans, Master of the HH, reported jointly on their classes and did not pull their punches — though they were unstinting in their praise where they considered it to be merited. Thus, Lady Meta was a very useful mare and a most improving sort, the winner of a very good Class XI was a particularly nice mare and a charming ride, 4-year-old geldings were good throughout. Class XIII was a very good class in numbers and quality, though some of them appeared up to more weight than 13.7 and were consequently passed over (no moving up in those days). Class XIV was exceptionally good throughout, the winner being a very good ride with power, liberty and action. Class XV was moderate, none showing to much advantage with the exception of the winner, though Big Game, *when standing still*, appeared the best-looking sort.

In 1903, Mr J. Cottrell-Dormer and Mr John Hill, the young stock judges, had some pertinent remarks to make. The two yearling premiums were awarded to two very promising colts. Prince was a nice one, with good shoulders and bone and plenty of quality. No. 117, the colt by Pantomime, hocks rather too far off the ground, otherwise a very good colt with great length and bone.

The single premium allowed the 2-year-olds went to McBede, a well-grown colt with action and lots of liberty. There was unfortunately only one entry in the 3-year-old class, but the colt that was shown was one of very high merit, and may be described as a typical hunter sire. The judges were unanimous in afterwards awarding him the Challenge Cup for the best animal in the Young Classes. 'He is a rich dark brown, with size, length, substance and quality, a particularly fine mover, getting his hind legs well under him, and flexing his hocks as a hunter should. Wexford should make a very valuable hunter sire, and his produce will be watched with interest. Owned by Captain H. Heywood-Lonsdale, he is by Great Britain out of Nellie by Herbertstown and was bred by A. Chambers in the stiff country whose name he bears.

'Without going into details of the individual merit of the animals shown in other classes, we may say that we considered the whole exhibition most satisfactory. Many of the fillies were of the highest quality, and from a breeder's point of view, the proper stamp of future dams of hunters. We noticed that a large proportion of the young stock were shown in a healthy, growing condition, with plenty of muscle and flesh, without being overloaded with fat and undesirable pampering. We are also of the opinion that every possible inducement should be given to breeders to keep and exhibit their colts, up to three years old at least, with a view to increasing the present number of hunter-bred stallions for registration in the *Stud Book*.'

Mr R. A. Barkley and Mr J. F. Hatfield-Harter were terse and to the point concerning the ridden horses, writing in generalities with the exception of their winner of Class XIII, a good class throughout, who was of special merit; and of Class XIV, a magnificent weight-carrier, and said to be clean-bred.

Tennis Ball, the ridden champion in 1902, was a 5-year-old by Court Ball out of Empress by Delight, bred by David Farrell at Courtown, Kells, Co. Meath.

Red Cloud, Mr John Stokes's ridden champion in 1903, was bred at Wooler, Northumberland, by the premium stallion Red Eagle out of a mare by another premium stallion, Prescription, and was ample testimony to the good work begun by the Society with its initial show in 1885.

The jumping classes introduced on Wednesday and Thursday afternoons attracted entries of 31 and 21 animals respectively, and large and interested audiences. The competition on the second day was very closely contested, and the performance of the winners was excellent. This nineteenth show of the Society was successful in every way. It was honoured by the presence of the King and Queen on Thursday afternoon, while on the preceding day the Prince and Princess of Wales witnessed the jumping.

In the report of the Council to the 17th Annual General Meeting of members on 11 March at the Agricultural Hall, it was announced that the *Hunter Stud Book* would replace the old *Register* and the principle of pedigree would receive full recognition, rather than entry being based, as heretofore, more or less exclusively on prizes. The *Supplement*, open to prize-winners at approved shows and to inspected mares, would act as a feeder to the *Stud Book*, and the automatic registration of the produce of qualified parents would act to stimulate breeders to produce colts and fillies on the suggested lines, an incentive absent from the old rules.

Three-year-old Thoroughbred colts had never mustered at the London show in large numbers, despite the fact that the class was probationary to entry to the District Classes of the Royal Commission on Horse Breeding in a subsequent year. In the show of 1904, therefore, the class was excised and one for Registered Hunter Sires substituted. In order to encourage breeders to exhibit in the Riding classes, 2 for 4-year-old mares and geldings respectively were set apart, but the £60 offered in prize money did not secure their support. The alterations were completed by the omission of the Charger classes, for which there was no longer a *raison d'être*.

In 1905, as the new Riding classes were so poorly supported, only that for 4-year-old Mares was retained. The surplus prizes went to a new class for fully registered Hunter Brood Mares, the Horse Show Committee feeling that encouragement should be given in the Spring Schedule to the prospective dams of Hunter-bred sires. The outlay of £50 for the four prizes was fully justified by the response. The three Riding classes were thrown open to 6- and 7-year-old Mares and Geldings and the weights amended again in the last two, over 13 stone 7 lbs. and not exceeding 14 stone 7 lbs., and over 14 stone 7 lbs. No further deviation was made from the previous schedule.

The 1905 show showed an all-time record entry of geldings, at 119, though the total entry, at 329, did not approach the record 1902 figure of 361, unless the jumping entries were added to bring the total to 383.

At the 1904 show, the Judges of the Riding Classes, Major W. Trocke and Mr Owen C. Wallis praised every class except a moderate assembly of 4-year-old geldings. The lightweight 5-year-olds they described as particularly good, with the winners showing breeding. Middleweights comprised an extremely good class, and heavyweights a very fine class, all the horses being up to the weight (over 15 stone), and many of them exceptionally good movers. They declared themselves to be much pleased with the horses brought before them, considering that the majority were of hunter type and there were many high-class horses.

Mr Romer Williams and Mr W. G. Peareth judged the young stock and only the hunter-bred colts drew from them the comment that, apart from the winner, they were a moderate lot. Yearling colts and geldings and 2-year-old fillies were indiscriminately praised, but their general comments on the classes overall sounded a warning as to lack of size and unimpressive movement: 'There were many good young horses, but we noticed very few that looked like carrying more than 14 stone to hounds in the future; a great many moved anything but true, many turned their feet in and more turned them out. There was any amount of quality, but distinct lack of size.'

At the 1905 show, Captain C. Fetherstonhaugh and Mr W. A. Harford found the 4-year-old bred on *Hunter Stud Book* lines a poor class, and the other 4-year-old mares very moderate, but the 4-year-old geldings were very good, with quality and size. The lightweight class was likewise very good and the prize winners showed great merit, although the one they placed first is described as a 'typical medium-weight hunter'. The middleweights were very good — seven especially nice hunters, and the heavyweights also, with several high-class horses.

'Taken generally, we consider the horses that came before us were exceptionally high-class; in only one of the 4-year-old mare classes was there any marked deficiency of merit. As a whole the horses showed good bone and straight action with quality; and gave evidence of the results of more systematic breeding.'

Reporting on the Breeding and Young Stock Classes, Mr E. H. Barlow and Major M. J. Balfe said: 'The quality of the entries was, taken as a whole, distinctly good. Commencing with the Brood Mares, Mr Carden's Katrine, the winner, is a high-class mare for breeding purposes. She is up to weight and clean-bred; as also was the second mare, Mr Prior's Darkie, a good type of a long, low, powerful blood mare. The class was one likely to show good results.'

The four groups entered in the Produce Class were by Wales, Pantomine, Riverstown and Red Prince II. The winning group by Wales was especially good, all three animals showing size, quality and exceptionally good limbs. 'These classes are interesting and should afford useful guidance to breeders.'

'Registered Hunter Sires, 4 years old and upwards, comprised three useful horses — Merry Matchmaker especially so; he is a fine, lengthy horse with great quality, and a good mover. Red Wings is compact, on good limbs, while Riverstown comes of one of the best hunting families.'

'Hunter-bred Colts. In the yearling class, Aurum is a colt with substance; and Sportsman, by Privado — himself a hunter-bred sire — shows such quality and breeding. Royal Fox in the class for 2-year-old sires is an exceptionally nice colt, with perfect quality and action. Templemore, a winner in the 3-year-old sire section, is a very strong colt, near the ground, and a bold, strong mover.'

Colts and geldings

YEARLINGS — The yearling colts were numerous and a strong class, three-fourths of the entry being animals of good size. Fog Signal, the winner, is quite a first-class yearling, of good colour, character and movement. The 5 Premium winners were all very promising young animals.

TWO-YEAR-OLDS — The 2-year-old colts and geldings were again a large class, and were as a whole decidedly good; some animals of much promise being among them. Royal Fox, by Foxhound, the winner, is a colt of the first water. Sugar Loaf, by Wales, the first Premium, is a very good colt also, well grown and on the best of limbs.

THREE-YEAR-OLDS — The 3-year-old geldings also produced some good young animals. Splasher, by King's Premium winner Burnock Water, is a very strong colt who looks like carrying weight and promises to make a valuable horse. Listener, by Whisperer, and Dervische, by Dan Dancer, are both very good colts of the right stamp.

Fillies

YEARLINGS — The yearling fillies were not so good a class as the colts, many of them showing an inclination to deficiency in depth and width, though the winner, Princess of Wales, by Wales, was an exceedingly nice filly.

TWO-YEAR-OLDS — The 2-year-old fillies brought out a lot of nice mares; the winner, Watercress, by Burnock Water, is a very strong, thick-set mare on capital legs and feet. Columbine, by Pantomine, is a fine mare of good type and Kitty, by Wales, has much character, good limbs and good action.

THREE-YEAR-OLDS — 3-year-old fillies formed a small class, but the winner, The Duchess, by Florismart, is quite tip-top, a very beautiful filly. Lady Peggy is a good sort and the grey Light Heart, by Basuto, is a big mare on good limbs.

'Altogether we think the Show of Breeding and Young Stock a good one — very possibly the best that has been brought together at this show. We are pleased to note that nearly all the young animals stood straight and went straight, and the great majority had good bone and limbs. 225 animals came forward for judging.'

At the 1904 show, there were three Registered Hunter Sires, two bred in Ireland and the third in Buckinghamshire. All received premiums. Merry Matchmaker had, as a 3-year-old Hunter-bred colt, received a Premium, while Wexford had been selected for the Society's Challenge Cup in 1903 as the best young hunter exhibited at the show.

In 1904 the honours rested with the Thoroughbred colts, contrary to the results at the two preceding shows. Four of them received Premiums, as opposed to two hunters.

Yearlings totalled 29, seven more than the 1903 total. Avonmore, the winner, was by the Premium sire Reveller and was bred in Shropshire. Antonio and Fearless, Premium winners in Class II, were again selected. They were bred in Leicestershire and Ireland respectively. Breeders from Nottinghamshire, Derbyshire and Wiltshire were represented in the three other awards. Fearless was by the registered Irish stallion Red Prince II and the English Premium sires contributing successful yearling colts were Dubuque and Alvin.

Two-year-olds totalled 32 — 12 colts and 20 geldings, an increase of four. This class produced the winner of the Society's Challenge Cup: Jupiter, by Johnny Morgan, exhibited by Mr Frank B. Wilkinson and bred by Mr E. R. Crossley of Clotham, Newark. Lifeboat sired one of the Premium winners and Templemore, bred and exhibited by Mr R. G. Carden of Templemore, Co. Tipperary, was subsequently awarded one of the Society's gold medals for hunter-bred colts at the Spring Show of the Royal Dublin Society. Two other winners were bred in Ireland and one in Yorkshire.

There were 21 3-year-olds, a decrease of two, the winner being bred in Northamptonshire, the second in Wales and the third in Ireland.

Of the fillies, yearlings totalled 17 — a reduction of three — the winner and one Premium winner being sired by Pantomime. Eight of the winners were out of registered mares and they were bred in the North, the West Country and the Midlands. Sister Anne, bred by C. W. Francis in Somerset and exhibited by J. L. Nickisson, was the winner.

There were 16 2-year-olds, a decrease of one, and the winner and reserve champion was Altercation, by Avington, dam Squabble by Discord, exhibited by Mr E. H. Barlow of Pateley Bridge in Yorkshire and bred in Berkshire. An entry of 12 3-year-olds (1 down) was headed by the brown St Brides, by Hartstown out of Miss Daly, bred by John Barrett of Co. Cork and exhibited by Herbert R. Cory of Castleton, Cardiff.

The Produce Groups attracted an entry of nine comprising 45 horses, but only two groups entered the ring. Pantomime was the winner through his three daughters Circus Maid, Sister Anne and Limelight. To ensure the due entry in the ring of all groups entered, it was proposed on future occasions to judge this class before the Young Stock section.

Many of the winning ridden hunters, including all four prize-winning 4-year-old mares, were bred in Ireland, but the champion ridden horse was Red Ruby, by Knight of Ruby out of a mare by Lord Derby, 5 years old, bred by Mr Auton at Bedale and exhibited by Mr Charles Wertheimer of Norfolk Street, Park Lane. Reserve was John Drage's Merry Tom, a brown 5-year-old to carry over 15 stone, by Tweeddale out of a mare by Conductor, bred by W. Coates at Brawby, Pickering.

At the 1905 show, the winning brood mare, R. G. Carden's bay 7-year-old Katrine, by Hackler, was bred by P. Shelly from Co. Kilkenny and shown from Ireland. John Stokes had the winning ridden mare, 5 and upwards, in Lady Emily, by Braggadocio, as well as the two following her, and the winning open lightweight, middleweight and heavyweight. John Drage, another dealer, had the runner-up in two classes but in two more two distinguished amateurs kept their flags flying — the Earl of Lonsdale and Sir Humphrey de Trafford.

Then, as now, the dealers were strong supporters of the showing classes, particularly those for ridden horses, which constituted a useful shop-window for their wares. William Gale of Waltham, Melton Mowbray, a well known hunting farmer-dealer with the Belvoir, was another who was a successful exhibitor in 1905.

Wales superseded Pantomime to win the Produce Groups, R. G. Carden, who had the winning brood mare, also brought off the double of the champion young horse, the 2-year-old Royal Fox, by Foxhound out of Romany Queen by Roman Emperor, a grand sort of bay colt which he bred himself at Borrisoleigh, Co. Tipperary.

Another name which was to become very famous in the HIS was also prominent in the prize list, this being Tom Wickham-Boynton of Burton Agnes, Driffield, East Yorkshire, with stallions such as Toledo and Pax, Harold Brassey of the Royal Horse Guards with Pontifex, who travelled in the Cotswolds while his owner was quartered in Regent's Park Barracks, and Thomas James Hillman from Warwickshire, whose descendants still have premium stallions in Worcestershire. This sort of continuity really makes 80 years seem a very short time — especially when two of the successful riders in the jumping classes, W. H. ('Gunner') Wellburn from Yorkshire and F. W. (Fred) Foster from Derbyshire are still remembered today.

At the 19th Annual General Meeting of members the financial position of the Society was declared to be most satisfactory. The Council had carefully considered the improvement of the ring telegraph-board, and had instructed the Royal Agricultural Hall Company to make a board — which they thought would greatly improve the posting of the awards. They had also arranged, in conjunction with the two other Societies, for a telephonic installation which would assist the stewards in the management of the show.

Gold medals for the best Hunter Filly, registered in the *Hunter Stud Book,* were to be offered to the Highland Agricultural Society and the Royal Dublin Society: while the RDS would be given two medals for stallions at their Spring Show, at which two classes had been opened for Hunter Stallions by Irish Registered Stallions out of mares registered in the HIS *Stud Book,* one for the best Hunter Stallion foaled in 1902 and one for the best foaled prior to that year.

The Council had also appointed a deputation to wait upon the President of the Board of Agriculture, to impress upon him the advisability of the compulsory registration and licence (embracing a certificate of soundness) of all stallions travelling for the public service in the United Kingdom, with a view to legislation on the subject. The nine stallions on the Society's *Register* had served a total of 402 mares, averaging 44 apiece.

At the 20th AGM on 7 March 1905, it was reported that at the June meeting of the Council, urgent representations were made concerning the necessity of opening an enquiry into the present unsatisfactory position of the breeding of hunters and other general utility horses. A special committee was appointed, and in response to ten questions covering the reference, 466 correspondents, representative of the highest professional and practical opinion in the country, sent in 4600 replies which were registered and collated, and from which the special committee presented to the Council an exhaustive report and analyses summarising the views and suggestions put forward to grapple with this national question.

The Council decided at their December meeting to appoint a permanent Committee of the Council, and invite thereon representatives of the Royal Commission on Horse Breeding, the Brood Mare Society, the Board of Agriculture, the War Office, and the Department of Agriculture and Technical Instruction for Ireland, in order that a serious and sustained effort should be made to organise the industry, with a view to establishing a recognised breed of Hunters.

Despite the acute depression affecting the agricultural and commercial interests, which naturally was reflected in a Society relying for its support upon voluntary contributions, the Council was enabled to report that the membership during the past financial year had been maintained and totalled 1695, an increase of seven on the previous figure.

Although subscriptions and general receipts did not diminish, the larger outlay on the 1904 show, and the publication of the first volume of the *Hunter Stud Book,* increased the expenditure of the previous year by £390. The total cost of the show was £452, entailing an outlay of £252 in excess of that of 1903, due to three causes — a large increase in the Schedule of Prizes, owing principally to the suspension of the limit rule in the young stock classes, the provision of the new award board, and a reduction in the admission receipts and at the Grandstands. The expenditure on the award board was fully justified, as, installed under the clock, it successfully met all the demands placed upon it, and the returns from the judging ring were promptly and efficiently posted.

The total value of the prize money for the 1905 show was £1194. The increase of £20 was practically devoted to the reintroduction of a class for Hunter Brood Mares, though open only to those registered or entered for full registration in the *Hunter Stud Book* with two crosses of qualified blood, or the inspected dams of winners under rules. Their colt produce would therefore, if by Thoroughbred or Registered Hunter sires, have the necessary pedigree required in a Hunter stallion qualifying for registration. The age limit in the Riding Classes was increased from 5 to 7 years, and the weights amended. The jumping classes were retained, their inclusion having favourably affected the admission and Grand Stand receipts of the last two shows.

The two prizes offered to the stallions registered in 1903, showing the best percentage of foals, were awarded to Privade (77.14%) and Clarendon (75%). The Deputation appointed by the Council waited on the President of the Board of Agriculture, and impressed upon him the advisability of the compulsory registration and licence (embracing a certificate of soundness) of all stallions travelling for the public service in the United Kingdom, with a view to legislation on the subject.

The Society had undoubtedly influenced public feeling by its prizes in London and the country, and its efforts had been a great factor in placing at the disposal of breeders sound stallions at reasonable fees. But its work was limited by its financial resources. It had, however, indicated in the report of its special committee the necessity for combined action in regard to the present condition of the national industry of horse-breeding:

Efficient and economic organisation was essential to the success of the proposals of the Committee, and the nucleus of the necessary machinery already existed in the representative character of the membership of the Hunters' Improvement Society, but the financial necessities of the scheme were palpably beyond the powers of the Society, and therefore the co-operation of the Royal Commission on Horse-Breeding, and the financial aid and assistance of the Government, must be evoked to deal with the condition of a national industry whose increasing decline cannot but be regarded with deep apprehension, and which, if allowed to continue, will at no remote period become a grave national danger.

The issue of this report, (even without its record of twenty years' work) amply justified the existence of the Society and its claims upon the support of all who have the welfare of horse-breeding at heart, who by becoming members of the Society would materially assist in furthering the interests of breeders of Hunters and General Utility Horses.

By Order of the Council,
A. B. Charlton,
Secretary.

CHAPTER 4

---========⊕========---

The Spring Show progresses

AFTER a reversion to two weight classes, under and over 14 stone, in 1906, the following year the Hunter Show schedule was exhaustively reviewed by a special committee, statistics dealing with the actual cost for each class were prepared, and those which lacked support were dropped. This enquiry left the Young Stock classes virtually intact, the entry for the three previous years having been maintained. Hunter brood mares, amply provided for at associated shows, and exhibitor-bred classes which were indifferently supported, were discontinued.

Finally, the status quo was recalled with three weight divisions and a new class for horses not exceeding 15.2 hands. At the 1906 show, Mr Thomas Anderson and Mr W. W. Jenkins judged young stock, considering yearlings and 3-year-old fillies noteworthy. In 1907, Mr R. G. Carden (Tipperary) and Sir Gilbert Greenall, Bart., Master of the Belvoir, considered the young entry particularly satisfactory, especially 2-year-old colts and 3-year-olds, who produced the champion.

In 1906 the riding classes were assessed by the Earl of Orkney and Mr A. E. West, and in 1907 by Mr Anthony Maude and Mr J. Maunsell Richardson. Both sets of judges were complimentary concerning the exhibits, though in 1906 the mares were thin on the ground, while the 1907 pair recommended dividing the 4-year-olds into two weights. The 1906 champion was John Drage's King Edward, a 5-year-old chesnut heavyweight of anonymous ancestry, bred in Co. Kildare. The champion young horse was the chesnut 3-year-old filly Watercress, by Burnock Water out of Mullinger Junior by Trundle Hill, bred by Francis Samuelson from Thirsk and shown by Frank Rickaby from Easingwold. The 1907 champion was John Stokes's 5-year-old Fable by Favoloo, bred by Garrett Barry in Co. Limerick. John Drage was reserve with the 5-year-old Red Earl, a heavyweight by Red Prince II out of Cora, by Ascetic, bred by James O'Hanlon at Naas, Co. Kildare. The champion young horse was William Butler of Ellesmere, Salop's Ian Hamilton, a brown 3-year-old by Surbiton and home-bred. Reserve was the 2-year-old filly Success, a chesnut by Enterprise, bred by J. L. Nickisson at Hinton Manor, Swindon, and exhibited by Major Leslie Renton, MP at Naseby Hall, Rugby. Mr Nickisson was a steward of the show with the Hon. Alexander Parker and John Cooper.

It seems barely credible that in 1907 the publication of the *Hunter Stud Book* every second year, which was distributed free to the 1693 members, cost £120 annually.

At the annual general meeting of members for 1909 the President, Col. the Hon. Charles Byng, submitted the report of the Special Committee appointed to define the conditions of entry in the *Hunter Stud Book*. Concerning the registration of stallions, they had to be 2 years old or upwards, by a Thoroughbred or Registered Hunter Stallion and out of a mare registered in Volume IV of the *Hunter Stud Book*—provided that he is inspected and passed by a member of the Society nominated and approved by the Editing Committee. The inspector may, at his discretion, call in a veterinary surgeon to examine a horse at the owner's expense.

A mare would be eligible if her sire is a Thoroughbred or registered Hunter Stallion, and if her dam is a mare registered in Vol. IV of the *Hunter Stud Book*; or if both her sire and dam's sire are Thoroughbred or registered Hunter Stallions. She was further eligible if her sire was a Thoroughbred or Registered Hunter Stallion and she was awarded one of the Society's medals, or if she wins or breeds the winner of a prize in Hunter Classes at a National, County or Associated show; if she or her produce win races under Jockey Club or National Hunt Rules; or if she is inspected and passed by a member of the Society nominated by the Editing Committee. The inspector may, at his discretion, call in a veterinary surgeon to examine the horse at the owner's expense.

The conditions laid down were greeted with acclaim, and the action of the Council in this important matter was endorsed. The proposal had long been advocated and the *Stud Book* would in future be on a really sound foundation, the means of establishing a breed of Hunters.

Mr G. H. Green, in seconding the resolution, said that their great difficulty was to find the right class of mares to breed from. They could not find them with enough substance. Some thirty years ago in the Midlands they had several horses that were not Thoroughbred; they had three crosses, and they produced mares of substance, which if put to Thoroughbred horses again turned out some of the best Hunters. The foreigners came over and bought these mares straight away, and there was hardly a mare to be found now in the country good enough to breed from. They could not find the right class of mare, but if they had the Hunter sires contemplated by the new rules they would get mares with more substance, so that they could put them to Thoroughbred mares and breed weight-carrying horses. He congratulated the Council most heartily upon their resolution, which he thought would do a great deal of good for horse-breeding generally.

Mr T. L. Wickham-Boynton understood that the inspector might at his discretion call in a veterinary surgeon to examine the horse at the owner's expense. He ventured to ask the Council whether it would not be better to have made that examination compulsory.

Mr Guy Fenwick thought that the certificate should state that the stallion should be free from hereditary disease, otherwise it would do a great deal more harm than good, and it would be better that the Society should bear the cost than that unsound horses should be registered.

Sir Richard Green Price said that if he understood it rightly, Mr Wickham Boynton suggested that instead of the word 'may' they should use the word 'shall'. Although he was a member of the Council which passed this, he confessed that he thought 'shall' was an improvement, so that they would not leave the door open for unsound stallions. Nor should it be left to the owner of the horse to choose the veterinary surgeon.

Mr Guy Fenwick thought that the veterinary surgeon should be selected by the Hunters' Improvement Society and not by the owner of the stallion.

Mr S. Nevins Bankart thought that anyone who owned a stallion would be quite willing to pay a guinea. The funds were none too large at present, they were not in a position to spend money and were only just getting on their feet, and as vice chairman of the finance committee he had to protest. Anyone with a sound stallion would pay a guinea to get it registered.

It was decided to state that the stallion was sound and free from hereditary disease, the wording being that the Council *shall* appoint a veterinary surgeon to examine the horse at the owner's expense. With regard to mares, the Council *may*, at their discretion, call in ... again at the owner's expense. The resolution was carried unanimously.

The Council during 1909 decided to take over the work and duties of the original Brood Mare Society. The discussion at the Annual General Meeting of members which initiated the proposal, and the report of the subsequent action of the Council to give it permanent record, and practical effect, were incorporated in the *Stud Book*. A Special Committee was appointed to promote the interests of horse-breeding by including within its functions:

(1) The duty of keeping before Parliament and the country the importance of making proper provision for the distribution of brood mares, and of supplying information and statistics to members of Parliament and others.

(2) The establishment of new branches, and the acquisition of mares by gift or purchase, and the obtaining of reports from local societies.

Major W. H. Fife said:

I do not think that there was ever a time when horse-breeding was more in need of the assistance of the HIS than it is at the present time, because there is no doubt about it that horse-breeding in England is declining. One of the first reasons for its decline, of course, as we all know, is that there is an decreased demand for horses, owing to electricity, motor cars, and mechanical traction generally. A great many people have an idea that the decline of horse-breeding is greatly due to the fact that foreigners buy our mares. I do not agree with that theory at all. I am of the opinion that the effect of foreigners buying our mares is a stimulus to horse-breeding. I maintain that there is no lack of mares in the country; there are plenty of mares, but as breeding does not pay, people will not buy them.

I will give you an instance by way of proof. I had a mare of my own — her dam was by Huguenot, and a Gold Medal mare, and her grand-dam was by King Crafty, another of the Compton Stud horses, and her great-great-grand-dam was a very good hunter in the Blackmore Vale and used to carry about seventeen stone. You could not have a better pedigree for Hunter breeding than that, and this mare was in foal to a good Thoroughbred stallion, and was due to foal two or three months after I wished to sell her. Her male produce would have been eligible as a Hunter sire, so that there was everything in her favour.

I wrote to Mr Charlton, the Secretary of the HIS, and asked him if he would make it known among the members. I also advertised the mare two weeks following in *The Field*, and I only got one reply from these two advertisements. Well, I think that pretty well shows that people are not very anxious to get mares. It is not that the mares are not in the country, but that people do not want them; they know it does not pay to breed. It is simply a case of supply and demand. I think the very fact of the foreigners coming and buying mares is a stimulus to people to breed mares for them.

I think that what we principally suffer from is importation of foreign horses. That is our evil. It is a far greater evil than the fact of the mares going out of the country. When I was abroad this winter I was being driven along by a Frenchman in his trap, and I began to talk to him about his horse. I said: 'Where did you get that horse?' He said 'I bought it in Italy'. Then he said he used to get them from Italy, and he could get them cheaper than he could in France, but the French people found out that they were going to Italy to buy their horses so they put a tax of 150 francs on every horse brought into France from Italy, so now they found they could buy them cheaper in France. That is what we want to do — to stop the foreigners coming in. That is what does us harm. Then look at it from this point; supposing we had a war; I maintain that the larger our exports of horses, the better we shall be prepared if war is declared. The larger our import of horses, the weaker would our position be in the event of war, and for this reason — if we had a large exportation and war were declared, we should stop it, and all those horses that had been bred to meet the foreign demand would be at our disposal for military purposes.

Conversely, if we were dependent on a large number of foreign horses to meet our usual requirements, and war breaks out, we are liable to have that supply stopped and we have nothing in the country to meet it.

I further think that the Brood Mare Society, which has done a great deal of good, and pioneered what can be done, it would surely be to the benefit of horse-breeding if it and the HIS could be combined. Of course, the HIS is of longer standing; it has all its organisation complete, and is in a position to carry the thing through, with better advantages for doing so than a young society, which has difficulties to contend with before it can get established.

Mr Algernon Turner, chairman of the Brood Mare Society, said that they had started under great difficulties some five or six years ago and made very fair progress. They had brought the subject of horse-breeding before Parliament on very many occasions and had had a great deal of support from the Royal Commission and other bodies. But they had always foreseen that to re-stock the country with mares of the right type, which he believed were quite obtainable if one had the money, would require the support of the Government who, after coquetting with it for a number of years have made speeches in Parliament on which he placed little reliance:

I would like to refer to some of the little difficulties we have had in our own domestic circle. I will not go into detail, but at our meeting last week we passed certain resolutions which will be published in *The Field* next Saturday, to the effect that the four branches which now exist in Herefordshire, Cornwall, Dorsetshire and Leicestershire should henceforth make their own rules, collect their own finance, and manage their own affairs entirely by themselves, with these qualifications: first, that any fillies bred from rented mares should be offered to the local committee for purchase, and we made no restriction at all as to price. The second was that annual reports should be furnished to the central authority, to enable them to judge the different schemes that were being carried out, and form an opinion as to the one which seemed most efficient.

We also passed a resolution to the effect that we should, in the event of these resolutions taking full effect, be quite willing to approach the Council of this Society in the sense which Major Fife has indicated. Many years ago I moved a resolution in the Council that this Society should create a Brood Mare branch, but it was not carried for technical reasons and that is why the Breed Mare Society started. I do not think a better step could be taken than to bring together under one roof all the different sections and departments connected with horse-breeding.

The Chairman was sure that if the 'sister society' were to approach the Society they would not meet with a deaf ear.

Mr C. W. Tindall from Lincolnshire, as one who had to do with the tenant farmer, said that there were plenty of mares, and they would be found: the real reason was that it did not pay to breed horses. Last year all the tenant farmers were breeding cattle; this year they were all going to graze sheep, because they were much cheaper than cattle. The moment that it pays better to breed horses than cattle and sheep they will breed horses and they will not ask anyone to find the mares, but do it themselves. 'That is the whole thing in a nutshell.'

He would not say a thing against the Brood Mare Society, but he understood another Society was cropping up, and he hoped that no one interested in breeding blood horses would subscribe to any society other than the HIS, which is known by everyone and was the only one which ought to exist. 'If branches come here and there away from this Society we not only weaken our own but they are all weak.'

Eventually a Brood Mare Committee of ten under the chairmanship of Mr Romer Williams was appointed and its first report was circulated to all members of the Society in January 1910.

The twenty-fourth and twenty-fifth shows at Islington marked the start of a new agreement of the Society with the Royal Agricultural Hall Company. The grandstand was enlarged, with increased accommodation for members and public, the Gilbey Hall with its improved and new boxes for the exhibits, and the large ring, with more scope for the showing classes and adaptability to the jumping competitions were all distinct improvements. The old boxes at the Upper Street end of the Hall were removed to make way for a collecting ring, adding both to the organisation and to the safety of the public.

The only alteration to the 1908 schedule was the omission of the rule in the Produce Class which required the contributing sire to be alive at the time of entry. The result was an increase in the number of groups.

In 1909 the 15.2 hands class was eliminated and in its place, in addition to separate classes for 4-year-old mares and geldings, a mixed class was provided. A new rule was also introduced, with a view to securing for the riding section the extended support given by exhibitors to the breeding classes. It provided that the first three classes were debarred to exhibitors (not being the breeders) who had won a first prize in the riding classes at the three previous shows.

The first prize in each of the jumping classes was doubled, with a corresponding increased entry. In 1909 it had grown from 24 to 56.

In 1908, Mr C. J. Furlong and Mr J. Simons Harrison commented most favourably upon the young Hunters, especially those selected for premiums; the classes calling for their especial encomium being the 2-year-olds in each section. They found the colts and geldings 'a class full of exceptional merit both in numbers and quality', and the fillies 'a splendid class all round, the five placed being a credit to any country breeding Hunters'. The 3-year-old classes were exceptionally good all round, though the yearling classes were weak, 'due probably to the exceedingly cold, wet summer of 1907'. The produce class was distinctly good.

The championship was won by Mr T. L. Bennett of Cross Hands, Chipping Sodbury, with the chesnut 2-year-old Sermon, by Royal Minister ex Hartstown, bred by Mr S. W. Carson of Ballyneety, Ardfinane, Co. Tipperary, who won a class of 29 entries. Reserve was the 3-year-old Zealot, a chesnut gelding by Whisperer, dam by Zeal, bred and exhibited by R. L. Fenwick of Wymondham, Oakham, who was also third in the class with Hark and sixth with Gay Boy, both likewise by Whisperer.

Royal Minister (1899), the stallion to which the highest honours fell at both shows, was bred by Sir Tatton Sykes, by Royal Hampton out of Mimi by Barcaldine.

In 1909, Mr J. W. A. Harris and Mr John Williams were well satisfied with the young stock and breeding classes. In the opinion of the former, the prize and premium winners in the 2-year-old colt and gelding classes and in the 3-year-old gelding class were very good animals and the firsts exceptionally so. Mr Williams thought that owners housed their yearlings too much after weaning, with insufficient outing during the winter.

The championship went to Sermon for the second successive year and the reserve was St George Littledale's home-bred 2-year-old Osprey, a chesnut gelding by Red Eagle out of Windless by Yard Arm.

The riding classes again developed into a battle for supremacy between Mr J. H. Stokes, who won six out of seven classes and thus may be said to have won the encounter hands-down, and Mr John Drage. The championship went to the former's middleweight Broadwood, a brown 5-year-old by Red Eagle out of Selby, by Selby. Reserve was the runner-up in the class, John Drage's Chatterbox II, a chesnut 6-year-old by Bergomask out of Dorothy, by Delight, bred by John Kenny in Co. Lonford. The champion was bred by J. Richardson at Saltown, York.

The judges in 1908, Captain C. Featherstonhaugh and Lord Penryhn, found their classes up to the average of excellence especially the lightweight class, with some typical exhibits. The middleweights included their champion, which they characterised as 'a magnificent type of mediumweight hunter. The heavyweight class, with the exception of the winner, was not strong, and some exhibits did not fulfil the requirements of the classification'.

In 1909, Major William Trocke and Sir Henry Hoare said that the quality throughout was very good, the first and second in the middleweights being exceptionally high-class. The heavyweights also were a very good lot, up to a great weight, with plenty of bone and quality, and the absence of under-bred animals was very marked. On the whole, the classes were most satisfactory, many exhibits high-class and the greater majority useful and saleable hunters. Major Trocke saw decided improvement since he last judged at the Hunter Show (in 1904), when he found the average quality of a high standad.

The champion and reserve again came from the first two placed horses in the middleweight class — J. S. H. Fullerton of Barnsley's bay 6-year-old Signal, by Beware, dam by Perfection, bred in Co. Cork by Jeremiah Leahy: and

W. A. Simpson-Hinchliffe of Harrogate's brown 6-year-old Broadwood, by Red Eagle, a winner for John Stokes the previous year.

At the 23rd Annual General Meeting of members of 1908, the Council had pleasure in announcing that, under the Presidency of Mr Romer Williams, the financial position had materially improved, due to a satisfactory increase in the membership, and to the co-ordination of the Society's programme at the London and affiliated shows. On 1 January the membership numbered 1750, an increase of 57. The debit balance of £207.3s.2d. on January 1907, had been converted into a credit balance of £74.4s. at the close of the 1907 financial year, and the greater part of the cost of publishing Volume III of the *Hunter Stud Book* had been met out of the past year's current receipts.

This was primarily due to the work of the special Show Sub-Committee who during 1906 made an exhaustive analysis of the whole of the Society's operations, and whose recommendations, adopted by the Council in the October of that year, yielded such excellent results. The reduction of £100 in the outlay on the Spring Show was the outcome of this policy, with a more economical distribution of medals and prizes at the country shows.

The special Sub-Committee recommended that a trial of three years be given to their schedule in the interests of both the Society and the exhibitors, who would thus be advised early of the Society's future programme.

At the 1909 meeting a further increase in membership was attributed to the initiative of the President, Col. the Hon. Charles Byng, who lived in Cornwall and brought a large influx of West Country supporters.

The operation of the new agreement brought the total cost of the 1908 exhibition down to £180.12s.7d. — a figure which does not seem relative to that charged by Olympia's executive in these days for staging a five-day show chiefly for international show jumping.

Volume V of the *Hunter Stud Book*, covering the years 1910 and 1911, had an additional section detailing Hunter Geldings awarded prizes at qualified shows, ensuring a permanent record, facilitating reference for future use. The whole field of registration and entry was now covered by the distinct sections for Stallions, Mares and Geldings and by the tabulated list of the 362 Premium and Registered Stallions and their 1371 successful produce.

The entry totalled 823 as compared with 677 entries in Volume IV, and was therefore the largest volume in the series issued by the Council. Numbers and numerals (in those cases where names had been previously registered) ensured that the registration certificates immediately provided:

(a) the official number and proof of registry — invaluable in all cases of transfer and export, with

(b) identity of the registered animal at time of exhibition, award of the Society's medals and — in the case of Stallions and Mares — upon entry of their produce.

Each entry in the thirteen previous volumes was transferred to a card, which in the case of re-entry indicated the various books in which the registered horse had appeared. All the cards were then arranged in drawers in strictly alphabetical order, a separate card index being opened for the current Volume. The previous use of a name and the necessary numeral are immediately available, while each registration certificate, bound up with counterfoils and in consecutive numbers, ensures that no duplicate can be issued. The registered number and numeral are then added to the entry form, which is bound up in the alphabetical order of the owner. The Secretary therefore has at his command three proofs of identity — the owner through the entry form; the animal through the card index; and the number through the counterfoil of the registration certificate. The provision of numerical indexes in the *Stud Book* completes the system.

Since the issue of Volume IV of the *Stud Book,* important developments supervened to affect favourably the national industry of light horse breeding in the United Kingdom, and ensuring from the funds available under the Development Act, two specific grants of £40,000 to Great Britain and £10,000 to Ireland. The Society regarded with satisfaction the results of their representations put forward by the Council in 1904 and 1910, as the new scheme, administered by the Board of Agriculture, embodied the suggestions of the Horse Supply Committee.

CHAPTER 5

———●❋●———

Report of the Horse Supply Committee

AT THE Council Meeting in October 1909, the Brood Mare Committee was instructed to consider and submit a report as to the best means of meeting the requirements of the nation in improving the condition of Light Horse Breeding in the UK. It appeared from the 12th Report of the Royal Commission on Horse-Breeding that the large majority of the members of the Commission were agreed as to the inadequacy of the supply, both in quality and quantity, of light horses in the country, and considered that it was due in no small degree to the exportation of the best of the stallions and mares for the use of foreign powers.

In the years 1907–8 there were in the United Kingdom (including Ireland) 184,602 horses under one year old as against 208,269 in 1904–5; the figures for Ireland alone — where there were few or no cart-horses — being 57,446 in 1907–8, as against 68,978 in 1904–5, a drop of 11,500 or thereabouts in three years.

It may be pointed out that there is no doubt that the breeding of light horses is annually diminishing to a large extent. It can hardly be disputed that although there may be sufficient horses to supply the normal requirements of the Army in peace-time, there is no sufficient reserve available in case of emergency. Had there been, the Government would not have been reduced to the straits in which they found themselves at the time of the Boer War. It has to be remembered that a very large quantity of horses is required for mobilisation long before approaching the question of how to replace the wastage of war, and there should be a sufficient reserve of horses available to meet this contingency.

The Committee were of the opinion that a sum of not less than £50,000 per annum should be allocated to the purpose in view. They pointed out that France spent £185,000; Germany, £370,000; and Austria £210,000 annually on horse-breeding.

They thought that the 28 King's Premium stallions which were allowed for Great Britain were totally insufficient for the needs of the country. They noted the great use made in some districts, not only of unsound, weedy Thoroughbred stallions, but also of inferior half-bred stallions, of no authentic breeding. They regretted the continual purchase by Foreign Governments of many of our best stallions, and thought that measures should be taken to counteract this evil which had been so appropriately referred to by the Royal Commission of 1887. They considered it essential, to assure a real and permanent improvement, that a considerable number of stallions which then went abroad, should be retained in the UK.

But if these stallions were to remain in the country, it could only be with the aid and resources of the Government, in view of the competition for their possession by Foreign Governments, and the Committee thought that arrangements for their purchase and retention in the country should be made by the Board of Agriculture on behalf of the Government.

The Committee were convinced that many parts of the United Kingdom, which are suitable for horse breeding, required to be re-stocked with brood mares. They were satisfied that many suitable districts were almost denuded of the class of mare required, the old strains of blood having been lost, chiefly in consequence of the exportation of the best mares.

They considered that, with good organisation and by acting in concert, the Board of Agriculture, the War Office, the Royal Commission on Horse Breeding, the Hunters' Improvement Society (which now incorporated the Brood Mare Society) could greatly improve the standard of excellence, possibly diminish the cost of production, and make the industry more profitable.

The Committee was prepared to submit for the consideration of the Commissioners of the Act a detailed scheme for the due development of the above suggestions, and recommended that any funds voted by Parliament for the purpose should be controlled by a Minister responsible to Parliament, assisted by a standing Council which should include representatives of the four bodies above mentioned.

The Council determined that this report should be distributed to all members of the Society, and appointed the Brood Mare Committee, with Viscount Helmsley, MP, as a Special Committee to draft a detailed scheme, based on the report, for the consideration of the Commissioners under the Development Act.

The Special Committee met on 17 February 1910, under the Chairmanship of Mr Romer Williams, when it was resolved to constitute the Horse Supply Committee, who should take the necessary steps to investigate the whole question, and who should report to the Council. The offer of co-operation of the Polo and Riding Pony Society was accepted and Viscount Valencia, MP, elected as their representative on this Committee, which was then constituted as follows:—

Viscount Helmsley, MP (Chairman)
HRH Prince Christian of Schleswig-Holstein, KG
Sir Merrik R. Burrell, Bart.
Mr J. L. Nickisson
Major H. N. Schofield, VC
Mr Algernon Turnor, CB
Viscount Valentia, MP
Mr Romer Williams
Mr R. G. Carden (*President*)
The Hon. Alexander Parker, MFH (*Vice President*) } Ex officio

Mr C. W. Tindall was co-opted a member at the first meeting of the Committee on 15 March 1910. The Horse Supply Committee met six times between 15 March and 23 May, and submitted a report to the Council of the HIS on 6 June 1910. Those parts which are still of interest today are appended:

46

(1) *Scope of Enquiry.*   In addition to the work of collecting evidence by the Special Committee in 1904, the views of several prominent breeders had been of great assistance.

(2) *Need for an Accurate Census.*   It became apparent during discussions of the Committee that there was a great need for an accurate census of horses in the UK which to be of value should provide for an accurate classification and be repeated at least every five years. It should be carried out by means of forms sent to owners of horses, who should be under statutory obligation to make the returns required.

(3) *Decrease in Light Horses.*   Partly due to the increase in mechanical traction, and the consequent decline of a market for the misfits, and partly to the fact that the majority of farmers can no longer afford to hunt, therefore, in the absence of any inducement or facilities either for acquiring brood mares or getting them served by suitable stallions, they have lost interest in light horse breeding.

(4) *No Restriction on Export Trade.*   Attempts to encourage breeding of this type of horse must depend for their success upon the breeder having a prospect of being able to dispose of his young stock to advantage. Because the Committee had this fact in mind they do not recommend any scheme which would have the effect of restricting the export of horses abroad. Foreigners are to a great extent the best customers for breeders of light horses in the UK. It is a question whether, had this not been so, light horse breeding would have declined even more seriously than it has done.

We are of the opinion that any restrictions on the export of horses or even mares would tend to discourage breeders, and to diminish the number bred. We hope that our proposals will result in a larger number of mares being retained in this country.

(5) *National Importance of Adequate Supply.*   Besides the foreign market, the demand for high-class hunters and polo ponies must be the main stimulus for breeders to engage in the production of light horses, and it is to these breeds that the Army must look for its supply of horses. Animals of hunter type are those most required, and though the pony of 14.2 is probably too small for general army purposes, yet the pony that grows too big for polo, say to 15.1 and 15.2, is extremely serviceable and just the type required. These breeds should therefore be especially encouraged, as being those from which the Army can draw what it needs, and also as being those unfortunately which offer the smallest prospects commercially.

The other breeds, such as the Hackney, the Shire and the Clydesdale can safely be left to themselves. Whatever may be the case with the Hackney, the Shire and the heavy horse generally are sufficiently profitable to breed to ensure a plentiful supply.

Hunter and riding pony breeding offer the smallest chance of profit, not because the prices of the best are not adequate — the best will always command good prices — but because it is more and more difficult to dispose of the misfits except at a loss. Mechanical traction has greatly diminished the demand for these misfits, and though no doubt there will always be a limited market for them, it is likely to decline in the future.

Hence, if breeders or hunters and riding ponies are to be encouraged, some prospects must be afforded them of disposing satisfactorily of those animals which, though perfectly serviceable, yet will not command high prices for the purposes for which they were intended. These are the very horses for the Army, and it is here that the War Office could assist.

(6) *Purchase of Three-year-olds.*   It is true that in time of peace, only about 3,000 horses annually are bought for the Army. Whether that number is sufficient or not to provide for a rapid mobilisation is not within the province of your Committee, but we may venture to point out that this annual purchase should be used to encourage the breeder rather than to discourage him, as is at the moment the case.

The Army horses are now bought at 4 years old and upwards, at a price which gives no profit to the breeder but probably means an actual loss. If horses were bought at 3-off, at the same average price as that now given for older horses, it would just pay the breeder, and although it might be a disappointment to him that his animal had not turned out to be of sufficient class to command a high price as a hunter or polo pony, yet he would not be out of pocket.

(7) *Advantages of this Course.* It may be that for military reasons it would be inconvenient for the Army to purchase all the horses at 3 years old. In that case, while buying as many as possible at that age, they should give a higher price for older horses. Although buying at a younger age than now at the same price, or at the same age as now at an increased price, would involve some increase in Army estimates, it would in reality be a national economy. Not only would the Army derive the advantage of being first in the market, but by utilising their annual purchase as an encouragement to the breeder they would be helping to maintain the supply they require and so fostering a very valuable asset in time of war.

(8) *Closer Touch with the Breeders.* The more closely the Army purchasing authorities can be brought in touch with the actual breeder the better; it would indeed be advisable to buy as many as possible direct from the breeder. It may be more convenient for the Army buyers to go to a dealer who has experience as to the sort of horses they want, who can collect together a considerable number of likely horses for their inspection. By so doing their time is less likely to be wasted than if they travel about to various places to see horses in the hands of breeders, a great many of whom are disposed to think that anything unsaleable elsewhere will do for the Army. But we cannot help thinking that by careful organisation, satisfactory arrangements might be made whereby breeders would have an opportunity of showing their horses to the Army buyers at convenient local centres.

At first, no doubt, a considerable number of unsuitable animals would be sent, but as experience was gained as to the sort of horse which the Army would buy, more and more would be up to the standard required.

If such a system were generally adopted, the Army would have a better selection, the breeder would get a better price, and most important of all, every breeder of light horses would know that he would have as good an opportunity as anyone else in the same line of disposing satisfactorily of his young stock.

(9) *Purchase of Mares.* The Army authorities could give further valuable assistance to horse-breeding, by making it part of their policy to buy annually a certain number of mares of rather a better stamp than the ordinary troop horse. Such mares, if bought at 4 years old, would probably command too high a price, if they had not already been snapped up by the foreigner, but they might be bought comparatively cheaply at 3 years old, or better still at 2. They could then be served by a Thoroughbred or registered sire and left with the breeder until the foal had been weaned, after which they could be passed into the Army in the ordinary way.

The inducement to the breeder to keep the mare should be that he would be allowed to retain the produce, which would be a set-off against the mare's keep. Some arrangements would have to be made as to insurance of the mare while she was in the hands of the breeder and as to compensation for expenses if she proved barren. It may be urged against the suggestion that breeding from mares so young as 2 would be injudicious; but your Committee are agreed in thinking that experience proves the contrary, and while there may be a certain amount of opinion opposed to this course, yet the majority of breeders would appear to be in favour of it.

If the suggestion as stated above were carried out, two advantages would follow:—

(a) A certain number of mares would be retained in this country which would otherwise go to the foreigner, and

(b) the mares, before being put to work would leave produce to carry on the strain. There is an additional advantage in breeding from mares at 2 or 3 years old, and that is they are more likely to breed again when older.

(10) *Distribution of Army Mares to Breeders.* Your Committee suggest that another way in which the Army could help horse-breeding would be to cast from service a few of their best mares, say at 12 years old, or preferably sooner, before they are altogether worn out. These mares could be distributed, either to their original breeder or to others who would be willing to undertake them. It would be necessary to make a very careful selection of mares for this purpose, but there would be some quite good enough to breed from, and if the suggestions contained in the preceding paragraph were adopted, the number of good mares available would be gradually increased.

(11) *Facilities for Acquiring Mares.* The suggestions above as to the help which might be given by the Army to horse-breeding, while important, and we believe valuable, only touch the fringe of the question.

There are many districts in which there is a great dearth of mares suitable for breeding, and we are of the opinion that they require re-stocking. If good mares were more easily obtainable, one of the causes which at present prevents a great many from breeding horses would be removed. The object should be to render the acquisition of mares as easy as possible, and to let it be known to likely breeders that they will be assisted in obtaining mares.

(a) By advancing the purchase price of an approved mare on loan to the breeder; the loan to be repaid within five years.

(b) By re-selling to breeders mares purchased by the Government; the breeder to pay by instalments.

(c) By purchasing mares and leasing them to breeders for a small annual rent, say £2, with conditions as to the refusal of the first filly produce being given to the Government at a fixed price.

The assistance given under proposals (a) and (b) should be without conditions except that the breeder should not be entitled to part with the mare until the payments had been completed. These proposals with regard to loans which are similar to those made below for stallions, are discussed in greater detail under that head.

We recommend that a sum of £7,000 should be devoted annually to the above purpose. A considerable proportion of that sum would be reproductive.

(12) *Nominations for Brood Mares.* On the lines of the system at present prevailing in Ireland, we recommend that free nominations to approved stallions be granted to a certain number of approved mares in each distict. Conditions provide that in each district there is an annual exhibition of mares, the property of *bona fide* farmers. Entries for this exhibition must be on a form provided by the local secretary, on which full particulars of the mare must be given. The judge is appointed by the Department of Agriculture and Technical Instruction, and preference is given to young mares under six years. Those selected must be passed free from hereditary disease.

Owners of selected mares are sent a selection docket on which to name the stallion of their choice from an approved list. The secretary then issues a service ticket to the owner of the mare. The ticket is given up at the time of service to the stallion owner, who receives payment on presenting them at the end of the season, on satisfying the Department that all the conditions have been fulfilled. The value of the nomination fee must be uniform for the county and must not be less than £2 nor more than £3. If the service fee exceeds the value of the nomination the difference is paid by the owner of the mare to the owner of the stallion. There are various other regulations designed to prevent fraud and to safeguard the proper working of the scheme.

Your Committee are of the opinion that a system of free nominations under similar regulations would work very well in Great Britain and be a distinct encouragement to breeders. We therefore recommend that the sum of £14,000 be devoted annually to this purpose. The question of the stallions necessary for this scheme is discussed later.

(13) *Stallions.* We are fully alive to the fact that at the root of the question is the necessity for the provision of an adequate number of good sound stallions. Hence our recommendations are directed towards giving facilities for the acquisition of stallions, thereby increasing the number available.

(14) *Purchase of Stallions.* There is no doubt that we lose annually from this country a certain number of Thoroughbred race horses having the necessary substance which, if retained, would be very valuable as stallions. They are bought very often by foreign governments who are prepared to outbid private purchasers.

In order to keep such horses for our own use we recommend that a certain sum — we suggest £5,000 — be set aside annually from the suggested grant, and that there should be an agent of the Government acquainted with the performances of racehorses and the strains of Thoroughbred blood who should buy such of these horses as it seems advisable to keep in the country.

We do not suggest that these horses when bought should be kept by the Government, but that they should be disposed of to such breeders (a list of whom should be kept) who had notified their willingness to take horses of this class. They might either be sold to these breeders at a reduced price, payment to be by instalments, on conditions as to the service of half-bred mares, in the district, at a low fee; or they might be let out to breeders at a reasonable rate on like conditions. The advantage of the latter course would be that many districts might in turn secure the advantages of the presence of a stallion which would be beyond the means of any one private owner.

We are fully conscious that the sum of £5,000 annually would not go far in this direction, but seeing that the proposed expenditure would be largely reproductive either by the resale of the stallions, or by the rents received for their hire, the amount available each year would gradually increase, so as to admit of more extended operations.

(15) *Loans for the Purchase of Stallions.* In order further to increase the facilities of acquiring stallions we recommend that an annual sum of £6,000 be devoted to the purpose of advancing loans to individuals and associations who wish to buy a stallion. A system of this kind is already in operation in Ireland, and it appears to us that it might well be extended throughout Great Britain.

Among other conditions, the regulations provide that no application will be considered coming from a locality in which, in the opinion of the Agricultural Department there is already a sufficient number of approved stallions.

That the purchase of the stallion must be approved by the Department.

That the applicant for a loan must pay to the Department one-third of the purchase price; the amount of the stamp duty; and the premium for the full insurance of the stallion at the full amount of the approved purchase price.

That sureties must be given for the repayment of the loan by five equal annual instalments.

That the applicant must offer the stallion for annual registration and must allow the stallion to serve nominated mares at a fee to be fixed by the Department, in any case not to exceed £3 per mare.

The expenditure proposed under this heading would be recouped in five years, and therefore the amount available would admit of extension if the system proved a success.

(16) *Registration of Stallions.* On lines analagous to those of the Irish system and in order to carry out the recommendations as to free nominations for mares (contained in para. (12)) we suggest that a certain number of stallions — Thoroughbred or regis-

tered in the Hunter or Polo and Riding Pony *Stud Books* — should be registered in each district, and that a list of such registered stallions should be published annually.

Stallions before registration should be approved by competent judges, and passed free from hereditary disease. They should be accepted for particular districts only and should not be removed to other districts without the consent of the registering authority.

Not more than 40 free service dockets will be allotted under this scheme for any stallion.

With the encouragement of nominations to the value of £2 and £3 being given to the owners of selected mares, there would probably be no difficulty in filling the list of each registered stallion.

The sum of £14,000 which it is suggested should be allotted to this purpose would provide for the registration of 175 stallions if the free nomination were fixed at £2, and if each stallion served 40 mares at that rate. Owners of registered stallions could allow these stallions to serve mares in addition to those receiving free Nominations, up to a number determined according to the age of the stallion.

(17) *Royal Commission on Horse Breeding.* Your Committee are of opinion that the scheme for the registration of stallions, and for free nominations of mares, need not necessarily interfere with a system of giving premiums for stallions under the directions of the Royal Commission on Horse-breeding. We feel that, with the very limited sum of £5,000 at their disposal, the Royal Commission have done a great deal of good, and we consider that the gathering of horses at the annual Spring Show exercises a very valuable educational influence, and affords breeders an opportunity of comparing the respective merits of the animals exhibited. We should therefore be extremely sorry to see it discontinued. After experience of the scheme recommended by your Committee, it might be a question for the Royal Commissioners to consider whether they could so modify their system of awarding premiums as to bring both forms of encouragement into greater harmony.

(18) *Purchase of Colts.* If the services of a sound and suitable stallion are to be easily available for mares in every district in the country, it is essential that the number of stallions should be increased. A great many promising colts which would make good stallions are annually castrated, largely because of the inconvenience, difficulty and expense which the private breeder experiences in keeping colts entire until they are old enough for use as stallions. It appears to us it is nearly impossible to obviate this difficulty, and to offer breeders sufficient encouragement to keep a larger proportion of colts entire.

We therefore recommend that part of the contemplated grant should be devoted to the purchase of colts by the Government.

These colts should be purchased for preference as yearlings; but considerable latitude could be allowed to the Government buyers in this respect. And if favourable opportunities occurred for purchasing colts at different ages, they should not be prevented from availing themselves of these opportunities. These colts should be either Thoroughbreds or by a Thoroughbred or Registered Sire, out of a Registered dam (registered in the Hunter *Stud Book*, or in the Polo or Riding Pony *Stud Book*). In our opinion these restrictions are necessary in order to ensure that the colts which it is contemplated to reserve as stallions should have a certain minimum amount of breeding away from coarse strains.

These colts should be reared on suitable land on a Government farm, and at 4 years old those considered good enough for use as stallions should be disposed of to breeders by outright sale, sale by instalments, or on the lease system as described earlier. Those not considered good enough for use as stallions should be castrated and disposed of to the best advantage.

There might be some difficulty in keeping a quantity of colts together on a Government farm, and in order to lessen this difficulty it may be found possible to find 'walks' for some of these colts among private breeders with extensive paddocks.

We recommend that the sum of £2,700, a large proportion of which would be reproductive, should be devoted to this branch of the scheme. That sum is estimated to admit of the purchase of about 30 colts annually, and to include the expenses of the Government farm.

(19) *Soundness of Stallions.* The question of the freedom of stallions from hereditary disease inevitably came before us. This is so important that we feel obliged to urge that legislation is necessary in order to prevent unsound stallions from travelling.

Some breeders are of the opinion that unsoundness is not hereditary. We cannot share that view. We are aware that some instances may be cited when the stock of a particular stallion affected with unsoundness have not shown traces of that unsoundness. But there are no sufficient statistics to prove that the unsoundness may not develop in subsequent generations, and indeed modern biological research goes to show that the influence of the grandsire or the grandam may be just as potent in the progeny as that of the sire or dam. Unsoundness, like other qualities, may miss a generation and reappear in the second.

Hence the use of unsound breeding stock cannot, in our view, be too strongly deprecated.

We therefore recommend that legislation should be enacted which would provide that no stallion should be allowed to travel the public highway for hire without a veterinary certificate of freedom from hereditary disease; such certificate to be produced at any time on demand.

It should be noticed that our recommendation refers only to stallions travelling the country. It would in no way interfere with the freedom of the individual to use his own unsound stallion on his own mares, nor would it prevent anyone desiring to do so from sending his mare to any particular stallion, even though unsound.

In order to minimise the hardships which might occur, we would suggest that after a horse had reached a certain age, say 8 years, without being declared unsound, he should be given a veterinary certificate for life.

(20) *Organisation.* It appeared to us that our suggestion would not be complete without a few recommendations as to the organisation which would be necessary for carrying out the above proposals.

We therefore suggest that the funds to be allotted under the Development Act for the encouragement of horse-breeding should not be distributed to various societies, but should be administered by the Board of Agriculture, the President of which would be the Minister responsible to Parliament. In order to assist him in the organisation and application of the scheme, we suggest that the President of the Board of Agriculture should appoint an Advisory Council on which there should be representatives from:

    (a) The Board of Agriculture.

    (b) The Royal Commission on Horse-Breeding.

    (c) The Councils of the Hunters' Improvement Society and of the Polo and Riding Pony Society; and

    (d) Officers recommended by the Army Council.

It should be part of the function of this Advisory Council to arrange for the appointment of small local committees (with a paid corresponding member) to perform such work in connection with the scheme as must be carried out locally.

No doubt the division of the country into districts would also be part of the work of the Advisory Council; but two points in connection with this division appear to us important:

    (a) That the districts in which local committees are first set up should be those that are most suitable for horse-breeding.

(b) That there should be considerable elasticity in the size of the districts, and that the boundaries of Hunts, or groups of Hunts, would in all probability be more convenient than the boundaries of counties or local authorities.

(21) *Ireland*. It was recommended that the funds allotted to Ireland should be left distinct from those allotted to Great Britain and should go towards the extension of the existing scheme in that country, which seems to us admirable. We suggest that out of the sum of £50,000 which we ask, £10,000 should be allotted to Ireland in addition to the grants they now have.

The report of the Horse Supply Committee was submitted at the Council meeting on 6 June 1910. The President, Mr R. G. Carden, said that the Council instructed the Brood Mare Committee to draw up a report to be presented to the Commissioners under the Development Act, and they referred the matter to the Horse Supply Committee to report direct to the Council. Therefore they had now to consider a report from the Horse Supply Committee, of which Viscount Helmsley was Chairman, before sending it to the Commissioners under the Development Act, and other interested Departments and individuals.

Lord Middleton then moved the adoption of the Report as presented. The Council was strongly of the opinion that no time should be lost in taking the necessary steps to complete the organisation without which no scheme could be introduced. Copies of the report should be sent to:—

The Prime Minister.
Chancellor of the Exchequer.
Members of both Houses of Parliament.
Commissioners under the Development Act.
Royal Commission on Horse Breeding.
Secretary of State for War.
Minister for Agriculture.
Army Council.
Inspector-General of the Forces.
Director and Assistant Director of Transport and Remounts.
Irish Department of Agriculture.
Members of the Society.
Affiliated Societies (with a request for Resolutions in support).

There were many recommendations which were most excellent; taken as a whole, the Report could not be better. In the first place, the need for an accurate census was unquestionable. Those that had been taken were most inadequate, failing to distinguish between light and heavy horses. All would agree to no restrictions being placed on the export trade. It was the universal opinion of breeders that the Army should buy 3-year-olds and give a better price, while the recommendation that the Army should be more in touch with breeders was essential. Then there were suggestions as to acquiring mares, how to acquire stallions and the purchase of stallions — all proposals of first importance, as there were many most valuable stallions which passed out of this country simply because people were not in a position to buy them. Buyers felt that they could not risk very much without the certainty of an adequate return. This, and the purchasing of colts by the Government, should be a great incentive to Light Horse breeding. Stallions should also not be allowed to travel on the road that were not sound, and all should be required to carry certificates of soundness.

The Hon. Alexander Parker seconded the adoption of this report. There were several points in connection with it that he thought should be emphasised. The chief was the composition of the Horse Supply Committee. There was not a single member on it who was not actuated by one disinterested idea — to ensure the provision of better horses for hunting (he was then Master of the North Warwickshire) and better horses for the nation. In formulating this scheme, the Committee had specially in their minds the fact that it was no use suggesting a scheme that went beyond the scope which could be carried out by the money that they were likely to get, and although they would all agree that the sum of £50,000 was an extremely small amount compared with the amounts that Foreign Governments were devoting to this purpose, yet he thought that the Committee had made the very best use of that £50,000. Another point was that the report had been signed unanimously. If they studied it carefully they would find that any section of the recommendations at the end of the Report can be amended without seriously impairing the utility of the scheme as a whole. That was a very strong point in its favour. In addition to those to whom Lord Middleton thought the report should be sent, he thought that it would be a great thing if everyone did their utmost to bring this matter before any agricultural meetings, and secure their support, thus ensuring for it the greatest possible publicity.

The Secretary then read a letter from Mr W. T. Trench as to the restrictions placed upon the qualifications of Hunter Stallions in the scheme. Viscount Helmsley, Chairman of the Horse Supply Committee, said that the point came before the Committee and was discussed at some length, but finally it was decided unanimously that it was very undesirable to admit stallions to the scheme without some restrictions, otherwise they would open the door to the admission of undesirable blood. The Committee failed to see how that could be kept out, indeed, without some distinction such as they ventured to suggest.

Mr Algernon Turnor, CB, urged the necessity of creating the necessary organisation without delay. It was obvious that if their proposals were to become effective in 1911, local Committees must at once be formed. Any delay would mean the loss of another season. It would be best to commence with a few districts, probably those in which were already established the Brood Mare Societies affiliated to the HIS and other suitable districts. Action was imperative to complete the organisation before the autumn.

The Chairman replied that this Society had already urged the necessity for national action so long ago as 1904, when they issued their Blue Book, and it was no doubt desirable to press the suggestions contained in that exhaustive report and in their present proposals upon the Government with an addendum that the HIS was the accredited representative of the Light Horse industry, established in 1885 to promote the National Horse Supply.

In response to other questions, the Chairman said the Committee was anxious to ensure by Act of Parliament that no stallion should travel for public use without a Government certificate of soundness, as was done in France.

The original application for the grant of £40,000 in respect of Great Britain was approved by the Development Commissioners in November 1910, and authorised by the Treasury in January 1911, when the following statement was issued by the Board of Agriculture and Fisheries:

The Lords Commissioners of the Treasury have, on the recommendation of the Development Commissioners, made a grant to the Board of Agriculture and Fisheries from the Development Fund of £40,000 for the ensuing year for the encouragement of Light Horse Breeding in Great Britain by means of

(1) The award of premiums to stallions.
(2) Grants for the purchase of half-bred working brood mares for location in selected districts.
(3) Free nominations for suitable mares for service by Premium or approved stallions.
(4) The purchase (for re-sale) of stallions.
(5) The voluntary Registration of stallions.

The President of the Board proposes at once to appoint an Advisory Council composed of persons intimately acquainted with the industry in various parts of the country to advise and assist the Board generally with respect to all matters connected with the industry of Horse-breeding. Until this Council has been constituted it is not possible for the Board to make public any details of the manner in which they propose that their scheme will be carried out, but in view of the necessity for making preparations for the breeding season of 1911 without delay, the Board think it desirable to give the following information on the subject.

Premiums to stallions

The premiums will be of two classes, viz:—

(1) *King's Premiums* King's Premiums will be awarded at the Spring Show to be held in London on the 7th., 8th. and 9th. March next in connection with the Hunters' Improvement Society Show, and will be made up (a) of a fixed amount to be paid on the award being made, (b) of a service fee for each mare covered during the season, and (c) of a further fee for each foal produced. The owner of a King's Premium stallion will be required in each case to enter into an agreement to allow the stallion to serve if required not fewer than 50 mares exclusive of mares for the service of which a free nomination has been given by the Board to the owner of the mare, and any mare which has been purchased or leased to a farmer or other person in connection with the scheme. Service fees will not be paid for more than 90 mares in any one year. The fee to be charged to the owner of a mare by the owner of a stallion is to be limited to £2, exclusive of the Groom's fee (2s.6d.). The amounts of the various payments have been so arranged as to secure that the owner of a King's Premium stallion which travels a district and serves 50 mares will, on an average, receive approximately £150 in the season, in addition to the fees payable by the owner of the mare.

(2) *Board's Premiums* The stallions to whom these Premiums are paid will be selected either at a local Spring Exhibition or by the Board themselves on the application of the owner and in all cases subject to approval as to soundness and suitability by a Veterinary Surgeon nominated by the Board. The Board's Premium will be made up of service and foal fees, and as in the case of a King's Premium Stallion, the owner of the stallion will be required to enter into an agreement to allow his stallion to serve, if required, not fewer than 50 mares exclusive of mares for the service of which a free nomination has been given by the Board to the owner of the mare, and of any mare which has been purchased or leased to a farmer or other person in connection with the scheme. Service fees will not be paid for more than 90 mares in any one year. The fee to be charged to the owner of the mare by the owner of the stallion is to be limited to

£1, exclusive of the groom's fee (2s.6d.). The amounts of the various payments have been so arranged as to secure that the owner of a Board's Premium Stallion which travels a district and serves 50 mares will, on an average, receive approximately £75 in the season, in addition to the fees payable by the owner of the mare.

Both in the case of a King's Premium Stallion and a Board's Premium stallion the covering fee will be larger in amount where the Stallion does not merely stand for service but travels in the district.

The Board also propose to award a limited number of Premiums of smaller amounts for Pony Stallions.

Purchase of brood mares

It is proposed that the moneys available for this purpose shall be expended locally through the agency of County Committees and Sub-Committees. The Board hope to be in a position to provide for the purchase of young half-bred working mares of good quality and of suitable conformation with a view to re-sell or lease them on certain conditions to the holders of suitable farms for the purpose of mating them with Premium or other approved stallions. The sum available for this purpose should suffice for the purchase of upwards of 200 mares during each year.

Free nominations for mares

The Board also hope to secure the distribution of a number of free nominations for service by King's Premium or Board's Premium Stallions, through the agency of the County Committees. A nomination, whether to a King's or a Board's Premium Stallion, will represent the fee which the owner of the mare would otherwise himself have to pay for the services of the Stallion. The intention is that these free nominations, about 1400 in number, shall be allocated by preference to the smaller tenant farmers and others in respect of the best of the young mares in their possession.

Purchase of stallions

The Board propose to expend a considerable sum on the purchase of Thoroughbred Stallions for re-sale on special conditions, with a view to securing the use in the district of a stallion of somewhat higher class than could otherwise be obtained, and of providing suitable stallions in districts where at present their services are not readily available. It is hoped by this means to secure the retention in this country of a certain number of Stallions which would otherwise go abroad. The number thus purchased in any one year cannot be large, but it is believed that in the course of time a substantial benefit to the industry will accrue.

Registration of stallions

The voluntary registration of Stallions by the Board is not to be confined to Light Horses only, but will be extended to Stallions of all breeds entered in the recognised Stud Books. It is intended that registration shall be carried out free of cost to the owner, except in the case of a Stallion serving at a fee exceeding £10, exclusive of the groom's fee, in which case the expense of veterinary inspection will be borne by the owner. The main object of the proposal is to establish a recognised standard of soundness for breeding purposes. The owner of a mare will know that any recognised Stallion has been examined by a competent authority and passed sound for service. As regards the suitability of the horse from other points of view, he will still have to rely on his own judgement, but in one important respect at any rate his choice will be made more easy.

The responsibility for the administration of the grant as a whole will rest with the Board, who will have at their disposal the assistance of the proposed Advisory Council representing all branches of the industry. In many important respects the detailed administration of the scheme will be left in the hands of the County Committees, without whose co-operation proposals of this magnitude could not successfully be undertaken. The Secretary of State for War has stated that the War Office will be prepared to purchase annually a certain number of the remount horses at 3 years off, and he has promised the co-operation and assistance of the Army Council, who will be represented at the meetings of the Advisory Council. If, as it is confidently believed, the willing assistance of all concerned in the industry can be secured for the carrying out of these proposals, there is good hope that the value of the industry can be materially increased and an important benefit to agriculture secured.

The Advisory Council were duly constituted and met in February, when Lord Middleton was elected Chairman, with the Hon. Alexander Parker as Vice-Chairman, and in July, when a statement was submitted as to the working of the scheme.

King's premiums

The time available between the authorisation of the grant by the Treasury and the Spring Show was so limited that it was not possible to complete the organisation of the County Committees, which by now had been appointed in every county but one. The service arrangements of the King's Premiums Stallions were therefore supervised by District Committees on the same lines as those of the Royal Commission on Horse-breeding. In all these circumstances the entries were adequate; and were in fact larger than they had been at recent shows, but it was impossible to suppose that the increased number of premiums could have had much effect on the entries, considering that the announcement was made at such a late date.

The grant of £40,000 was apportioned under the following heads:—

(1)	The Award of Premiums to Stallions	£13,000
(2)	Grants for the purchase of half-bred working Brood Mares in selected districts	£10,000
(3)	Nominations for Mares for service by Premium Stallions	£3,000
(4)	Purchase (for re-sale) of stallions	£5,000
(5)	Registration of Stallions of all breeds	£5,000
(6)	Administration	£3,800

The Advisory Council, upon which are five members of the Royal Commission on Horse-breeding, and leading representatives of the Hunters' Improvement Society, met on 7 February 1911, and appointed a Standing Committee of 20 members with whom the Board are in constant communication, and to whom are referred for their advice and their suggestions many matters in respect of various points under consideration. Upon their recommendations it has been resolved in respect of the 1912 show:

That the rules should be answered as follows:

(a) That no stallion shall be accepted for entry at the show unless it has been examined and placed on the Board's Stallion Register in the current year (November, 1911 to October, 1912). No veterinary examination will be made at the Show.

(b) That exhibitors be allowed to enter as many stallions as they like in a District Class, and that they be allowed to take all the Premiums awarded to them.

(c) That every King's Premium Stallion should 'travel', and not be allowed the option of 'standing' in a district.

(d) That the method of payment for 'travelling' be altered from 19s.6d. a service to an award of 50 guineas to be paid at the close of the season.

(e) That the 'Service Season' now fixed for 1 April to 31 July be considered the 'Travelling Season', but that King's Premium Stallions be allowed to serve mares prior to 1 April provided that the service takes place in the district for which the award is made, and that it is duly entered in the Service Book of the Stallion owner.

(f) That a King's Premium Stallion be allowed to be exhibited *for competition* on or after 15 July in the district for which the Premium is awarded, provided that sanction for such exhibition is first obtained from the Committee which is supervising the service arrangements of the stallion.

(g) That no Service Fees be paid by the Board to the owner of a King's Premium Stallion for the service by that stallion of more than one mare belonging to him.

(h) That no fee in excess of the prescribed fee be charged (unless the owner of the mare offers to pay for it) for the service of half-bred mares located in the district for which the Premium was awarded, unless and until 70 half-bred mares have been served, inclusive of mares purchased by a County Committee and mares in favour of which nominations for free service have been issued.

(i) That after the commencement of the Travelling Season, no Kings Premium Stallion be exhibited in any town or village along or near the route of another King's Premium Stallion without the permission of the Board.

(j) That a Stallion which has been admitted to the Agricultural Hall cannot be withdrawn from Exhibition, and that a Premium awarded to it cannot be refused by the owner, except by permission of the Board.

(k) That a King's Premium Stallion be not sold or let, during the Service Season, without the approval of the Board except in the event of the death of the owner, and that in such a case his executors be prohibited from selling or letting the stallion without giving notice to, and obtaining the agreement of, the purchaser or lessees to observe the Rules and Regulations that were binding on the owner of the stallion.

Board's premiums

That Light Horse Stallions of any other recognised breeds should be eligible also for these Premiums provided that in the event of a Premium being awarded, payments by the Board should be made only in respect of registered mares of the same breed as the Stallion.

Purchase of Brood mares

That grants be allocated only to those counties where a Brood Mare Organisation existed or where the necessary machinery could be put in motion without delay, and that the organisation of the scheme in such Counties should be completed on a substantial basis, before the scheme be extended to other Counties.

Registration of stallions

(a) That the Rules should contain a Schedule of Diseases and defects which should absolutely disqualify a stallion for Registration, as follows:—Cataract, Ringbone, Roaring, Navicular Disease, Sidebone, Shivering, Whistling, Bone Spavin, String-halt, and defective Genital Organs.

(b) That the registration year be from 1 November to 31 October.

(c) That the Veterinary Surgeon employed to examine a stallion should be required to report on the *suitability* of the Stallion for breeding purposes as well as its soundness, and be required to report fully as to any diseases or defects other than those scheduled which in his opinion render the Stallion either unsound or unsuitable for breeding purposes.

The Rules for Custodians of Brood Mares were also submitted to the Standing Committee before issue, and were framed in accordance with the views of the Committee.

The Committee also had before them certain proposals of Mr Phillpotts-Williams, a Member of the Council, as to the reconstruction of the Board's scheme for the purchase and placing in the hands of custodians, of Brood Mares, but they did not consider the time to be opportune for the reconstruction of the scheme which was, at the time, being put into active operation.

The Committee have further been asked for their advice as to the manner in which a gift of £10,000, by an officer in the Army, could be expended to the best advantage in the furtherance of the Board's Horse-Breeding Scheme.

In this connection they have had under their consideration schemes for experiments in Horse-breeding put forward by

(1) Prof. Ewart and Mr Hurst;
(2) Mr John Hill;
(3) Mr Algernon Turnor;

but they have not yet arrived at a decision on this important question.

At the Meeting on 6 July 1911, Mr A. W. Anstruther, CB, an Assistant Secretary of the Board of Agriculture and Fisheries, gave to the Advisory Council a detailed statement as to the working of the Scheme, expressing their indebtedness to Lord Middleton (the Chairman) and the Standing Committee for the valuable advice afforded and for the consideration given by its members to the difficult questions submitted to them. The Board also appreciated the co-operation of the County Committees, and the work of their secretaries, who for all practical purposes filled what were merely honorary positions. The success of the scheme would largely depend on County Committees, as by means of the information which they divided the Board would have at their disposal much useful information which would enable them to select the routes to be travelled by the Stallions.

The short notice at which the Board took over the work of the Royal Commission, with the consequent meagre information on which they had to work, necessitated unusual haste in the arrangements for the 1911 season. With the co-operation of the County Committees they would be better able to obtain details as to the location of mares whose owners would use Premium Stallions and a list of gentlemen prepared to supervise the service operations. The routes would thus be well organised, though the short time between the award of the Premiums and the date upon which the horses should be in their districts — an interval of less than three weeks — presented an element of difficulty, in view of the preparation of the travelling cards.

Practically the whole of the Grant for Brood Mares had been allocated. The scheme had proved popular, and no substantial difficulty had been experienced in purchasing mares or in getting suitable custodians. The future success of the scheme would depend upon the discrimination shown by the County Committees in the purchase of suitable mares. From reports it appeared that on the whole the mares seemed to have been wisely chosen, though some would not be likely to make suitable brood mares for the particular purposes of the scheme. In such cases the County Committees should arrange to part with the mares and substitute something better for them. The Board hoped to forward this part of the scheme by obtaining the grant in advance, to enable mares to be purchased before the commencement of the financial year, and thereby establish a better sequence in their operations for the next and subsequent seasons.

The free nominations to a certain number of mares in the district travelled by each stallion had been well taken up. Unsoundness in a large proportion of the mares presented had necessitated their refusal for free service, with the result that the County Committees had had to examine more than half as many again before they could get the number of sound mares to which they could give nominations. To avoid the consequent increased cost of veterinary examination, the County Committees would be invited to arrange a previous lay inspection, and only send before the veterinary surgeons mares which were palpably suitable.

The returns of the other mares presented for service were not yet available, but a return obtained from the stallion owners for the first two months of the season showed that the average number of mares covered by Premium Stallions by that date was 43. As one stallion served only five mares and others were below the 50 anticipated, the average was satisfactory. The maximum number of mares served before 31 May by one stallion was 82.

The registration of stallions had been well received, and with the co-operation of the Breed Societies its application would become universal, as it was hoped that all shows would recognise as sound any stallion certified by the Board as sound for the year for which it was registered. The number of registered stallions to date was 305, of which 102 were Thoroughbreds. They had rejected 43.

Major-General Brocklehurst suggested that the examination of Thoroughbred Stallions at 4 years and upwards should hold good for life, as they had been tried and proved themselves sound ȯn the race-course. Veterinary reports differed, and owners would not risk sending up a good stallion to the show.

The Duke of Portland agreed with General Brocklehurst in the main, but considered that as hard training on a racecourse was not enough for all purposes, 4 years was rather young, and he would rather have the horse passed sound at 7 years old.

The Hon. Alexander Parker and Professor Penberthy strongly urged that this point had been exhaustively discussed by the Standing Committee, who considered that no age limit was safe. Horses which developed roaring or unsoundness after a certain age were equally likely to transmit it to their stock as animals that developed it at the age of 4 up to 8. The professional evidence before the Committee indicated that the majority of cases of unsoundness developed after 4 years rather than before. Horses examined annually in successive years for 7 years gave no evidence of unsoundness for the first 6 years and yet in the seventh year developed most palpable unsoundness, which was acknowledged to be hereditary. No loophole should therefore be left as they were all agreed that the element of unsoundness was that which detracted most from Horse Breeding at the present moment.

In response to an inquiry from Viscount Helmsley, Mr Anstruther said that, up to the present, no portion of the grant had been expended on the purchase of Thoroughbred Stallions for re-sale to persons in this country, on the condition that they remained in the country. The question was under the consideration of a Committee, though they had not yet been able to formulate conditions that would be satisfactory to owners of stallions or which would not involve a heavy loss to the Board on the re-sale of the animals. Their present intention was that such a stallion should come up to the show annually, and that it would therefore be annually examined for qualification to enter the Show.

Mr Nickisson thought that the present system of allocating the Premiums did not ensure the best 50 horses getting the awards. One District class might contain eight or nine exceedingly good horses, any one of which a breeder would be anxious to use, though there were only three Premiums available, while in another class these went to moderate and indifferent horses.

Mr Anstruther, in acknowledging that it was a difficult point, stated that the judges were not bound to select such horses, and could utilise, as was done at the 1911 show, the reserves in the better classes.

The Hon. Alexander Parker also raised the question, for the consideration of the Standing Committee, of the desirability of giving free nominations to mares for service by other than Premium Horses, provided such a stallion was a registered horse, and such service was approved by the County Committee. The Premium Horses did not cover the whole of the county, and an owner of a mare who wished to benefit under the scheme could not do so, as he was not always able to get the service of a Premium Horse.

At the 1910 Spring Show, no alteration was introduced into the schedule of prizes. The ridden hunters were judged by Gordon Cunard and Major G. Franks, who awarded the championship to W. A. Simpson-Hinchcliffe of Harrogate's brown middleweight 7-year-old Broadwood, by Red Eagle, for the second year running. Reserve was Frank Rickaby's bay lightweight 7-year-old Reckless, of unknown breeding. H. Cholmondeley and Major F. H. Wise judged the Breeding classes, and for the first time the championship went to a yearling, Sir Merrik Burrell's chestnut home-bred Sunbeam, by Rousseau, with the reserve going to W. S. Ridehalgh's bay 2-year-old colt Midland, by St Pancras, bred at Bridlington by Edward Hodgson. The champion appears from his photograph to be exceptionally mature and well-grown and beautifully proportioned, with wonderful limbs.

In 1911 the Earl of Kenmare and W. G. Lambarde gave the ridden championship to the grey 5-year-old Monarch, by Boykin, bred by William Jordison at Thirsk and exhibited by Stephen Furness, MP, of West Hartlepool. Reserve was W. Guy Mewburn's brown heavyweight 6-year-old Barometer, by Roswal, bred by Robert Curtis at Winslow. Sir Henry Hoare, Bart., and Anthony F. Maude gave the led championship to Mrs R. C. Bainbridge's Mephistopheles, exhibitor-bred in Devon by Red Prince II and 3-years-old. Reserve was the runner-up in the class, Major-General W. T. Goldsworthy's chestnut Emerald, by Masterman Ready.

For the first time in 1911, the number of Premium Stallions was increased to 50 and His Majesty the King (Edward VII) offered for competition a Champion Cup for the best stallion in the show. It was awarded to Mr Henry A. Cholmondeley's Berrill, a bay-brown 16-hand son of Rouge Dragon, foaled in 1896, who stood at Burton Agnes and won District Class VI for the East and West riding of Yorkshire. Reserve was John Drage's Drummond's Pride, who stood at Chapel Brampton and travelled Market Harborough, Kettering, Thrapston and Wellingborough. He was by Drummond.

The HIS was able to celebrate its first quarter-century with the Annual General Meeting of Members in 1910. An honorary list of 51 veterinary officers was appointed for England and Wales to administer the new rules for inspection and examination. Membership was kept up to strength by the election of new candidates to offset annual wastage, and the financial position of the Society was most satisfactory. After discharging the annual expenditure and considerably more than half the cost of Volume IV of the *Hunter Stud Book*, the reserve fund was strengthened by an additional £500 invested in $3\frac{1}{2}$ per cent India Stock.

At the 26th AGM in 1911, it was recorded that the Society deeply deplored the death of His Late Majesty King Edward VII, whose interest in its work was evinced by frequent visits to the Spring Show. The Council duly conveyed to His Majesty the King (George V) and Her Majesty Queen Alexandra their loyal feelings of sincere and deep regret so universally shared by the whole Empire. The Council had the honour to announce that His Majesty the King (George V) had been graciously pleased to continue the Royal Patronage which the Society had enjoyed under the two previous reigns.

At the Meeting of the Advisory Council on 27 June 1912, Mr A.W. Anstruther, CB (an Assistant Secretary to the Board of Agriculture and Fisheries) presented a report indicating the action taken since 31 October 1911.

CHAPTER 6

———————◄❋►———————

Report of the Advisory Council

THE recommendations of the Standing Committee were endorsed by the Advisory Council and incorporated into the Regulations for the 1912 season. It was further decided to offer for competition at the 1912 Show ten super-Premiums, which would entitle the owner of a stallion to which such a Premium might be awarded to a payment, on award, of 100 guineas in addition to the ordinary Premium, provided that he undertook to enter the same stallion for the show to be held in March, 1913, subject to the forfeiture of the additional Premium should he fail to do so. As regards the King's Premiums awarded in 1912, it had also been made a condition that every stallion should travel an allotted district, and that a fixed sum of 50 guineas should be paid to the owner of the stallion at the close of the service season in respect of travelling, in lieu of the method of payment adopted in 1911 whereby an additional fee was payable — in cases where stallions travelled a district — in respect of each mare served.

The regulations as to the award of Board's premiums to stallions for the 1912 season has also been amended. In future £20 would be paid to the owner when the award was made. The average value of the Premium was increased from £75 to £80.

A further grant of £10,000 had been made for the purchase of brood mares, in selected counties, which would later be extended to the country at large. An arrangement had also been reached with the War Office for the sale to the Department of 20 selected Artillery mares, to be placed out with certain County Committees as brood mares. Six had gone to Wiltshire, four each to East and West Sussex, three each to Northamptonshire and Warwickshire. They were of an exceptionally good and suitable type and the recipients were approving and satisfied. A committee concerned with the breeding of ponies had also been formed under Lord Arthur Cecil.

During the winter special schemes were elaborated for dealing with the revival of some of the hardy old native breeds of horses and ponies in Scotland and Wales. A sum of £400 had been granted to the Invernesshire County Committee, with which arrangements would be made for the purchase of some of the best available Highland Pony mares, to be mated, under the direction of the County Committee, with suitable stallions, service fees to be paid by the Board.

In Pembrokeshire and Carmarthenshire similar schemes had been set in train for the revival of the old Welsh light cart horse, or roadster breed, which was rapidly disappearing. In each case a grant of £400 had been made for the purchase of mares, and provision had also been made for the acquisition of stallions of the breed.

Similar arrangements were contemplated for the revival of the old Devon-shire pack horse — remains of which were said still to exist in south-west Devonshire and in eastern Cornwall — but sufficient information was not yet available.

Steps were also being taken to encourage the revival of the old strain of Welsh cob. No grant had been made for the purchase of mares by a limited number of Premiums, for Welsh cob stallions were to be given by the Board, under conditions which would allow free services being given to 25 mares of the breed, provided that they were certified by the County Committee as being suitable in breed and type.

Special premiums would also be awarded to six New Forest Pony stallions, to be selected by a judge appointed by the Board, to run on six selected portions of the New Forest for the service of mares belonging to commoners. Similarly, four Premiums would be allotted to stallions to run on the commons under the control of the Church Stretton Hill Pony Improvement Society. In neither case would a premium be awarded to a stallion unless it had been accepted for registration under the Board's scheme.

Since the registration of stallions had been tightened up as regards soundness and suitability, the number of owners applying had increased from 312 to 613, made up of 162 Thoroughbreds, 56 Hackneys, 18 Hunters, 3 Cleveland Bays, 3 Yorkshire Coach Horses, 1 Dartmoor Pony, 18 Highland Ponies, 14 Polo Ponies, 14 Shetland Ponies, 2 Trotters, 11 Welsh Cob Ponies, 17 Welsh Ponies, 215 Shires, 48 Clydesdales, and 31 Suffolks.

Of this number, 214 were also registered in 1911. Nineteen submitted for re-registration were not accepted, and 53 submitted for the first time were rejected. The right of appeal was taken advantage of in 14 cases, six of which confirmed the decision of the examining veterinary surgeon.

With regard to the very generous offer of Captain Dealtry C. Part, 21st Lancers, to place £10,000 at the disposal of the Board to be expended on the improvement of light horse breeding, it was ultimately decided that the object could be best attained were this sum to be expended directly by Captain Part in consultation with Major C. C. Hurst, one of the scientific members of the Advisory Council, and Mr F. W. Carter, a superintending Inspector of the Board, in accordance with the following conditions (*inter alia*):

(1) That the Mendelian experiment, on the lines suggested by Professor Ewart and Major Hurst, should be carried out by Captain Part on behalf of the Board.

(2) That the experiment should be carried out at the expense of Captain Part for a period not exceeding six years, and that at the end of this period, or at such earlier date when a definite result of the experiment shall be considered to have been attained, the mares used shall be handed over as a gift to the Board, should they wish to continue it on a more extended scale.

(3) That if at the end of the period, which is not to exceed six years, the Board wish to continue, Captain Part will hand over to them, at valuation, the

stallion and such produce of the animals used for the experiment as Major Hurst considers the Board to require.

It is believed that this experiment may furnish information of the highest value in connection with the applicability of the Mendelian theories to the breed of Thoroughbred horses.

In connection with Captain Part's original proposals as to the allocation of his gift, it was at one time contemplated that a portion of the money thus to be made available should be expended specially in the direction of the encouragement of the breeding of hunter-bred sires. In view of the revised arrangements alluded to above, this question has had to be deferred.

Thoroughbred Show, 1912

It is satisfactory to be able to report that in the opinion of the Judges, namely Sir Gilbert Greenall, Bart., cvo, Captain C. H. D. Fetherstonhaugh and Mr E. P. Rawnsley, the stallions exhibited at this show were considerably superior in merit to those exhibited in 1911, and the judges expressly state that in their opinion the ten horses to which Super-Premiums were awarded 'were of an exceptionally high standard'. It is a significant fact that no fewer than fifteen stallions to which premiums were awarded in 1911 failed to secure a place in the list of Premium winners this year, doubtless because a number of young horses of merit were exhibited for the first time at this show. The following horses which only came out of training last season, *viz*. Lousby, Carrousel, My Bird Sings, Explorer and Cock of the Walk were awarded Premiums, and the first three were also awarded Super-Premiums.

In presenting the report, Mr Anstruther furnished further details of interest. Of the 50 Thoroughbred stallions awarded King's Premiums in 1911, 46 travelled and 4 stayed at home. Free nominations were awarded to 625 mares; the total number of mares served was 3,245; and the amount paid by the Board in fees was £6,232.5s., to which of course had to be added the sum of £2,625 for the original Premium — the sum of 50 guineas paid on award to each stallion, and the amount to be paid for foal fees.

375 Brood Mares had already been purchased, and about half that number had been examined by the Board's Veterinary Officers and the Superintending Inspector. The results could be regarded as satisfactory. Twenty-eight of the mares examined were considered unsuitable and the County Committees concerned were advised to dispose of them. Others were not likely to turn out suitable, but should be kept for a year or two to see what class of stock they produced. The Board was endeavouring to place in the hands of custodians a type of mare suitable for the purpose, such as would really encourage farmers to take up horse-breeding again. Thirty-seven counties had received grants, in Pembrokeshire and Carmarthenshire to purchase mares of the old breed of Welsh Light Cart Horses to preserve the hardy native breed and ensure its reproduction. Crossing them with a Thoroughbred ensured a rapid profit, as from such crosses the Pembrokeshire hunter had been produced.

Investigation had revealed the existence of a very much larger number of these mares in the country than was anticipated, some of an excellent type. Farmers were disposed to use a sire of this native breed for their mares, and would in time form a reservoir from which County Committees in England could buy their light-legged brood mares suitable for breeding hunters. It was on these lines that the Irish Department was endeavouring to revive the Irish Draught Horse, from which were descended the dams of some of their Irish hunters. Greater difficulty was experienced in Devonshire with regard to the pack horse, owing to the absence of suitable foundation stock. With reference to the registration of stallions the following additional figures were given: —

Up to 29 February 1912, 509 stallions had been registered, and a further 199 since that date. Of the 509, 48 were Hackneys, 15 Hunters and 159 were Thoroughbreds, the remainder of the light horses being American Trotter, Arab, Cleveland Bay or Yorkshire Coach. Since February the additions had been to the Hackneys 12, to the Hunters 3 and to the Thoroughbreds, making a total of 60 Hackneys, 18 Hunters and 170 Thoroughbreds. During the full period ended 31 May they had registered 261 Light Stallions and 109 Pony Stallions. The ponies embrace the following breeds: — Dartmoor, Fell, Highland Pony, New Forest, Polo and Shetland, and also Welsh Cob, Welsh Pony and Welsh Mountain Pony. Of the heavy breeds they had registered 338, of which 56 were Clydesdales, 246 Shires and 36 Suffolks. The total number was 708, compared with 313 the previous year.

The average number of mares served by the King's Premium Stallions up to 31 May 1912 was 47 as compared with 41 in 1911. Twenty-five Board's Premiums had been awarded, and up to the same date 989 mares had been served — an average of 40 per stallion. In 1911 there were 10 Board Stallions, averaging 24 mares.

Major-General Brocklebank referred to the age limit for stallions in regard to their soundness, and urged that it should be fixed at four; though in Ireland they had it at six.

Mr Campbell of the Irish Department said it was only this year that they had fixed the age at six. In the early years each stallion was examined for wind; now the veterinary surgeon examined them for other unsoundness after that age, but not for wind. If a horse went on the register at three or four, and remained sound until six they did not require that it should be examined again for wind. If it could be proved that any of his stock were unsound, then the horse was removed from the register. If a sire was known to be getting good sound stock he was not again examined after six, but they retained the power to do so in respect of any other unsoundness. The reason given for not examining a horse after six was the sort of life these sires lead. They got fat and heavy, were not perhaps always very well cared for, and owing to their inactive life made a noise of some kind or other — though not necessarily unsound. It was not considered hereditary. Representative Irish breeders were strong advocates of an age limit of four.

Viscount Helmsley and Mr J. L. Nickisson urged that if a horse had a clean bill of health up to eight he should for the rest of his life be certified as an absolutely sound animal.

Major-General Brocklehurst said the difficulty about eight was that the horse they wanted came off the racecourse at three, and in five years' time would 'blow' a bit if he ran a mile.

The Hon Alexander Parker said that a great many horses that were cast as unsound after they got fat were really in themselves not unsound, and it was entirely due to the life that they lead. His experience with Hunters showed that though perfectly sound in condition they had been cast when got up for sale. He instanced a case of a horse passed as sound when in hard condition by a veterinary surgeon, which he had originally cast when fat as making a noise.

Major-General Brocklehurst said that they could not get the veterinary surgeon to differentiate between the horse at Tattersalls when he was fat and when he was lean.

Sir Merrik Burrell, Bart., thought that the veterinary profession was inclined to put too much stress upon wind as one of the hereditary diseases. All light horses went in their wind if they had a bad cold, but the veterinary surgeon, not being able to tell whether the horse had a bad cold or influenza, would not listen to the owner's explanation. He (Sir Merrik) would not use a stallion that made a noise when it was racing, or immediately it came out of training, but if a horse had been trained for three years and passed sound at six they had, for all practical purposes, a sound horse.

His view was that of a great many veterinary surgeons about the country, who had large practical experience, especially with Thoroughbred stallions.

It was resolved to refer this question back to the Standing Committee.

A communication was read from the President of the Board inviting an expression of opinion from the Advisory Council as to the expediency of controlling by legislative enactment the travelling, or service for a fee, of stallions other than those which had received an official certificate of soundness and suitability for breeding purposes.

The question had been before the County Committees and several had suggested that it was advisable to legislate to prevent the travelling of unsound stallions. The experience of Lord Saltoun and his Committee of Aberdeen indicated the need for such regulations. The services of a sound and suitable stallion had been keenly taken up there last year, but during 1912 three horses, not on the Board's register, had appeared to compete and serve at ridiculously low fees. There was no evidence available as to the soundness and suitability of these horses, and any unsatisfactory results would discourage the farmers who had taken up light horse breeding. Lord Saltoun felt it to be important that steps were taken to check practices of this kind, and he had under consideration the preparation of a Bill to be introduced into the House of Lords on the subject. If the certificate of soundness became a matter of necessity owing to an act of Parliament, the lines upon which such certificates should be granted with a possible age limit for soundness for breeding purposes would require careful consideration.

Mr Campbell outlined the action taken in Ireland in respect of this subject. They had been at work for some twelve years on horse-breeding schemes, and although they had some 2,300 stallions in Ireland, yet they had only succeeded in getting some 400 registered. Of the remainder, about 100 might be considered as high-class Thoroughbreds standing at a high fee. Some 1,800 had been rejected on account of unsuitability. In Ireland a farmer kept only the worst as a stallion. He had small fields and he would not keep them entire after a year, as, expecting every yearling to turn out a winner, he had them castrated. If obviously it was not going to be a winner then he might keep it for a stallion. When first they offered to register half-bred stallions hundreds were offered for inspection, but of these only a dozen were selected as sound and suitable. Their Council of Agriculture (of which in England there was no counterpart), which was to a large extent nominated by the County Councils and therefore composed of a good number of the leading-farmers, took the question up and passed three times the following resolution:

That the time had come for the Irish Department to seek Parliamentary powers to prevent the great injury being done to horse-breeding schemes by the number of unsound and unsuitable stallions which had been offered for service; and requested the Vice-President to promote legislation making it illegal for any stallion, save Thoroughbred Stallions serving Thoroughbred mares only, to be employed for the public service, unless passed as sound and suitable for breeding purposes.

Their Advisory Committee also adopted a resolution urging that the efforts of the Irish Department and the local authorities to improve the breeds of horses in Ireland were being, and would continue to be, seriously hampered, and to a great extent nullified so long as no supervision or control was exercised over the very large number of stallions standing in Ireland for public service which did not come within the operations of the Department's scheme. They therefore recommended that, with the exception of Thoroughbred stallions entered in the *General Stud Book*, no stallion should be permitted to stand for public use unless licensed by the Department; and that no stallion should be licensed unless passed by the Department as being free from hereditary disease and up to a certain standard of excellence and suitability for breeding purposes. Such standard should not at first be so high as to interfere seriously or injuriously with the present race of stallions in the country.

The co-operation for the Vice-President of the Department was invoked with a view to the immediate introduction of a Bill to give legislative effect to the foregoing recommendations which were adopted in 1909. Thirty-two out of the 33 County Committees appointed with statutory power under the Act to deal with Horse-breeding approved it, indicating that the general principle had been accepted throughout Ireland.

It had been suggested that Thoroughbred sires serving half-bred as well as Thoroughbred mares should be exempt, and that such exemption might include any Thoroughbred Stallion serving at a fee of over £5. No interference was desired in respect of very well known race-getting sires. They desired to put out of action very bad stallions that were competing with their registered sires. They certainly wished to exempt Thoroughbred sires after six years of age from being tested for wind.

The difficulty was to secure agreement about the unsuitability of an animal for breeding purposes, involving the probable adoption of a lower standard than that required in their registered sires. The register would still be retained, and sires on it would continue to receive certain subsidies. The best of their half-bred sires would be licensed, but would not necessarily be put on the register — these two things, registration and licensing, would be kept distinct. Application for the licence should be made by 1 March in each year and remain in force until 31 December in the same year. Surrender of the old licences would be essential to secure a new one each season, and licences might be suspended, revoked or cancelled by the Department if, after due enquiry, the Department was satisfied that the stallion was suffering from disease either infectious, contagious or hereditary, or that the progeny of the stallion was developing hereditary unsoundness which had been transmitted by the stallion.

A new licence was to be obtained whenever a stallion was sold or leased: all licences were to be issued free and all expenses defrayed by the Department, who would keep the register. Licences were to be produced on demand to any officer of the Department, and all owners of licensed stallions had to keep for inspection a list of the mares served. A list of unsoundnesses would be scheduled, with the provision of a board of appeal consisting of three persons, one of whom to be a veterinary surgeon, who would be the sole judge as to the question of unsoundness.

The chances of obtaining legislation of this kind would be greatly increased if the Board of Agriculture and Fisheries were also to take up the matter. Considering the experience each had had of co-ordination in the past, it should not be difficult for the Board and the Irish Department to arrive at some system applicable and satisfactory to both countries.

Mr Tindall moved that the whole question be referred to the Advisory Committee for consideration and report. Nearly all the breeds of horses were represented in the various Stud Books, and these were invaluable in indicating how to select, and how to breed with a fair chance sound or unsound horses. The percentage of unsound animals was very high, and he would like to propose that anyone in the future who wished to keep a stallion, or who kept a stallion, should not be allowed to travel it on the road for public service unless it was sound. In dealing with the allocation of public funds they must be consistent, and if anybody wished to keep a horse, let the age be what it might, if it were unsound and had not got a Government certificate it must be kept at home. The principle applied to Thoroughbred stallions as precedent to their exhibition at the Spring Show, *viz.* registration as sound and suitable by the Board of Agriculture and Fisheries, and whether they were 4 or 20 should be equally applied. Associations in his own county, paying for the hire of horses from £500 to £800 for the season, found in the first week of April, when the hired horses were shown on parade, a dozen horses going to compete against them at any price during the travelling season. They had no Government certificate, some not even being eligible for registry in their own Stud Book, but covering at any sort of fee. The breeding of the horses registered in the different Stud Books was available, and they could guard against unsoundness, an evil which had been the greatest detriment to horse-breeding for two or more centuries. In these days of mechanical traction everything possible must be done to help the breeders. They must be supported by the Government, who should enact that after a prescribed date stallions without a certificate should not be allowed to travel the country for fees. He would move that for the good of the country; it was essential that only sound horses should receive premiums.

Mr J. L. Nickisson supported the resolution, recalling the action taken by the HIS when in 1904 a deputation waited on Lord Onslow on this very question. An unsound stallion could get 50 or 60 unsound foals, and a man who used the public highways for a horse should be compelled by legislation to produce a certificate of soundness.

Viscount Helmsley seconded the resolution, and it was unanimously agreed to refer the question to the Standing Committee.

The following report on the administration of the grant for the encouragement and improvement of Light Horse Breeding for the year 1 November 1911 to 31 October 1912, was issued by the Board of Agriculture and Fisheries in January 1913:

A preliminary report on the Administration of the Horse Breeding Grant from January 1911 to March 1912 has already been presented to Parliament. In order, however, to give a complete account in the present report of the proceedings for the period 1 November 1911 to 31 October 1912, it will be necessary to repeat some of the information contained in the original report.

The operations connected with the award of premiums to stallions extend over a period of 18 months from the date of the awards to the completion of the foal returns, and the whole of the information respecting them cannot be given in the report for the year. It has been decided, therefore, that the period from 1 November to 31 October — which is the period during which the registration of stallions is carried out — may, for the purposes of the annual review, be regarded as the horse-breeding year.

The grant, which is approximately £40,000 a year, is made by the Development Commissioners for the purpose of encouraging and improving the breeding of light horses, in the numbers of which there has been a serious decline in recent years. The chief means by which the Board are endeavouring to secure the object in view is by the provision of an increased number of high-class Thoroughbred Stallions for the service of half-bred mares at a low fee, and of about 1,000 selected mares free of charge. And in order to encourage farmers and others to keep Brood Mares of substance and quality for mating with Thoroughbred Stallions, the Board also arrange, through the agency of County Committees, for the purchase of mares of this type for leasing out to suitable custodians at a small annual rent. Every possible action is at the same time being taken to encourage breeders to use only sound stallions for the service of their mares, and with a view to placing on the road as many stallions as possible that are free from hereditary disease and suitable for breeding purposes, the Board undertake the veterinary examination, free of charge, of all stallions, the service fee of which does not exceed £10, and the issue of certificates of soundness to all that pass inspection. Action is also being taken to improve the native breeds of Mountain and Moorland ponies as being the foundation stock from which the improved pony, the cob and the polo derive their origin, and to which they owe many of their valuable characteristics of temperament, courage, intelligence and hardiness. In addition, experiments are being carried out to test the possibility and commercial advisability of reviving the old 'packhorse' and 'roadster' breeds, which have, with the advent of good roads, railways, and mechanical traction generally, become almost defunct.

The Board appointed in 1911 a Council to advise them on all matters pertaining to the breeding of light horses. Its members are all intimately acquainted with the conditions and needs for the industry, and represent also various public departments and societies concerned therewith including the War Office, the Department of Agriculture and Technical Instruction for Ireland, the late Royal Commission on Horse-Breeding, the Hunters' Improvement and National Light Horse Breeding Society, and several pony Societies. The Council has appointed a Standing Committee with whom frequent conferences are held, and their advice has been of the greatest value.

Committees have also been appointed in almost every county to assist in the administration of the scheme. Their services are voluntary, and in the great majority of counties they have been given most readily and wholeheartedly. It is on the co-operation of these Committees and their Secretaries that the success of the scheme must to a great extent depend, and the Department are greatly indebted to the members of these Committees for their assistance.

Such, in short, are the measures which are at present being taken to encourage Light

Horse Breeding. Their extension and development will be a matter for consideration in the light of experience gained in the administration of the scheme. At present it would clearly be premature to express any opinion as to the ultimate value of the operations which are being undertaken in reviving the industry of Light Horse Breeding. The measures adopted must be judged not only by the increase which is already apparent in the actual breeding operations, but by the financial results of such operations. Five years at the very least must elapse before an opinion of value could be expressed, and ten years would not be too long a period to be passed under review before any final judgement should be recorded. It will only be in another two years that the earliest of the foals bred under the present scheme will come upon the market, and many of them will not be sold until a year later. The problem for immediate consideration is that of how far the central authority can assist the breeder in the profitable disposal of his young stock, and in this matter the Board have the promise of sympathetic co-operation from the Army Council.

Before detailing the operations for the year 1 November 1911 to 31 October 1912, the full results of the service season of 1911 may be reviewed.

Service season, 1911

At the show which was held at the Royal Agricultural Hall, Islington, in March 1911, the King's Premiums were awarded to 50 stallions. These stallions served or tried during the season (1 April to 31 July) 3,245 mares, being an average of 65 mares per stallion — an average number which is considerably in excess of that attained in the past under the operations of the Royal Commission on Horse-Breeding with about half the number of stallions.

The success of a service season, however, does not depend so much on the number of mares served as on the number of foals produced, and in this respect the season of 1911 cannot be regarded as very satisfactory; allowance must, however, be made for the fact that, owing probably to climatic conditions, the season was a somewhat abnormal one.

Of the 3,245 service fees paid, 80 were in respect of trials, which are not, of course, taken into account in arriving at the number of foals produced, and of the 3,165 mares actually covered no information could be obtained of the results of the service of 245 of them. The foaling particulars received for the remaining 2,920 mares show that 1,567 foals were dropped, giving an average foaling percentage of 53.66. This record of approximately one foal to every two mares served cannot be considered altogether satisfactory, and it is hoped that it will be possible to report an improvement in this direction in future years. In the regulations for the Thoroughbred Show it is provided that the entry of any stallion can be refused if its foal-getting record as a premium stallion in two consecutive years does not exceed 40% of the mares served, but blame in this matter does not always attach to the stallion alone, inasmuch as many mares are sent to Premium horses which cannot be considered to be really suitable for breeding purposes. The custom of sending an old mare which is past work, to the horse, in the hope of taking a foal off her before her days are numbered, is perhaps responsible for many 'no foal' returns — it is a haphazard method of breeding which is not generally successful, and one that does not give the stallion a fair chance, nor is it likely to result in healthy, sound stock being bred.

With the completion of the foal returns the value of the Premiums, which to a great extent are payments by results, can now be given. The average amount paid by the Board in respect of a King's Premium Stallion for the service season of 1911 was £196, and the maximum amount £259, and when it is borne in mind that in addition a fee of £2 per service is payable by the owner of the mare, it will be seen that the average earnings of these stallions can amount to £300, and in exceptional cases to over £400.

In addition to the King's Premiums, ten Premiums of half value, known as Board's premiums, were awarded to stallions recommended by County Committees.

These stallions served or tried 552 mares during the season, being an average of 55 mares per horse, and the percentage of foals got by them was 44. The average payment by the Board in respect of these Premiums worked out at £93, and the maximum at £143. With the additional service fee of £1 chargeable to the owner of a mare, the average value of a Board's premium was £135, and the maximum £219.

Service season, 1912

The Show of Thoroughbred Stallions was held at the Royal Agricultural Hall, Islington, on 12 to 14 March 1912, and important alterations were made in the regulations that had previously been in force. No stallion was accepted for entry unless it had been registered for the current year as sound and suitable for breeding purposes. This innovation was welcomed by all concerned, as it obviated a veterinary examination at the Show and the possibility of a stallion being rejected after considerable expense had been incurred in sending it there. Another important amendment was that exhibitors were allowed to enter any number of stallions in any class and to take all the Premiums awarded to them.

In order to attract the entry of stallions of more substance and quality, ten Super-Premiums of 100 guineas, in addition to the ordinary Premium, were offered on condition that the owners of the stallions to which they were awarded undertook to show them again at the Show in 1913 or in the event of their failing to do so, to forfeit the value of the Super-Premium.

It was also made a condition that every Premium winner should travel the district assigned to it, and in lieu of the payment made in 1911 for each mare served by a travelling stallion it was provided that a fixed sum of 50 guineas should be paid at the close of the service season.

The number of entries for the Show was 111. If consideration is taken of the number (23) of Thoroughbred Stallions rejected for registration, the majority of which, if passed, would no doubt have been exhibited, the entry compares very favourably with that of any previous year.

It is satisfactory to be able to report that, in the opinion of the judges at the show, who were Sir Gilbert Greenall, Bart., cvo, Captain C. H. D. Fetherstonhaugh and Mr E. P. Rawnsley, the stallions exhibited were considerably superior in merit to those exhibited in 1911, and the ten stallions to which the Super-Premiums were awarded were of an exceptionally high standard. The improvement in the quality of the stallions exhibited is evidenced by the fact that no fewer than 15 stallions to which premiums were given in 1911 failed to secure awards this year. A satisfactory feature of the show was that a number of young horses of merit, which had only recently come out of training, were shown, and three of them secured Super-Premiums and two others the ordinary award.

The routes to be travelled by the stallions were arranged by the Board in consultation with the County Committees and owners concerned, and on the whole they proved satisfactory. In defining a route, first consideration has to be given to the owner of the stallion, as from his local knowledge and experience he is generally in a position to know the number of mares likely to be available in the district for which he has entered his horse, and he naturally prefers to travel it there rather than on a route of which he personally has no knowledge. Any suggestions as to routes which are made by County Committees are also valued, and endeavour is made, as far as possible, to adopt them.

The service arrangements of the Premium Stallions were, as in previous years, supervised by local committees, to the members of which the Board are greatly indebted for their valuable assistance.

The service season, so far as the number of mares was concerned, proved very satisfactory — the number being 3,438, an average of 69 per stallion. The payments made by the Board in respect of stallions (exclusive of foal fees) averaged £226 per horse with a maximum of £334.10s. With the addition of service fees of £2 payable by owners of mares, the average earning of a stallion could amount to £336, and the maximum to £441.10s.

Board's Premiums

The procedure of awarding Board's Premiums in 1911 proved so successful that it was again adopted in 1912. Under it the selection of the stallion is made by the County Committee, and provided the horse has been registered and conforms in other respects to the prescribed conditions of award, approval is given to the recommendation of the Committee.

In 1912 Board's Premiums were awarded to 25 stallions (20 Thoroughbreds, 3 Hunter Sires, 1 Yorkshire Coach and 1 Cleveland Bay) an increase of 15 on the number given in 1911 — to travel various districts in England (16) Scotland (5) and Wales (5), and the results of these seasons may be considered very satisfactory. They served 1,655 mares, being an average of 66 per stallion. The owners also have reason to be satisfied with the results, as the average amount paid to them by the Board was £102, giving an average earning capacity of £156, inclusive of fees payable by mare owners. The maximum earnings of one of these stallions was £204.10s., of which £129.10s. was paid by the Board. The above payments were exclusive of foal fees of 5s. per foal, which would be paid after the close of the foaling season of 1913.

Premiums to Welsh cobs and pony stallions

With a view to encouraging the breeding of cobs of the old Welsh stamp, five premiums of an average value of £50 were awarded in 1912. The awards were made on the recommendation of County Committees to stallions selected by them, and it was a condition that the mares, for which nominations for free service were authorised, should be of the old Welsh type and entered or accepted for entry in the *Welsh Stud Book*. The number of free nominations so authorised was 25 to each stallion.

Six premiums of £20 were given to Fell Ponies with satisfactory results, and assistance was also given to mountain and moorland pony breeding by the award of Premiums of £5 to six selected Pony Stallions that were turned out in the New Forest, and to four Welsh Mountain Pony stallions that were turned out to roam the hills at Church Stretton. Measures were also set on foot to encourage the breeding of Highland Ponies.

Procedure on the lines which had already been laid down was approved by a Committee, which the President appointed in February, 1912, under the Chairmanship of Lord Arthur Cecil, to advise the Board as to the measures to be adopted for the improvement of mountain and moorland breeds of ponies. The Committee, after careful consideration of the question, issued an interesting report, which has been printed separately, in which they recommended that encouragement and improvement of the breeding of mountain and moorland ponies can be best secured by the formation of pony associations, registration in stud books, the award of premiums to mountain and moorland stallions to roam at large, and to polo-bred ponies to travel, the award of premiums to young mares until they produce a foal, the exercise of the Commons Act, 1908, and by various other measures, all of which are receiving careful consideration.

Free nominations for mares

Free nominations to Premium Stallions were given to small farmers and others to whom the fee charged for the use of such high-class sires is a serious item, and it was hoped that this form of encouragement would be that owners of mares would realise that there were commercial advantages to mating their mares with sound sires of quality, and give up the use of nondescript and often unsound stallions, the chief and perhaps the sole merit of which is a low service fee.

The value of a nomination to a mare for service by a King's Premium stallion was £2, and £1 in the case of a Board's Premium Stallion. Nominations were issued by County Committees in favour only of mares which have been examined by veterinary surgeons and passed as sound for breeding purposes. It was recognised that County Committees were put to considerable trouble in the selection of mares for free nominations. The educational value of this part of the scheme was, however, very generally admitted, and the labour involved would, it was hoped, be amply repaid, provided that the Committee continued to exercise the same care as hitherto.

In 1911 the County Committees issued 676 nominations to King's Premium Stallions and 625 of these were used. 138 free nominations were issued to Board's Premium Stallions and 128 of them were taken up. For the year 1912, 738 free nominations were issued to King's Premium Stallions and 696 were used. The comparative figures for Board's Premium Stallions were 340 and 305.

Purchase of brood mares (1911–1912)

Before giving particulars of the procedure adopted for purchasing mares and leasing them out to custodians for breeding purposes, it may be of interest to review briefly the reason for this part of the horse-breeding scheme. There is, and no doubt there always will be, a good demand and a good market, both at home and abroad, for high-class light horses. But with the increase of mechanical traction and the consequent decrease in demand for light-vanners and cab horses, the market for misfits is necessarily on the decline. The hunting farmer, too, is fast disappearing, and his successor, who finds it more profitable to breed heavy than light horses, takes little interest in breeding horses fit to carry him to hounds. To these reasons may be attributed, at any rate in part, the diminution in the number of light horses bred in recent years. Representations were made to the Board that in many parts of the country there was a serious shortage of mares of the hunter type, and that farmers and others were giving up breeding, owing to the difficulty which was increasing, of getting good brood mares of that class, and to lack of suitable Throughbred stallions available for mating with them at a reasonable fee. The Board recognised that it would be very inadvisable to encourage farmers to breed light horses of a type for which there is but little demand, and in view of the fact that there is always a good market for horses of the heavyweight hunter type, they decided to provide funds for the purchase of mares which, when mated with suitable Thoroughbred stallions, are likely to produce stock of the class mentioned.

With this object in view, grants amounting approximately to £20,000 have been made to 36 County Committees for the purchase of mares for leasing at a rental of £2 to suitable custodians for breeding purposes. One of the conditions of a grant is that the average price of the mare is not to exceed £50, and though representations have been received that this amount is insufficient, it is satisfactory to report that many excellent mares have been bought below the figure mentioned. The question of whether any alterations should be made in the amount of the purchase price already authorised will, however, be considered in the light of further experience. Over 400 mares have been purchased after veterinary examination, and nearly all of them have been inspected for conformation and soundness by Inspectors of the Board. The majority of these mares are reported to be suitable for the purpose in view, but there are also, unfortunately, a considerable number which are not of the type desired, and arrangements are being made for their disposal. The County Committees have been most zealous in their endeavours to satisfy, without delay, the applications which they have received for mares, and, in their anxiety to expend the grant made to them, have not perhaps always exercised sufficient care in the selection of the animals purchased. The extreme pressure of work on the staff of the Animals Division occasioned by the recrudescence of Foot-and-Mouth disease, made a heavy call on the services of Inspectors who, in the ordinary course, would have been more fully available for advising and assisting the County Committees in their difficult and responsible duties in purchasing mares. The Committees are, however, now fully aware of the type of mares which should be purchased, and there is no reason to suppose that, in future, other than suitable mares will be bought. Some years must necessarily elapse before it is possible to determine whether these operations are likely to have the effect desired. It will be necessary to wait and see how the produce of the mares turn out, and whether a ready market can be found for them. This will be the real test of the value of the scheme, for unless it is found to be of commercial advantage to those who engage in it, it is not likely to prove an ultimate success.

In addition to the mares purchased by the County Committees the Board, in 1912, availed themselves of an opportunity that offered to purchase from the War Office 20 mares that were specially selected for them out of Artillery batteries. These mares had been thoroughly tested, and proved to have powers of endurance and stamina, and with these qualifications they may reasonably be expected to breed useful stock if suitably mated, and the Board understand that the custodians with whom they are leased are very well pleased with them. The purchase has only been made as an experiment, but the Board are in close touch with the War Office, and it is hoped that other schemes may be developed which will prove of value and advantage to the breeding of light horses.

Registration of stallions

The results of the registration year 1911–12 (1 November to 31 October) clearly show that owners of stallions are beginning to recognise the advantage of having their horse registered by the Board. In the previous year 313 stallions were registered and 44 rejected. In the year under review 715 were accepted for registration — 220 of these had been registered in the previous year — and 90 refused, and of the latter 20 had been registered in 1911.

Of the number registered in 1911–12, 247 were Shires, 172 Thoroughbreds, 116 Ponies, 60 Hackneys, 57 Clydesdales, 36 Suffolk Punches, 19 Hunters, 4 Cleveland Bays and 4 Yorkshire Coach Horses. Of the number rejected, 38 were Shires, 28 Thoroughbreds, 6 Ponies, 5 Hackneys, 7 Clydesdales, 5 Suffolk Punches and 1 Hunter.

There were 15 appeals made in 1911–12 made against the reports of the examining veterinary surgeons, and with success in nine cases. Six stallions were also reported by veterinary surgeons to be unsuitable in conformation for breeding purposes, but in only one was the opinion confirmed by the referee — an acknowledged judge of the breed — who was employed by the Board to make a further examination subsequent to that of the veterinary surgeon.

A stallion is never rejected for registration on an adverse report of a veterinary surgeon until the owner has been given an option to appeal against it, and when a veterinary surgeon reports unfavourably on the conformation of a stallion, another inspection is made by a recognised authority on the breed to which it belongs, and on his advice the decision is made.

Although the figures mentioned show a decided improvement on those of the previous year there is undoubtedly a large number of sound stallions which are travelling the country without the certificate of the Board, but it is hoped that many of these will, before long, be placed on the register. Owners of mares can do much to further the object in view by refusing to put their mares to stallions that are not certified to be sound for breeding purposes.

The efforts that are being made to eliminate the unsound stallion are receiving the active support of the leading horse-breeding societies. Many of them publish in their stud books the regulations for registration, and lists of stallions that have been registered by the Board. The majority of them, too, accept, at either their London or provincial shows, without further veterinary examination, stallions that have the Board's certificate. Negotiations are also preceding between the Board and the societies, the results of which will, it is hoped, secure for registration many of the best sires in the country.

Arrangements were made this year for the issue of a register of stallions which have been certified by the Board to be sound and suitable for breeding purposes, and it is hoped that it will prove of value, not only to the owners of stallions mentioned therein, but also to the owners of mares who wish to know of sound stallions in their districts.

Many representations have been made to the Board that statutory powers should be obtained for the purpose of making the registration of stallions compulsory, and the Advisory Committee to the Board have recently passed a resolution to this effect in respect of stallions that travel. Those interested in horsebreeding are no doubt tending towards this opinion, and it is significant that a Bill embodying this principle was introduced in the House of Lords and secured a second reading in December 1912.

During the year under review the schedule of diseases in accordance with which examinations for registration are made was submitted to the National Veterinary Association. The Association approved it, with one slight modification which has since been adopted, and it is hoped that this schedule will, in time, become the recognised standard by which stallions are judged as to their soundness for breeding purposes. It has frequently been urged that the regulations for registration should be amended so as to provide exemption for stallions that have been passed sound on one or more occasions, up to a certain age limit. No satisfactory or convincing evidence has been submitted showing that any period can be accepted after which hereditary disease will not appear, and until information of this nature is forthcoming it would seem very undesirable that the Board should exempt horses of any age from the annual examination at present prescribed. In this connection, it is of interest to note that the ages of the stallions rejected for registration in 1912 included all ages from 3 to 18, with the exception of 11 and 13, but as many of these stallions had possibly been unsound for several years prior to their examination, more instructive data is afforded by the ages of the 20 stallions rejected in 1912 which had been certified as sound in 1911. Five of them were 4 years old, four 5 years old, and there were two each of 6, 7, 8 and 12 years old. The ages of the remainder were 16, 17 and 23, thus showing a very wide variation in the ages at which stallions may develop hereditary diseases.

Proceedings of the Advisory Council and of its Standing Committee

During the year under review a full meeting of the Advisory Council was held on 27 June 1912, and a report of the procedings thereat has been printed and can be obtained on application to the Board. Six meetings of the Standing Committee of the Advisory Council had been held.

By the death of Major Fife-Cookson and the resignations of Lord Granard and Mr John Hill, three vacancies occurred on the Committee which were filled by the appointment of Lord Helmsley, Lord Arthur Cecil and Captain M. S. Adye.

The questions discussed and recommendations made were as follows: —

The advisability of the publication by the Board of a list of stallions registered by them as sound and suitable was considered, and the Committee, who had had the advantage of hearing from Mr J. R. Campbell what is done in that direction in Ireland, recommended that an alphabetical list of registered stallions and their owners should be issued annually in April. The desirability of accepting half-bred stallions for registration was considered, but the Committee advised against the acceptance of any horse that was not entered in the recognised stud book of its breed.

The committee considered various suggestions made to the Board in regard to the exhibition and judging of the stallions exhibited for King's and Super-Premiums.

Among these was a proposal that a proportion of the Super-Premiums should be specifically allocated to young stallions recently out of training, with a view to encourage the purchase of young stallions of merit. The Committee were favourably disposed towards any scheme calculated to secure this desirable object, but they were not able to recommend the adoption of this particular proposal, as they considered that more useful, though older stallions might thus be deprived of the chance of securing the higher award. In connection with the offer of Super-Premiums at the show last March, the Committee had put on record their opinion that these special Premiums had attracted a better entry of high-class stallions, and they have recommended that the existing arrangements should be given another year's trial before any amendment was made.

The possibility of specifying a standard of merit for King's premiums was discussed, but the Committee recommended that no action should be taken in this direction as, in their opinion, it was not possible to lay down any hard and fast regulations, and that the matter should be left for the Judges to decide.

The Committee, with a view to giving the Show Judges all possible information and assistance, have recommended that the racing performances, if any, of the stallions exhibited should be given in the Show catalogue, and that the particulars supplied by the exhibitors should be carefully checked by the Board, and, if necessary, added to or amended before publication.

The possibility of sub-dividing the present stallion districts and of definitely allocating a stallion or stallions to a county prior to the Show was discussed, but the Committee agreed that under the existing circumstances no alteration could with advantage be made in the present arrangement.

The Committee recommended an alteration of the existing rule as to the dis-qualification of a stallion which had changed hands between the time of entry for the Show and the date of the Show, so as to provide that 'where the seller of the stallion entered for the Show gives notice to the Board of his intention to dispose of it, and the purchaser enters into an agreement similar to that binding on the vendor, the horse so entered should not be disqualified from competing'.

The Committee agreed to the proposal of the Board that the owner of a Premium Stallion, in the case of its death, or its inability owing to illness or other cause to fulfil its engagements, should be required to report the matter to the Board and to furnish a certificate from a veterinary surgeon, and if required by the Board, to arrange for the substitution of another stallion, having first obtained their approval thereto.

A discussion took place as to whether any action should be taken to recover wholly or in part the portion of the Premium paid on award to the owner of a stallion which died before serving any mares, or during the service season. The Committee considered that in such cases the loss should be borne by the Board, and recommended that no action should be taken.

The delay which had occurred in settling the routes of some of the King's Premium Stallions was brought to the notice of the Committee, which considered that the information which the County Committees were able to supply was valuable. They suggested that some of the delay involved in consulting them might be obviated if County Committees were asked to furnish the Board with general information as to the districts in which mares were to be found, without attempting closely to define the routes to be travelled by stallions.

The question as to whether an age limit could be fixed for the veterinary examinations of mares for free nominations was discussed, but no decision was reached pending further consideration of the matter.

The advisability of exempting stallions from examination after reaching a certain age was fully considered on being referred back to the Committee by the Advisory Council, but in view of the full inquiry made into the matter in 1887 and 1892 by the

Royal Commission, and the conclusion they arrived at, and by a sub-committee of the Advisory Council also in 1911, that no age limit could be fixed, it was decided to defer the making of any recommendation.

The Committee considered the advisability of awarding Premiums to Polo-bred stallions and Eastern sires, but deferred making any ruling pending the receipt from County Committees concerning the existing demand for sires of these types.

The price authorised for the purchase of brood mares by County Committee was considered, but no alteration was recommended. Discussions took place on other matters, including a scheme proposed by Mr Sewell Rigg for the revision of the method of awarding Premiums, but it was not approved. An interesting discussion took place at another meeting as to the breeding of hunter sires. The Committee was favoured on that occasion by the presence of Mr Campbell, Captain Fetherstonhaugh and Mr Carden, who explained at some length the steps that had been and were being taken in Ireland to promote breeding of this character. The Committee decided to consider the matter further.

The Advisory Council in July 1913

The Advisory Council held its fourth meeting under the Chairmanship of Lord Middleton, who presented a report from the Chairman of the Standing Committee, parts of which (if the subject matter has not previously been publicised) are herewith appended.

Since the last meeting of the Advisory Council on 27 June 1912, the Standing Committee had met on five occasions to consider questions referred to them by the Board and to discuss generally its horse-breeding operations.

The suggestion of the Judges on their report of the last Spring Show that additional King's and Super-Premiums should be offered for competition was considered by the Committee, who recommended the addition of two Super-Premiums and as many King's Premiums as the funds available would allow.

As a result of the conference with horse-breeding Societies on 9 December 1912, the Committee again considered the question of giving assistance to the breeding of Hackneys. The subject had already been considered twice, but no recommendation was made, other than that Hackney stallions should be entitled to Board's Premiums provided that they served Hackney mares that had been entered, or accepted for entry, in the *Stud Book*.

The Committee were of the opinion that the breeding of Hackneys could no longer be regarded as a national industry, and that in view of the fact that the Development Commissioners were suggesting a reduction of the grant for light horse breeding, they thought that the money available could be more usefully expended in other directions.

The Committee had before them a letter from the Development Commissioners in which enquiry was made as to a reduction in the grant for Light Horse Breeding in view of the expenditure to be incurred in the Heavy Horse Industry.

The Committee were all agreed that the light horse industry was in far greater need of assistance than that of the heavy horse, and they also considered that any reduction in the grant would tend to militate against the success of the scheme, which must be given at least five years in which to operate before any useful conclusions as to its value could be reached. After some discussion, the following resolution was carried unanimously: —

'It is impossible within so brief a period to review with any advantage the experience gained, inasmuch as none of the horses whose breeding has been affected by the operations of the Board are yet twelve months old.

'So far from being able to reduce the expenditure, the experience of the Committee leads them to think that the grant could usefully be increased, and they are unanimous in thinking that it would be most unwise to divert money from Light Horse Breeding to the Heavy Horse Industry.'

Mr Cheyney (as Assistant Secretary to the Board) detailed the results of the working of the Board's scheme. It had only been in operation for little more than two years. Its object was to secure an improvement in the *quality* of the horses bred by farmers and others. An idea seemed to have got about that the object of the Board was to induce farmers to breed light horses for remount purposes. This was certainly not the primary object of the scheme, as the Board were endeavouring, by the provision of high-class sires, to secure the breeding of horses of a better stamp than that which satisfied the War Office for remount purposes. The scheme would, incidentally, no doubt produce many horses suitable for remount purposes, as there were bound to be many misfits produced in the attempts that were being made to breed horses of superior quality of the hunter weight type. He emphasised this point so as to correct this idea that the scheme was one for breeding remounts — a business that could not be advocated by the Board, as it was not sufficiently remunerative to the breeder.

Another mistaken idea that seemed to prevail in some quarters was that if a Free Nomination was given to the owner of a mare, the Board would have a lien on the progeny of that mare. This misunderstanding was preventing a good many owners in some districts from applying for Free Nominations. There was, of course, no claim on the progeny of a mare to which a Free Nomination had been issued, and the Board would be glad if members of the Council and of County Committees would make this as widely known as possible.

It was, of course, much too soon to express any definite opinion as to the ultimate value of the operations which were now being carried on for the improvement of Light Horse Breeding. At least five years must elapse before any opinion of value could be based on results — in fact, it would probably be ten rather than five years before any final judgements could be recorded.

There was, however, no doubt that the operations of the scheme were re-awakening interest in Light Horse Breeding, and though the market for horses of the misfit type was becoming smaller every day, there was still a good demand among home and foreign buyers for hunters of substance and quality.

In response to the invitation of the Chairman for any remarks or suggestions, Major-General Brocklehurst moved the following resolution: — 'That a life certificate for wind should be given to any Thoroughbred stallion of six years old, if passed for registration at that age, and if he has been placed first, second or third as a three-year-old or over in any race under the rules of racing.'

This resolution was passed by a full Rutland Committee. It was sent round to the other County Committees with the result that 15 agreed, four were against, six were neutral and the others did not answer. Of the 15 that agreed, 11 were unanimous, three recommended 8 years instead of 6, and in the case of one it was only passed by a small majority. Support was also forthcoming from several important stallion owners, urging that a horse that had been passed sound for registration at 6 years old should be given a life certificate for wind, and that with regard to racing qualifications, a horse being Thoroughbred was sufficient provided he was otherwise suitable.

He (Major-General Brocklehurst) was convinced that unless an early age limit for veterinary inspection was adopted in regard to Thoroughbred stallions it was impossible to get the class of animal they required. The risks were too great and the rewards too small for anyone to buy and keep as a business proposition a Thoroughbred stallion with a view to taking Premiums. If they wanted good stallions kept in the country by private individuals they must decrease the risks and increase the rewards. With the continued improvement of motor traction the day would not be far distant when almost the only support of Light Horse Breeding would be the remount buyer and the dealer in horses that were ridden and driven for pleasure. The Government grant was to prevent the remount horse from becoming an extinct animal, and in the belief that it would benefit the cavalry he had moved the resolution.

It was the racehorse and only the racehorse of proved speed that could impart endurance to its stock. Good stallions could not be bought cheaply, and if proper stallions were wanted the Government must buy, or encourage others to buy them as they came into the market one by one, and be prepared to pay the market price, say up to £3,000. With this class of horse travelling the country at a low fee, the mare question would settle itself. If consequently there were not enough stallions to go round they must limit their operations to those districts which were most suitable for breeding, but never let anything but a first-class horse serve in the name of the Government.

There was much divergence of opinion in the veterinary profession on the question of roaring. His view, upheld by that of practical veterinary surgeons, was that it was only hereditary to the extent to which conformation is hereditary. In regard to hunters that made a noise, his experience was that horses going wrong before 6 were of small good as hunters, but those only failing to pass after 6 years old, given a turn of speed, were worth buying and generally little the worse for it. As the racehorse matured much earlier than the hunter he would put the safety age at even less than 6 years.

Their present system of examining horses year by year and taking no note of their stock was surely wrong. The value of the stallion was the value of his stock; and the corollary of this resolution was that when a stallion got a life certificate at 6 years old he would then be judged by the report on his stock.

Mr Nickisson seconded the resolution and said that they should clearly understand that this was really a matter for racehorses, and for those racehorses only that had stood not only the very severe ordeal of training but that had won or been placed as a 3-year-old or over. If a horse could stand that severe course of training and win a race there was no doubt that with his early maturity he would probably to all intents and purposes remain sound for the rest of his life.

Mr Rea ventured to think that the Council would be taking an undue risk in recommending that it should be agreed to by the Board. As a member of a local Committee ever since the system of Premium Stallions was instituted in 1887, the first consideration which the members of the Committee had brought before the users of stallions was that they had an absolute guarantee of soundness. Under this proposition that guarantee would be gone, because, though it might be right that a stallion that passed sound up to 6 years old should have a life certificate, he did not think that it would satisfy the prejudices or the rightful demands of breeders of hunters. They would argue that the racehorse for all practical purposes had finished his useful career at 6 years old, when the best of a hunter's life was only just beginning; and though the stallion stood sound up to 6 and might beget sound stock, on the other hand he might beget broken-winded or roaring horses. The first principle of the

Board should be to encourage a scheme which gave absolute security to horses above suspicion in the way of soundness of any description. He agreed that the Board should only encourage the use of first-class stallions, but no stallion which was first-class but which possessed any infirmity should be encouraged. There was no more insidious disease than wind troubles, and there was probably no disease which militated so severely against the value of a horse. Though there were absolutely first-class hunters which made a noise, yet, from a breeder's point of view, the breeding of this class of horse must be discouraged because he was not a horse that would be remunerative. He hoped that this Council would not give its sanction to this motion, which would not only be a retrograde step, but would be introducing an element of danger which the Board would not be well advised to take upon its shoulders.

Major Gilmour, as connected with the Committee that had to consider this question, and also with the Royal Commission, who had it before them on previous occasions, said that he would be the first to admit that the last word upon roaring or whistling had perhaps not been said. But the duty of the Advisory Council, and the paramount duty of the Board, in dealing with this horse-breeding question was to put before the country the soundest horses possible and to run absolutely no risks. Any change in their regulations at the present time, say, in favour of a Thoroughbred horse which had presumably been tested by being in severe training and racing, would immediately bring them up against the difficulty of dealing with many horses of excellent quality which had not actually raced and had not been tested. He agreed that the best test was in the stock, but he was not satisfied that in the case of many of the horses that they recommended to the public at 6 years old with a certificate for all time, they would have had the opportunity, or those who were working the scheme would have had the opportunity, of making certain as to the soundness of those horses' stock. He did not think there would be any lack of horses for their work in the future.

The Chairman was opposed to Major-General Brocklehurst's resolution. He tried to get stallions as sound as possible, and would not buy one of these horses at 7 years old without a most thorough examination — in fact, he should not keep in his stud a horse which had gone wrong in his wind after 6 years old. He would not feel sure of being able to breed sound horses from him, and would probably part with that horse directly. Any such change would cause a great deal of confusion in the scheme of Premium sires, and would lead to a great deal of misunderstanding. A man paying a fee for a horse should be certain, so far as it is possible to be certain, that that horse was sound. They could not vouch that these horses were sound after 6 years old. No one could prove that a horse did not propagate wind unsoundness after 6 years old. They were there to do as much as possible to provide sound horses for use in the country. The HIS were the first to initiate a Premium Stallion scheme, and their chief object was to secure that only certified horses should travel the country.

Mr Sewell Rigg urged that the Board should subsidise the veterinary profession in some way to elucidate this very complex question. Whistling, in the judgement of many people, was of very little detriment to horses until it became a question or roaring, when it oppressed them.

Prof. Penberthy urged that the Council had at their disposal veterinary advice which was as good as they were likely to get anywhere. If anything could be done to settle this question, nobody would be better pleased than the veterinary profession itself. But there was a danger just beyond this. There was an operation for what was called curing roarers at the present moment which was rather largely in vogue. He was consulted by a Colonial Government a few weeks ago as to the means which were adopted for preventing these sires that had been operated on from coming into service in the UK. From special enquiries made he discovered that this operation had been performed on a considerable number of roarers, and three roarers were mentioned to him which had already, to the knowledge of a person on whom he could depend, taken prizes at Breeding Societies' shows. They were all passed by the veterinary officers, and it was therefore a veterinary question which was worthy of consideration. He had never heard of a horse being hurt, or never heard it substantiated, as the result of examination. They, as breeders, would naturally want to know whether the horse which was going to serve their mare was sound or not.

Major-General Brocklehurst said that if it was agreed that suitable and sufficient horses were forthcoming it was unnecessary to pass his resolution. 'Every practical man I speak to says the same, that unless there is some further help given the horses will not be forthcoming, and we shall not get the class of horse that we want'.

Mr Sewell Rigg said that as all stallions entering for the King's Premiums were examined at home, he did not see that the owner of a horse had any ground for complaint now if his horse was rejected as an unsound horse. He had the alternative of an appeal, and if it was pronounced on appeal an unsound horse, he did not think that the Council would be wise in advising the Board to recommend the use of unsound horses.

Major-General Brocklehurst said that last year Mr Campbell brought it to their notice that what he was asking for today was adopted in Ireland. The reason he gave was that in Ireland they found that unless something of the sort was adopted they would miss the stallions they wanted to get. For that reason they passed the rule that for wind, horses should be allowed a life certificate at six.

The Hon. Alexander Parker thought that it would become a great point in the years to come whether the Irish Department had adopted a wise step. From what he had heard from a member of the French Jockey Club who imported Irish horses, he thought that it was all the more necessary that in England they should keep their horses sound.

The Chairman put the motion to the meeting, and it was rejected by a large majority.

Mr Lort Phillips said that he did not agree with the Brood Mare scheme, and did not believe in giving the Government grant to breed half-bred horses. He felt that encouraging the breeding of half-bred horses was simply destroying the brood mares of the different countries. He had always considered that the scheme was by no means a wise one, though he had done his best to carry out the wishes of the Board, and their efforts in Pembrokeshire would compare favourably with other counties in this respect. The scheme was not sound economically, and was certainly not so scientifically. It was not economically sound because the capital laid out would never be seen again, nor would the effect of the scheme be efficacious in carrying out its object — to create a stimulant to light horse breeding. It was scientifically unsound in the sense that all breeding of half-breds was unscientific. They could not continue to breed half-breds without breeding one side of the breed out of existence — as had already been done to a great extent throughout Ireland and in Pembrokeshire. They were destroying and not setting up or permanently improving a breed, however grand an animal might be produced for the moment. The root principle of the Brood Mare scheme — to give farmers higher-class mares than they could otherwise afford to keep — was an admirable scheme in theory, but it was by no means a new or untried idea; and it had done a certain amount of good indirectly. In a small way he had tried it, and the Duke of Portland had tried such a scheme and found it wanting. There was only one way to put the Horse Breeding Industry on a sound footing, and that was for the Government to pay such a price for its remounts as would induce the farmers to breed them. They would have to come to this sooner or later, and in the long run the sooner they did so the less it would cost the country. He thought that the Government could not spend too much money on improving the present breeds of horses now existing, and that it was absolutely necessary to spend money on creating one type that was badly wanted — the Artillery type of horse. At present they depended upon the misfits; but the time must come when they would no longer be able to rely on misfits and unless they were prepared to meet the deficiency with an alternative, they would be in a very bad way. Breed pure-bred animals and fixed types and the law of supply and demand would determine the numbers of half-breds required. Money laid out on pure-breeds would always remain as capital, and the demand for these pure breeds would increase as the supply of horses diminished.

Mr Rea suggested that this Council should recommend to the Board the advisability of having the disease of strangles included in the schedule of notafiable diseases. From the breeders' point of view it was a very important matter, because it was a disease that spread very rapidly, was most contagious, and was most destructive when it got among a lot of young horses, or even among horses of more mature age.

Mr Sewell Rigg criticised the outlay on the Super-Premiums. It was the very best medium they could adopt of advertising to the foreigner the best horses the country possessed, and the very animal that the Board should be trying to keep in the country. The money expended in large sums like that should be capitalised in the shape of buying the best stallions to be owned by the Board of Agriculture themselves. The Board should become the owners of 50 stallions in the course of ten years, or five years, as the case might be. The £5,000 which was allocated to purchasing stallions would buy five horses a year, probably 10, at prices ranging from £400 to £1,000. The £1,000 for Super-premiums could be used to set up an insurance fund which would provide the horses in case anything went wrong. On reckoning it out, he found that they would have the service of so many mares at much less cost to the Board of Agriculture. He did not agree with this advertising the best of our stallions for the foreigners to come and purchase and take them away out of the country, which was practically what it amounted to.

The Chairman: 'I believe that we are generally agreed that it is impossible to run the two schemes together — namely, the Government owning some of the stallions and private owners the rest'.

Mr Sewell Rigg: 'Do you not think it could be done in the course of ten years?'

The Chairman: 'As to the Super-premium, I think it is a great incentive and a help towards buying stallions. I do not think the Premiums for stallions are too large'.

Mr Sewell Rigg urged that the result of the scheme of the Super-Premiums would be just what he wished to avoid — the purchase of stallions by the foreigner at a big price.

Mr Lort Phillips said that facts in his county confirmed this view. Could it not come as a suggestion from them to the Government that they should be allowed to buy the stallions on their taking Super-Premiums to keep them in the country?

Colonel the Hon. Charles Byng said that as the Super-Premiums were to be won year after year, foreigners could not be very much helped in picking out the most valuable stallions.

Viscount Helmsley suggested that the Board should attach some further conditions to the award of Super-Premiums to prevent the selected horse being sold to go abroad within a certain time, and make the award of a Super-Premium subject to the acceptance of such conditions. For some years they would have had the value of its services.

The Chairman thought that Lord Helmsley's suggestion was one that might be considered by the Board.

The 28th and 29th Spring Shows

The 28th and 29th Spring Shows were held on 12–14 March 1912, and on 11–13 March 1913 respectively, honoured by Their Majesties the King and Queen on both occasions, and well attended by members and the general public. Her Majesty Queen Alexandra also honoured the Society by a visit on the Thursday afternoon in 1913.

At both shows the King's Champion Challenge Cup, graciously offered by His Majesty the King, was awarded to the Champion Thoroughbred stallion in the Show, selected from among the Super-Premium winners. On each occasion the honour was gained by King's Courtship, bred by Mr Donald Fraser and owned by Messrs T. L. Wickham-Boynton and H. A. Cholmondeley. A bay horse, 16.0 hands and foaled in 1904, he was by Matchmaker out of Be Cannie, by Jock of Oran out of Reticence, by Vespasian out of Seclusion, by Tadmor.

The judges were Sir Gilbert Greenall, Bart., Captain C. H. D. Fetherstonhaugh and E. P. Rawnsley, MFH, who gave the reserve award to Lord Middleton's Wales, by Belgrave. Super-premiums went to these two, plus:

Eustace Barlow's Birk Gill, by Marcion.
Southwold Hunt Sire Association's Akbar, by Ladas.

J. F. Rees's Lousby, by Desmond.
R. L. Fenwick's Carrousel, by Pietermaritzburg.
John Drage's Drummond's Pride, by Drummond.
W. G. Maxwell and James Heys's My Bird Sings, by Thrush.
Sir Merrik R. Burrell, Bart.'s Hanover Square, by Matchmaker.
W. and H. Whitley's Golden Grebe, by Grebe.

In 1913, Sir Gilbert Greenall and Captain Fetherstonhaugh officiated again, this time with J. Simons Harrison. Reserve to the champion, King's Courtship, was Eustace Barlow's Birk Gill, by Marcion. Others to gain Super-Premiums were:

Wales.
Lord Willoughby de Broke's Pure Caster, by Uncle Mac.
Eustace Barlow's and Donald Fraser's Ulpian, by Gallinule.
J. F. Rees and W. V. Howell Thomas's Neyland, by Milford.
E. and P. Hodgson's Kilbrook, by Santry.
Golden Grebe.
Sir Walter Gilbey, Bart.'s Stortford, by Thrush.
Hanover Square.

In a joint report on the Young Stock in 1912 the judges of this section, Mr R. G. Carden and the Hon. T. Cecil Parker stated that they found the classes extremely satisfactory, showing much improvement. The yearling classes called for special comment, both colts and fillies, and the 3-year-old geldings were magnificent, all the award winners combining quality and substance.

The champion was Edward Hodgson of Bridlington's dark chestnut 3-year-old Mince Pie, by Favonian out of a mare by Sir Reginald, bred by T. O. Hutchinson of Birtown, Athy, Co. Kildare. Reserve was the chestnut yearling colt Jasper Red Heart, by Red Heart out of Diamond by Eglamore, owned by E. W. Goldsworthy of Kensing, Sevenoaks, and bred by his father the late Major-General W. T. Goldsworthy, CB.

In 1913, under E. H. Barlow and P. Fitzgerald, the champion was the grey 3-year-old Splendour, by Splendour out of Snowdrop III, owned by Frank B. Wilkinson of Edwinstowe, Newark and bred by F. E. Bowser of Boston, Lincs. Reserve was A. J. Dorman of Nunthorpe's bay yearling Golf Ball, by Tennis Ball ex Ladybird, who was home-bred.

In 1912 the riding classes were assessed by Captain C. Fetherstonhaugh and T. L. Wickham-Boynton, who found that the exhibits on the whole were an improvement on previous years, though the four-year-olds were moderate. The lightweights were good and the heavyweights made up a very good class of big horses.

A 5-year-old won the championship for Geoffrey Kenyon of Wigginton, York. A 15 stone horse of unknown breeding, bought from Miles Kenyon of Bury, he was a bay-brown horse with a white face and three white joints. Reserve was another of anonymous ancestry, John Stokes's middleweight 6-year-old Chieftain, bought from G. M. Wilson of Hawick.

In 1913 Lord Annaly, Master of the Pytchley, and Mr W. P. Hanly were the ridden hunter judges and found that though the lightweight classes were moderate, the upper weight divisions were very good. Their champion was John Drage's heavyweight 6-year-old Alarm, a brown horse bought from the Marquess of Cholmondeley; and the reserve was the lightweight chesnut 5-year-old MP, by The Gull out of Fancy Princess by Red Prince II, owned by Edward Hodgson of Bridlington and bred by Hugh Murray of Newbridge, Co. Kildare.

At the 27th Annual General Meeting in 1912, the title of the HIS was altered to *The Hunters' Improvement and National Light Horse Breeding Society*, in order to define its extended scope to include light horses generally.

Careful consideration had been given to the two proposals put forward in 1911 by Colonel Little and Mr Charles Richardson, as to the precautions taken to prevent the importation and distribution of horses affected with infectious diseases into the UK, and if any steps of a similar nature had been taken in Ireland. The Board replied that under the Glanders or Farcy Order of 1907, Article 2, no horse brought from abroad should be landed in this country without a Veterinary certificate of freedom from disease. Further, in the case of stallions and mares brought from countries in which the disease of dourine is believed to exist, the consignee is warned by the Board to take special notice of the animal, and to communicate with the Board if at any time it shows signs of wasting or chronic illness. He is also asked to acquaint the Board if he disposes of the animal within three months of the date of its landing in this country, so that the person to whom it is sent may also be warned.

CHAPTER 7

———◦❁◦———

The Society in the war years

VOLUME VII of the *Stud Book*, the sixteenth in the series, covered the years 1914–1915 and the Presidencies of Sir Merrik Burrell, Bart., and Sir Gilbert Greenall, Bart., CVO. The Preface states that the war had affected all breed societies and their records, many representative shows had to be abandoned and all suitable horses had been commandeered for use of the Army.

Yet the report of the 1914 show, attended by the King and Queen, when His Majesty entered the ring to present the King George V Cup to the owners of the champion stallion, Eustace Barlow's Birk Gill, by Marcion, supreme in both 1914 and 1915, states: 'No shadow of the impending conflict which has convulsed the whole of Europe was then discernible.' The 30th exhibition was successful in every way, both as regards attendance and entries. But the 1915 show (31st), attended by Queen Alexandra, was determined upon and carried through in the midst of a war which had already taken heavy toll of well-known supporters of the Society. Practically all the members were engaged in national duties, either on service with their Regiments or in remount work. The supreme importance of maintaining the continuity of the Spring Shows in the interest of horse breeding was the deciding factor in the Council's unanimous decision to go on, which was amply justified by the results.

This show was the first held under the new agreement with the Royal Agricultural Hall Company in the first week in March 1915, which avoided the previous clash with the National Hunt Meeting at Cheltenham. Owing to the mobilisation demands made on all hunting stables, it was thought advisable to restrict the show to the Thoroughbred and Registered Hunter Stallions and Young Stock classes, with two classes for 4-year-old mares and geldings under saddle. The programme was therefore compressed into two days, with the Pony Show, as an integral section, on Thursday. This enabled the Council to offer the last two days of the week to the Hackney Horse Society, whose arrangements with the Olympia Company for their initial show at Kensington had to be cancelled owing to its occupation by the Government. The total value of the schedule for the show of 1915 was over £18,000 — the largest sum ever offered for breeding classes.

For the first time, this volume was illustrated by three copyright photographs by W. A. Rouch, that legendary cameraman. The 1914 ridden champion, a lightweight exhibited by John Drage, was Gold Fish, a chesnut 6-year-old with no breeding, bought in Yorkshire from W. Brown of Slingsby. The led champion was William Holmes's brown 3-year-old Wilton Drummer, by Drummer Kelly, also bred in Yorkshire. In 1915 the led champion was A.J.

Dorman's Golf Ball, by Tennis Ball, bred in Yorkshire by the owner. Birk Gill, the champion stallion, had changed hands and was now the property of Capt. T. L. Wickham-Boynton and H. A. Cholmondeley of Burton Agnes Hall, Driffield, Yorkshire.

Major-General Sir W. H. Birkbeck, KCB, Director of Remounts, compiled a pamphlet on French Horse-Breeding and Remount Organisation, based on notes he made during a brief visit to France. They were reproduced for their interest value, 'more especially at the present juncture when our Army is fighting shoulder to shoulder with these gallant Allies, and indicate how very systematically the French are dealing with Light Horse Breeding.' They are still of considerable interest 70 years on; particularly as the national studs still not only exist but flourish, while in England the whole horse-breeding industry is the prerogative of private enterprise without any form of state aid, though the grant of the Horse Race Betting Levy Board thankfully provides the money for the premiums. Extracts from this pamphlet follow:

Connection between horse-breeding and remount department

The production of sufficient and suitable horses for military purposes in peace and war has long been the object of solicitude in France.

Breeding of all kinds of horse is directed by an efficient branch of the Ministry of Agriculture, staffed by highly-trained professional enthusiasts. Their aim is to guide production along sound lines to provide for the agricultural population horses most suitable to the soil, and the most profitable to breed, without losing sight of the essential object, that horses used in civil life shall be suitable for the Army in war.

The Minister, in shaping his equine policy, has the advantage of the advice of a Joint Council of horse-breeding department and remount officials, including the most prominent civilian breeders of various types of horse. The working connection between the breeding department and the Remount Service is very close. Organisation of the latter is designed to fulfil the State's obligation to purchase as many as possible of the annual contingent of remounts direct from the man who has bred them, under the guidance of, and with means supplied by, the Breeding Department.

Outline of breeding department's organisation

First established in 1639, the system of State aid for breeders has continued, with varying success and only one break (during the Revolutionary period). The Loi Organique des Haras, passed in 1874, established the system as it now stands. There are six circles (each presided over by an inspector-general) and there are 25 directors and 45 sub-directors and superintendants, with a corps of attendants of various grades called *Palfreniers*. Within the circles are 25 stallion depots containing 3,450 stallions: 545 Thoroughbreds — Arab, Anglo-Arab and English — 2,175 half-breds (Anglo-Normands and a few roadsters) — and 730 draught horses (Percherons, Ardennais and Boulonnais). The most important are at Pin, St. Loe, Tarbes Compiegne and Pompadour. These depots serve 756 stations. Pompadour has the only brood mare stable in France, and there are produced the Anglo-Arab stallions so largely used in the South of France.

The policy of the Department is based on a system of zones, the aim being to provide, in each, stallions of the type best suited to the soil. For example, at Compiegne, in the Northern zone, where heavy draught horses abound, the stallion depot contains only Boulonnais, Ardennais and a few English hackney stallions. Possibly the breeders would prefer heavy draught horses of Shire or Clydesdale type, but the military consideration forbids. The Boulonnais and Ardennais are heavy enough for the plough, quick, active,

The thoroughbred stallion Orville (1799), winner of the Doncaster St Leger in 1802. Bred by Lord Fitzwilliam and forerunner of the premium stallion.

Peppermill. He won his first premium in 1890, as a 3-year-old.

Huguenot (1888). Premium stallion owned by the Compton Stud Company.

Eglamore. One of the 1891 Queen's premium horses for North Wales.

Lady Helen McCalmont's Handley Cross. Champion hunter at London Spring Shows,
1931 and 1932.

Premium stallion Scarlet Rambler, winner of the King's Challenge Cup, 1924.

Top Game Rights. Reserve Champion at 1962/63/65 Shows. *Below* Sporting Rights (by Game Rights). Champion Middleweight Hunter at Shows in 1967/68.

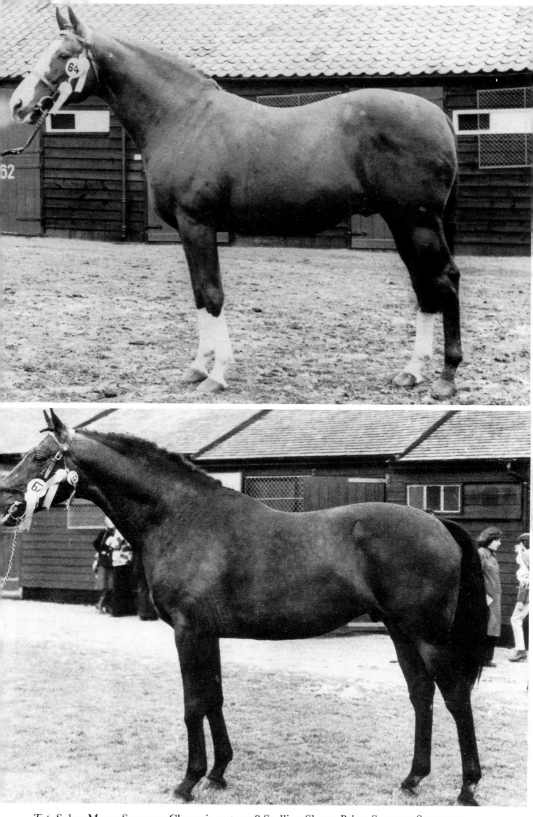

Top Solon Morn. Supreme Champion at 1958 Stallion Show. *Below* Saunter. Supreme
Champion in 1978 and 1981.

Mrs M. H. Tollit's Seaward II. Champion Hunter Brood Mare 1954–1956.

Formula. Winner of the HIS Challenge Cup for the Best Brood Mare at the 1961 National Hunter Show.

Top Cuillin Hills. Supreme Champion of breeding classes at Newark and Notts Show, 1982.
Below Arch Guard. Best Young Hunter at the National Hunter Show, Shrewsbury, 1957.

Boothby. Best Young Hunter at the 1959 National Hunter Show.

Prince's Grace. Ridden Hunter Champion at National Hunter Show 1962 and Champion Brood Mare at the same show in 1964, 1965 and 1967.

hardy, live on a comparatively small ration and above all they are suitable for military purposes, for transport and even for artillery, the strain of hackney being intended to increase their activity for this latter purpose.

At Pin and St. Loe, in the central zone, where lighter draught horses, high-class carriage horses and the heavyweight hunter class of saddle horse are produced, the stallion depots contain Thoroughbred stallions, Anglo-Norman or half-bred, Percherons and a few English hackneys. At Tarbes, in the Southern zone, we find nothing but Anglo-Arabs and Thoroughbred stallions, and the use of heavy sires is absolutely forbidden.

Privately-owned stallions

In addition to the 3,500 sires maintained by the State for service at nominal fees, there are three classes of privately-owned stallions standing for public service. In 1911 their number was 8,140.

(a) *Approved stallions* (total 1,736) —
  1) Those whose covering fee is over £4 get no premium.
  2) Those whose covering fee is less than £4 receive premiums from a minimum of 300 francs (£12) in the heavy draught class to a maximum of 2,000 francs (£80) in the Thoroughbred class. The premium depends on the value of the produce got by the stallion. £30,000 is the sum thus distributed annually.
(b) *Authorised stallions* are not good enough to win premiums, but are good enough to have a formal certificate of excellence.
(c) *Accepted stallions* are certified as free from hereditary diseases, but that is all. Without such a certificate, no stallion of any breed is permitted to travel or stand for public service.

Brood mares

The provision of brood mares is not neglected. Shows are held in every circle at which, in addition to prizes locally provided, the State gives handsome premiums for mares with foal at foot and for young brood mares which it is desired to devote to the stud. Permanent premiums for a certain number of years are given to the owners of these young mares, conditional on their appearance at subsequent shows a certain number of times with foal at foot by a State stallion.

Personnel of the Stud department

The stud department is not easy to enter and the officials are, in this democratic country, invariably gentlemen of good family. The training is thorough; after two years at the college of agriculture candidates may compete for the three stud department vacancies offered annually. Successful competitors must have proved not only their agricultural knowledge, but their aptitude for the special duties of the department. They then go through a two years' special course at the Haras du Pin, which includes a study of the characteristics of all equine breeds, of the objects of and results obtainable from judicious mating, practical care of stallions, foaling mares and young stock, veterinary studies, shoeing, dietetics, treatment, etc. The lectures are carefully chosen and the students observe the management of a mixed stud of 300 stallions in the most important breeding circle of France. Finally they complete three years' service with mounted branches of the Army, where they learn the work of the animals in the production of which they are to spend their lives.

The director of a district has arduous and responsible duties. He has the care of the stallions in his depot, where he himself resides, usually in some charming old royal *château*, the property of the State. During the autumn and winter he and his staff tour the district inspecting, holding breeders' meetings, advising them as to the care of their young stock and the mating of their mares, and gathering information to guide them in the distribution of stallions for the following year.

In the Spring he sends his stallions in groups to out-stations in charge of *Palfreniers* — old soldiers, ranging from stable helper to stud groom. The communes apply for a certain number of stallions and provide accommodation for horses and men. Stud grooms have considerable responsibility and the director and his staff are continually on tours of inspection.

The only real national stud is at Pompadour, where 50 brood mares of English TB, Arab and Anglo-Arabs are maintained. There are also 100 stallions, which serve the surrounding districts. The French have a tremendous opinion of the Anglo-Arab as a war horse, and to keep up the supply of sires of this type the stud exists. The two Eastern Arab stallions I saw did not strike me as of the type which we are taught to look on as the highest caste, but they have a marked effect on their progeny.

Every precaution is taken to develop the young stock and give them bone, by liberal dressing of their pasture and careful feeding as soon as they can eat. As 3-year-olds they are put in training and tested for speed and stamina. Surplus mares are auctioned and command high prices for the value of their particular strains. Colts deemed unworthy to sire progeny are gelded and go to the Remount Department.

The establishment is maintained on lavish lines, worthy of the French nation.

General Remarks

Breeding is at present in a transitional state in France. In Normandy, the most important breeding district, very high class carriage horses used to be produced in large numbers. Motors have destroyed this industry, and this foundation stock of big, upstanding carriage mares is being used more and more to mate with Thoroughbreds to secure true cavalry horses. The present *cuirassier* horse, which seems to me altogether too big for war, will doubtless lose in size and gain in quality, and a first-class cavalry horse will result. In France the army is always up against the fact that it is practically the only large buyer of saddle horses, whereas we fortunately have the hunter market to keep our breeders busy. However, all French remount officers say that the quality of their cavalry remounts is improving, though they cannot breed the bone and substance that Ireland produces.

At their great horse show in Paris, the height, weight, girth and bone of the saddle horse is given in the catalogue. A 16-hand horse rarely has as much as 8 inches of bone, weighs more than 1,050 lbs. or girths more than 74 inches. Undoubtedly the best French cavalry horse is the Anglo-Arab, which, though light to look at, is extra-ordinarily enduring.

Provision of funds for the upkeep of Stud Department

When one studies the elaborate organisation devoted to the guidance and stimulation of the horse-breeding industry, one naturally wonders where the money comes from. The reply is from racing, the collection being made through the *pari-mutuel* or totalisator which so largely supplants the bookmaker on French racecourses, and which pays a percentage to the State. Racing in France is thus compelled to fulfil its duty to the State, i.e. the improvement of the national breeds of horses. Two-year-old racing is discouraged, and long distance races and steeple-chases are looked on with favour. In short, those responsible for the government of the French turf seem to pay more regard to the national aspect of racing than do similar authorities in England.

Organisation of the Remount Department

The Remount Department includes —

(1) A directorate at the War Office.
(2) Inspectors in charge of remount circles.

(3) Superintendents of the purchasing remount depots.

(4) Officers attached to these depots as purchasers.

(5) Superintendents of 'Annexes' or establishments for the storage of young remounts until ready for issue (normally veterinary officers).

(6) Personnel of remount depot. Total five companies, of which four are distributed among depots and one serves the military college.

Purchasing depots are located to serve the districts where horses are bred, being designed primarily for the encouragement of horse breeding by the purchase of young horses direct from breeders. Purchasing of the specified number is carried out by three officers, of whom the superintendent is president, at the depot on certain days each month, during regular tours in the district from July to March, at fairs and horse shows and wherever horses are gathered together. These tours, designed to tap all centres of breeding, and bring the market to the farmer's door, concern the purchase of 4-year-olds as chargers and troopers. After 15 November the Army buys TBs at $2\frac{1}{2}$ out of training, mares going as chargers direct to regiments, colts first gelded at a remount depot. *No horses are bought from dealers under 5 years old, and French commissions never go abroad to purchase.* This year, owing to increase of establishment, a number of foreign horses have been bought from dealers in France, including some 2,500 Irish and English horses. Freight and import tax total £9, so there is not much profit for English dealers at French trooper prices. The officers' chargers at the Montrouge depot appeared cheaply bought at £55 to £64, considering their age and the freight and import tax. The total to be bought in 1914 is 15,000 horses. French law permits the return of all horses within 9 days from date or purchase which may be found to suffer from certain diseases and vices, i.e.

Intermittent lameness.

Chronic roaring.

Crib-biting and wind-sucking.

Jibbing.

Intermittent ophthalmia (30 days).

After purchase they are usually sent to a remount depot, of which there are 17, to remain under veterinary observation for 20 days before being drafted to their corps. Five-year-olds are issued as they are bought.

Annexes to remount depots

The establishments where young horses are matured for issue are either on Government land, as at Chalons, or on the property of communes or individuals. Other than Chalons, they are superintended by the remount depots, in charge of a resident officer. The men are all grooms, jockeys or farm labourers, there is a warrant officer and NCOs drawn from the regiment to which the young horses will belong. Animals are divided into stables of 40, which always remain together. The stable consists merely of four light walls, a cement floor and tiled roof; there are two large doors in the middle and mangers, hayracks and rings all the way round. They are always brought in for the night, the whole stable being bedded down and the horses turned loose. They are always fed in the stable, tied to the rings. There are no bales or other divisions but the hind shoes are off and they stand quietly together. There is only one man to ten horses, so the work is confined to keeping the stables clean, feeding and watering, and the animals spend most of their time in the paddock, coming in to feed and escape the sun, flies, rain or cold. In every annexe is an exercising track round which each lot is driven daily for exercise. They certainly look well and are quiet.

Census and classification of horses for impressment

It is interesting to compare with our own the system of horse classification and impressment carried out in France, where possibly mobilisation is regarded more seriously than with us. Early each December notices are issued to all horse owners, and by 1 January they are legally obliged to attend at the local Mairie and declare the details of their horses. This declaration is verified by the gendarmerie and proceedings are taken against anyone who omits or falsifies any particular.

On 20 January an abstract (in duplicate) is sent by each commune to the sub-prefect, who forwards one copy to the district recruiting office. Then military commissions classify the horses at the Mairie as *cuirassier*, dragoon, light cavalry, artillery and so on. The cost of the census is £25,000 yearly. On mobilisation a military commission selects the horses required to fill the quota allocated to each commune, payment being made according to classification and price fixed by budget.

Report of Lord Selbourne's Committee

On 3 August 1915, after consultation with the Chairman of the Advisory Council on Light Horse Breeding, the Right Honourable The Earl of Selbourne, KG, GCMG, President of the Board of Agriculture and Fisheries, appointed a Committee to consider and advise what steps should be taken to secure the production and maintenance in England and Wales of a supply of horses suitable and sufficient for military purposes, especially on mobilisation.

The Committee was constituted as follows:

> The Lord Middleton (*Chairman*)
> The Right Hon. Henry Chaplin, MP
> The Rt. Hon. Sir Ailwyn Fellowes, KCVO
> The Hon. Alexander Parker
> Major Sir Merrik Burrell, Bart.
> Sir Gilbert Greenall, Bart., CVO
> Captain M. S. Adye

The report of this committee opened by emphasising the urgency of the pleas addressed by the War Office to the Board. The Committee entirely agreed with the expressions of opinion of the War Office, and considered that they did not exaggerate the seriousness of the present position of light horse breeding. The Committee sat on thirteen days, from 4 August. Prior to 1911 the only assistance given by the Government was an annual grant of £5,000 to the Royal Commission. Of this amount, £3,000 had been given annually since the reign of Queen Anne by way of a Royal Bounty, and expended on the provision of Royal Plates to be won at race meetings in various parts of the country.

This method of encouraging breeding was not considered altogether satisfactory, and in 1887 the grant was increased to £5,000, a Royal Commission was appointed to administer the grant and to consider how the funds could be more usefully expended. The grant at their disposal being wholly inadequate to enable them to do anything to improve, in either quantity or quality, the horse supply of the country, they decided to award premiums for Thoroughbred stallions suitable for getting half-bred horses of general utility, and from 1888 to 1910 they awarded annually some 28 premiums, originally £200, and subsequently £150 in value, limiting their object to the promotion of soundness among the stallions and their progeny.

Unsatisfactory condition of the horse supply of the country for military purposes

So long as Racing and Hunting continue unchecked, there is no reason to anticipate any very large reduction in the number of horses of the highest quality, but owing to the war, racing, except in Ireland and at Newmarket, is entirely stopped, and hunting, though not suspended to any great extent, is conducted under unusual difficulties. If present conditions continue for any length of time, the horse-breeding industry must be disastrously affected, as the breeding of Thoroughbred horses would be immensely diminished, and we should be in danger of losing the sires on which we depend, not only for military purposes but for the civil supply as well.

In 1906 and subsequent years representations from various other quarters were made to the Government as to the urgent need for further financial assistance. The Government recognised that the breeding of light horses was being adversely affected by the increase in mechanical traction and the consequent diminution in the number of horses required by the export of good stallions and brood mares, and by the insufficient supply of sound and suitable stallions for service at a moderate fee. In January 1911, a grant of £40,000 was made out of the Development Fund to the Board, to assist and encourage the horse-breeding industry. The present scheme has been in existence for only four years, and it is therefore premature to expect any marked improvement.

The War Office made a series of biting criticisms. In April 1914: 'No one who goes carefully through the horses in either a country or urban district can fail to be appalled at the number of animals which, by faulty conformation or obvious unsoundness, are quite unsuited for hard work.'

'I am to call the immediate attention of your Board to the grave concern with which the Army Council view this question of the production and maintenance of an ample supply of light horses of a suitable stamp for military purposes. The supply of this type of horse is indeed so vital to the successful mobilisation of His Majesty's Forces that the Army Council are impelled to ask for a definite assurance that the Board contemplate taking urgent and adequate steps to allay anxiety on this point. (20 July 1914.)

On 13 December 1914: 'Owing to the inferiority of many of the sires, a large number of these horses are of so poor a stamp as to be of no military value.'

On 9 July 1915: 'Unhappily, the experience of the recent mobilisation has proved that though this country produces many super-excellent horses, the number of unsound and utterly worthless animals, which ought never to have been bred, is deplorably large.... This clearly points to the necessity of levelling up the horses in general use throughout the country and the production, instead of nondescripts, of animals of a type which will command good prices both in the home and foreign markets.'

In a letter, finally, dated 20 July 1915, from Lord Kitchener to Lord Selborne, the former says:

'... I have no hesitation in saying that from a military point of view it is of the utmost importance to ensure an ample supply of light draught and riding horses of a really good stamp, suitable for Cavalry and Artillery work, if this country is, in the future, to be fully prepared for war... Even the numbers available have not been sufficient for our largely increased wants, and consequently we have had to purchase heavily in America, some £12,000,000 having been spent there since war was declared. Some, at any rate, of this expenditure might have been saved had the Home breeding been on a proper footing. The main difficulty, however, is quality, and to secure this the first requisite is a good supply of high-class Thoroughbred sires readily available to the small breeder at a reasonable price, together with a corresponding number of good brood mares, capable not only of producing a good foal, but also of earning their keep on a farm... I hope, therefore, that you will do your utmost to secure the approval of the Treasury to the adoption of some scheme of State aid. The question is one of military importance, and it is essential that it should be dealt with on large and comprehensive lines, and at the earliest possible date.'

Inasmuch as the War Office have purchased many thousands of horses in England and Wales since the outbreak of war, they are in a better position than anyone to know and judge of the character and condition of our present horse supply, and it must be admitted from their evidence that the present position is a menace to the State, and that urgent necessity exists for the improvement of the Horse Supply, both in the interests of the nation generally, and of the Army in particular.

Decline of light horse breeding

It is well known that the breeding of light horses has been on the decline for many years past. The increase of mechanical traction may be held to be responsible to some extent; but there are other contributory causes, and by no means the least of them is that farmers have not found the industry a paying one. It is recognised that the market for the misfit light horse is daily growing smaller. As a business proposition, it does not pay to breed misfits, but only animals for which there is a good demand at a remunerative price. The hunter is a class of horse to which the latter definition applies at the present time: but hunter breeding is not a branch of farming that appeals to farmers as a general rule, unless they are good horsemen; for however successful a breeder may be, it is only the breeder who can convert his young stock into 'made' hunters who finds light horse breeding a really profitable industry.

The number of farmers who possess the necessary qualifications and opportunities for 'making' hunters is comparatively few, and they are men who can probably look after themselves without Government assistance, but there are many farmers who, without being skilled horsemen, are ready to breed light horses if sufficient encouragement and facilities are afforded them, and if they find that they can do so without losing money.

Continuity of policy is absolutely essential to the success of any horse-breeding scheme, and radical alteration should as far as possible be avoided, unless and until it has proved ineffective. After a careful examination of the Board's scheme it appears sound in principle and has already undoubtedly revived interest in light horse breeding in many parts of the country.

There follows a lengthy review of the current situation. Voluntary registration of stallions was introduced in 1911, and the number registered annually was:

	Registered	Rejected
1911	313	44
1911–12	715	90
1912–13	837	65
1913–14	1220	106
1914–15	1471	103

The War Office recommended compulsory registration, and maintained that the levelling up of horses in general use throughout the country can only be effected by the elimination of worthless stallions. It was recommended further that the number of King's Premium stallions should be increased in 1916 from fifty to sixty, and progressively to 150 as soon as stallions of sufficient merit were available. There were several parts of the country where no premium stallion was available, and many had to travel much too wide an area. With a view to preventing the export of premium stallions which are deemed by the Board suitable for country service, it was recommended that a condition of acceptance of a premium was that the Government should be given first refusal to purchase if the owner had an offer to sell the stallion abroad, such condition to remain in force for twelve months after the award of the premium. Change of ownership should not nullify this condition.

Another recommendation was for the purchase of mares and stallions by the Board. The mares would be leased out to suitable custodians at an annual rental of £2, to be stinted to registered stallions approved by the Board. Stallions should be purchased by the Board to prevent them being bought for use abroad, especially when private enterprise, as hitherto, has so often been outbidden by the foreign agent with a Government purse behind him. The purchase of horses by the Board was quite compatible with the Premium system, which was undoubtedly successful, but Board stallions should not compete for premiums.

It was considered that the Board should appoint a competent buyer, who should make it his business to know of every horse in training suitable for country service. In all arrangements for the purchase, maintenance and use of Thoroughbred stallions, under the Premium system or otherwise, the first consideration and guiding principle must be what was best for the national object of the improvement of the breed of horses. Attention must be called to another source of danger to the horse supply which would add to the anxieties of the War Office and might quite conceivably become quite serious to that supply in the future — the abnormal number of Thoroughbred colts, both among the yearlings and older horses in training, which, owning to the partial suspension of racing, were being castrated.

Stallions, including yearlings after a certain date, could not be turned out together lest they fight and get injured, and in the great majority of cases there was not accommodation available to turn them out alone. In consequence, castration was being widely resorted to. The question of how this process might be arrested was one for prompt decision. It was thought that the Board might reasonably step in without delay and ask for the means, as a measure of emergency, to acquire from the Thoroughbreds still in training which would otherwise be cut, such animals as might be held by competent judges to be really suitable for the breeding of the horses of the quality and stamp required for military purposes.

Encouragement of breeding

If improvement of the quality of horses bred was to be secured, it was vital to give farmers every facility and encouragement, as there was always a market for good horses both at home and abroad. Up to the present, little encouragement had been given to breeders by the War Office in their method of buying horses in time of peace. The Committee opined that the system of giving prizes for foals deserved every encour-agement, as it was most desirable to educate breeders concerning the necessity of looking after and doing their young stock well, especially during the first year after birth. The system of giving foal prizes was much appreciated by breeders, providing a quick return for their outlay. They therefore recommended that liberal grants be provided for foal prizes, each foal being limited to one a year. These grants should supplement, not replace, prizes already given at shows. Liberal grants should similarly be expended in the award of futurity prizes to mares from 3 to 8 years old, in respect of those who produced living foals the following year, the produce of a premium or registered stallion, approved by the Board or County Committee.

It was not suggested that suitable horses would not be available in sufficient numbers to meet all War Office requirements in time of peace. Hitherto the Army has been a comparatively small customer in the horse market of Great Britain — the normal purchases at time of peace amount only to some 3,000 a year, and 80% are bought in Ireland. The fact that the purchases are made through dealers and consist of horses over 4 years old does not tend to bring the War Office into touch with breeders, nor will any breeder in Britain attempt under existing conditions to breed horses especially for remount purposes; it would not pay him to do so.

95

The system of purchase has no doubt been adopted because it is economical and convenient, and provided the Army can secure, at the price they are prepared to offer, horses in sufficient numbers and of the type, age and quality required (and they can in peace time) there would seem no good reason to alter the methods employed. The middleman (dealer) saves an enormous amount of trouble and expense, as he knows the requirements of the Army buyers, collects batches of suitable horses for their inspection, and does not waste their time by trying to sell animals that are evidently unsuitable. Again, horses between 4 and 7 are ready and fit to go into the ranks much sooner than horses bought at 3 from breeders.

But, and it is a very big 'but', the present method of buying remounts gives no encouragement at all to the breeder and does not bring him into touch with Army buyers. If the Government want farmers and others to breed horses suitable for remount purposes, they must in some way make it profitable to do so, and give further assistance and encouragement to the industry. Joint action by the War Office and the Board is required, and it is recommended:

(1) That in peace time the War Office should buy a much larger number in England and Wales. Since the outbreak of war only 15% of the horses purchased in the UK have been bought in Ireland, and the remainder in Britain, though in times of peace this is usually reversed. This anomaly is due, we understand, to the fact that impressment of horses was not practicable in Ireland except in towns and certain garrison districts.

(2) That the peace establishment should be materially increased to provide a larger market for breeders.

(3) That more horses should be bought direct from breeders, who must be educated as to the types required for military purposes, the advantage of having them in suitable condition by Army buyers, and as to their fair commercial value.

(4) That as many should be bought when rising 4 as possible, as the earlier he can get rid of his stock the better pleased he will be and the more ready to study the requirements of the War Office.

(5) That if there are any specially good 3-year-old fillies they should be bought and left with breeders until they have produced and reared foals, though great care should be taken in determining the conditions and selecting the breeders.

(6) That mares which appear suitable for breeding should be drafted from the ranks at ten years and transferred to the Board for disposal under their brood mare schemes.

Artillery horses

We consider the encouragement of the breeding of horses suitable for artillery and light draught to be of the utmost national importance, bearing in mind that on mobilisation a greater number of these horses is required than of the riding type. This type of horse, weighing from 1200 to 1400 lbs., from 15.2 to 15.3 hands, on short clean legs, with deep, well-placed shoulders, short back and quick, well-balanced action, has always been hard to find, but of late years, owing to the replacement of all omnibus horses and many vanners by motors, it is rapidly becoming extinct. But on light land, and in the hilly districts, small active draught horses are still to be found, and it is recommended that steps should be taken by the War Office and the Board to encourage the improvement of that type of horse in such districts. It is essential that a sufficiency of these short-legged active stallions and mares should be maintained. It may be impossible to find enough sires of the requisite stamp, and it may be necessary for special efforts to be made by the Board to breed this particular type of horse.

These horses are more economical for use on light land and in hilly districts than the taller, heavier, slower-moving breeds, so that if the number bred is increased, there is no reason to anticipate any difficulty in finding a ready market for them. We understand that the use of the Shire horse during the present war has proved that although he possesses certain advantages he is, on the whole, unsuitable for campaigning, and can never therefore take the place of the smaller, hardier horse.

Repatriation of army horses

We are glad to learn that it is anticipated that large numbers of army horses will be available at the close of war for disposal in this country, and we hope the War Office and the Board will use every endeavour to secure their distribution to the best possible advantage. We are well aware that many thousands of horses — mares as well as geldings — have been taken for military purposes since the outbreak of war, and the drain on the country has been severe. We cordially approve, therefore, of the proposal to repatriate Army horses; and the opportunity of replenishing the horse stock of the country, especially breeding stock, will be very welcome.

We realise that it is impossible for the War Office to furnish reliable information at present as to the number, according to sex or type, to be demobilised, so we are not in a position to recommend the most suitable methods of dealing with them. We feel, however, that all the best mares, of every type used in the Army, should be repatriated and made available for absorption in the civil horse stock, and that their subsequent export should be prohibited as long as they are suitable for breeding.

Exportation of horses

It is common knowledge that many of our high-class sires and mares are exported annually, but the official returns available are not given in sufficient detail for any definite conclusion to be reached as to the actual breeds and value of the horses exported. There is no doubt that some Thoroughbred stallions, very suitable for country service are purchased for studs abroad, and at prices with which home buyers are unable to compete. On the other hand, it must be remembered that it is the foreign demand that encourages the horse-breeding industry, and gives the best incentive to breeders to produce the best class of stock. This consideration must not be lost sight of, as the object in view is to increase the number of high-class horses in the country so that in a crisis they will be available for military purposes.

We are of opinion that in normal times no restrictions should be placed on the export trade in horses, *provided that effective steps are taken to secure the retention of suitable stallions and mares in sufficient numbers for use in this country.* This we urge should be done by the liberal provision of facilities and encouragement for breeding, and by Government purchases of suitable animals for retention in the country.

Census of horses

We have considered the information available as to the number of horses in the country, the number exported and the number imported, and are of the opinion that a census of horses should be taken annually, not only of horses on agricultural holdings but throughout the country, in urban as well as rural districts: this return should be compulsory and made in as great detail as possible, classifying the horses, so far as practicable, according to breeds, sexes and ages. We would also urge that the returns collected in regard to the exports and imports of horses should show in greater detail the breeds, sexes, ages and values of the animals as to which information is obtained, and that arrangements should be made that no Thoroughbred stallion should be exported without his name being given, and also the names of his sire and dam.

Appointment of Advisory Council and County Committees

The Advisory Council and its Standing Committee, appointed by the Board to advise them in the administration of their scheme, are in our opinion too large for practical purposes, and we recommend that their appointment should lapse and that

97

a small permanent Council of not more than seven members should be appointed in their place.

We are also well aware, from our knowledge of County Committees, that their present constitution is not altogether satisfactory. Few members have sufficient leisure, even though they may have the keenness and initiative, to carry out efficiently the duties entrusted to County Committees; other members have not the necessary practical knowledge and experience for doing so, and in the circumstances we are of the opinion that the Committees should be reconstituted, and that small committees of not more than three members should be appointed by the Board to take the place of the present Committees, and that great care should be taken that only thoroughly experienced and practical men are appointed as members of the new Committees.

Appointment of an expert staff

We consider the appointment of an expert and adequate staff of officers of the Board to be absolutely essential, inasmuch as the success of any national horse-breeding scheme must depend on proper supervision. We recommend therefore that the country should be divided into districts and that in each district there should be stationed an officer of the Board, whose sole duty should be to promote and supervise the light horse breeding operations of the Board. The staff should consist of men who are fully qualified by practical experience and knowledge to carry out the following duties:

(a) To advise breeders as to the selection, mating, rearing and disposal of their stock.

(b) To supervise the service arrangements of stallions purchased by the Board, and of Premium Stallions, and to inspect and keep records of their stock.

(c) To keep in close touch with War Office buyers, and to arrange for collection of horses for inspection and purchase.

(d) To act as secretaries to County Committees and to supervise generally the horse-breeding scheme of the Board.

Finance

The present scheme of the Board is financed almost entirely by a grant from the Development Fund, which has been materially reduced since it was first made in 1911, when it amounted approximately to £40,000. The grant has been reduced annually during the last three years, and for the present financial year amounts only to £26,500, which is totally inadequate to afford the encouragement necessary to secure an improvement in the quality of the horse supply of the country. We make no recommendation as to the amount necessary for the purpose, as that does not appear to fall within the terms of our reference.

We consider, however, that continuity of policy is absolutely essential to the success of any horse-breeding scheme and that, as the Board should be responsible for the policy, we recommend that the provision of funds for financing the scheme should be borne on the Board's Vote, and that encouragement of horse-breeding should be recognised as a permanent activity of the State.

Finally, we wish to express our entire concurrence with the contents of the following extract from a statement forwarded to the Board by the War Office in a letter dated 16 April, 1914:

'Without an adequate supply of suitable horses in civil life upon which to draw it would be impossible to mobilise the Army as it is now constituted, and if such a supply were non-existent we should be compelled at vast expense to maintain not only establishments constantly at war strength but adequate reserves as well.'

Unfortunately this supply did prove on mobilisation to be inadequate for military purposes, and it therefore appears to us to be essential to the national welfare that steps should be taken by the Government to deal with the situation, and on comprehensive lines. We are aware that the adoption of our proposals will involve very considerable expenditure, and a progressively increasing one for a few years, but even if it eventually approximates an annual outlay of £100,000 the amount would be small compared to that expended by many Continental Powers, or with the sum that would be required if it were found necessary for the War Office to set up establishments for breeding remounts.

We fully recognise the need for national economy in every possible direction, but in view of the serious condition of the light horse industry of the country, we are of opinion that it would be false economy to defer taking action on the lines suggested.

We have the honour to be, my Lord,
Your Lordship's obedient Servants,
(*Signed*)   Middleton (*Chairman*)
Henry Chaplin
Alwyn E. Fellows
Alexander E. Parker
Merrik Burrell
Gilbert Greenall
M. S. Adye

Reservations and supplementary report by the Rt. Hon. Henry Chaplin, MP

I have signed the Report which has been agreed to by my colleagues, but subject to certain reservations on some points on which I am not in entire agreement with them, and others on which I go perhaps further than they do. With the general purport of the Report and the absolute need for continued Government aid I warmly concur. I have also added a statement, which seems to me desirable, explaining more fully the causes which have produced the deplorable change in the character of the horse supply of the country.

That supply is a matter to which I have given much thought and attention, and with which I have been familiar for years. The whole question was raised in Parliament so long ago as 23 April 1875, in which I took a leading part; and it was also my fortune to serve on the Royal Commission, afterwards appointed upon it, throughout its career until it ceased to exist in 1911.

When, therefore, I was invited by the Minister of Agriculture to serve on a Committee 'to consider and report as to the steps that should be taken to secure the production and maintenance in England and Wales of an ample supply of horses suitable for military purposes' I assented at once, being one of those who have been convinced, from my own personal experience, that the horse supply of the country had been steadily going from bad to worse for a number of years.

Among the papers we found submitted by the Committee the correspondence between that Department and the War Office is of the utmost importance. It must not be forgotten, moreover, that the War Office wrote on this subject with a weight of authority which was unique, having regard to the information before them, and the sources from which it had been derived — *viz*:

(a) The horse census and classification taken by them in the winter 1912–13 by some 500 officers; and
(b) The vast number of horses purchased by them for mobilisation after war was declared, through a great number of buyers in the United Kingdom.

What was the purport of their information? It will be found in the quotations contained in paragraphs 10–14 in the Report of the Committee and is taken from the communications addressed to the Board by the War Office on 16 April, 20 July and

13 December 1914, and on 9 July, and 20 July 1915, and may be summarised as follows:

13 December, 1914: 'that there is a sensibly diminished supply in the number of horses used in civil life owing to the development of motor traffic; although there would still be sufficient to meet the requirements of the Army, if they were of good type.'

9 July 1914: 'But a great many of them are of so bad a type as to be of no military value, while the number of unsound and utterly worthless animals which ought never to have been bred at all is deplorably large.'

16 April 1914: 'The number of faulty and unsound animals in either town or country districts is described as appalling.'

13 December 1914: 'And the Board is informed by the War Office that it is of the utmost importance that steps should be taken at once to arrest the deterioration of the horse stock in this country.'

This is indeed a stupendous disclosure, a deplorable change in the character of the horse supply of the nation; and the more remarkable when, by universal consent, it is admitted that at one time, and for a vast number of years, England was famous throughout the world for its breed of horses, and for the stamp and the quality of the supply which it possessed. Nor has it occurred without warnings upon the subject addressed to successive Governments, again and again, by the Royal Commission already mentioned and otherwise, but without any avail; and it has been reserved to the War Office during the last two years to bring to light the true facts as to our present supply of horses for military purposes, as they have been disclosed by the census and the recent mobilisation.

Here it may not be out of place to quote the Resolution, already referred to, which was moved in the House of Commons in 1875, as follows:

'That this House views with apprehension the large and continued export of the best and soundest stud horses and brood mares for general purposes from this country, and wishes to direct the attention of Her Majesty's Government to the national importance of taking such steps as may be desirable to prevent the deterioration of the stock which remains.'

It will be seen that it indicates some of the causes which even then were beginning to injure the home supply, while the disclosures of the War Office today bear out to the letter the force of the apprehensions which it expressed at that date. With two exceptions, however, which are dealt with in the Report, little or nothing has ever been done from that time to this, to arrest and repair the mischief to which attention was drawn in 1875 and which, in greater or less degree, has been going on ever since.

The first exception was when the Royal Commission was appointed in 1887, but with a grant so small — under £5,000 a year with office expenses deducted — that it could do nothing to add to either the quantity or the quality of the supply of horses excepting in one respect; to improve by a very limited system of Premiums, the soundness of some of the stallions in use and therefore some of their progeny also, and in which, having regard for their very limited means, they were, as a matter of fact, more successful than could have been hoped for. The other was when a Council of 55 members, appointed by the then President of the Board of Agriculture (Lord Carrington), to administer a much increased grant of £45,000 a year in aid of horse-breeding, but the results of the policy which they pursued, whatever its merits, has not found great favour, it seems, with the Development Commissioners.

But before dealing further with this branch of the subject, it seems to me that a somewhat fuller explanation than was given in the Report, of the causes which have occasioned the deplorable change in the character of the horse supply of the country, which is disclosed in the graphic descriptions of the War Office, is needed for the information both of Members of Parliament and of the public, the great majority of whom are probably not closely acquainted with this particular subject.

It is to be found in the widely differing methods by which horse-breeding is and has been conducted in the United Kingdom, and in the other leading countries on the Continents both of Europe and, more recently, of America also.

Hitherto, with the exceptions referred to, the breeding of horses adapted for the Army has been left entirely to private enterprise in Great Britain. But the conditions as regards horse-breeding in the leading countries of Europe are entirely different; and there, horses for their Armies for years have been largely supplied by great Government establishments, including Depots for stallions and extensive Haras for mares. But for the purposes of these establishments created to supply the Army, they have had to draw very heavily upon England and Ireland for the country mares, and the right class of Thoroughbred sires, only to be found at that time in the United Kingdom — and with this result: that the UK has been drained year after year, by one country after another, of great numbers of our best Thoroughbred country stallions and our best half-bred country mares, for a period so prolonged that it began in the late sixties or the very early seventies and has been steadily continued ever since, to the great detriment of the general excellence of our own breed at home.

Having watched with great care the mischief progressing for forty years, I am convinced, and have not a doubt, that this is the real cause that lies at the root of the deplorable position into which the horse supply of the country has fallen, as described by the War Office today. And as long as we continue to lose the best of our breeding material in such large proportions as we have done for years, common sense tells us that it could not be otherwise.

In support of that view, moreover, we have an accumulation of evidence which seems to me to be conclusive as to the facts. Take the War Office first, what do they say of the character of the present supply? To those who can remember what it once was, the change is deplorable. With their unique opportunity for ascertaining the facts, they trace the cause of the mischief to the 'inferiority of so many of the sires now being used'. They are equally clear as to the remedy: 'to ensure that thoroughly good sires are available to all private breeders at a low price'. Again, in a letter of 9 July 1915, in reference to the deplorable number of worthless animals now being bred, the War Office say:

'This, as Lord Selborne indicates, can only be effected by the elimination of worthless stallions, the provision of good ones, the use of good mares, and' (the Council ventures to add) 'the creation of a staff of trained inspectors to carry out the policy of the Board. Finally, in a letter dated 20 July 1915, from Lord Kitchener, the same remedy is insisted upon again in paragraph 14 of the Report, which I recommend to the attention of all who are interested in this very important question.

Lord Kitchener's letter points to the necessity of a corresponding number of good brood mares, and these latter, the War Office explains, can be obtained by the repatriation of a number of high-class brood mares which were taken abroad for the war. The War Office — and I do not say this without reason — would be glad to consider sympathetically any proposal put forward by the Board of Agriculture for the selection and repatriation of any high-class brood mares with the Army in France, with a view to their being placed with suitable custodians, on a guarantee of their being bred from.

Again, we are told in the annual report of the Board on the administration of the grant for the year 1912–13:

'It is frequently urged that more stallions of weight and substance should be sub-sidised to travel the country, and effect would gladly be given to these representations if such stallions were available in greater numbers than is the case . . . The Thoroughbred stallion of the stamp required, that has stood the test of the racecourse, is sound and has weight and substance, is said to be increasingly difficult to find.'

This statement, no doubt, is absolutely true, and is more than confirmed by the information and letters which constantly reach me from breeders, among them one of great eminence, as to the scarcity of sires of the right class. Further support for our proposals is found in the 12th Report of the Royal Commission, in which they review their work from the time of their appointment in 1887 until very shortly before their demise was decreed by the Board under Lord Carrington. They say that the first thing they did was to ascertain clearly the causes of the deterioration of the stock in the country, which even then was the subject for complaint. Their conclusions were stated in four brief paragraphs in their first report on 20 December 1887. They seem to me to embody the policy for which I have never ceased to contend. 'From these views' the Commissioners say 'they have never departed.' They conclude a very important report:

'The main causes of the trouble are still in operation. The best of our sires and our mares, which are so greatly needed for our own requirements, continue steadily to leave the country, purchased by foreign Governments, to improve the breed of horses in foreign lands.

'No efforts on the part of this Commission to assist the industry, unless they are provided with further means, can effectually help it, and it becomes our duty once again to urge with all the force we can that the difficulties which confront an interest of so much importance to the nation, its welfare and even its safety, are increasing every year; and with every day's delay in dealing with the question they will continue to increase more seriously in the future.'

The Report, dated 13 April 1908, was agreed to by the whole Commission, with a single reservation by one of its members on a question affecting the Brood Mare Society, and among those who signed it will be found those of the Chairman of this Committee, Lord Middleton, and the author of these reservations.

I have thought it right to cite the Commissioners in that Report for two reasons:

(1) Because they have never wavered in their opinions, from the time of their first appointment, either as to the cause of the troubles we see today, or the real remedies for them; and

(2) Everything that we have learned in our inquiry and that we know now points to the conclusion that in the appeals of the Commission, which were never attended to, it is proved today to have been right; and their views should carry, in consequence, no little weight in support of the new departure for the Government purchase of stallions.

Unfortunately we have no returns of the export of horses of which they complained, sufficient to tell us precisely what we have been losing year after year of our most valuable stock, among them the class of stallions which we ought, above all, to keep for our own use at home. But happily I am able to give a concrete case of what happened some years ago, in one European country, when the drain upon our resources had not long begun, which will show quite clearly what was going on then. And, indirectly, we are able to learn by a recent and timely change in the form of the Returns since 1912, by which stallions of the value of £100 and over are classified, that the same kind of thing is going on still on an extensive scale, and it leads very strongly to the belief, that concealed by the previous form of the Returns, the drain on our resources has quite possibly been going on the whole of the time.

I will take the concrete case of Germany first, which was quoted in the House of Commons in 1875. It is very striking and will be found extremely interesting, and it throws much light on the causes of the unhappy change in the character of the horse supply in the United Kingdom at present. The whole of the information and the figures which I quoted at that time were supplied to me by the courtesy of the Count Münster, at that time German Ambassador in London. He was good enough to obtain them for me from Berlin, and gave me permission to use them in moving the Resolution I have already referred to. They are taken from an extract which will be found in the *Appendix*, from the Statement I made on that occasion.

'In Prussia there were three principal breeding studs which were originally intended for supplying the Royal stud. In addition there were 11 depots, containing about 1450 stallions. From those depots at the proper season of the year, those horses were distributed in number varying from one to six, in the charge of Government servants; and they were located at 540 different stations throughout the country...

The whole cost of maintaining these studs was £170,000 per annum, of which there was received back in fees £70,000; and the annual results of these establishments was a produce of something like 50,000 foals at a gross cost to the State of £100,000, or £2 per head...

The most serious part of that question as affecting us was that all those 1,700 horses in Germany were of English extraction — that was to say, were bred either from English horses or mares, and one-third of the whole had been imported straight from this country.'

From this Summary it will be seen that some 567 of the pick of our stallions for country purposes at that time were taken for one foreign country alone, besides numbers of others which had been taken previously from whom the remaining two-thirds were bred. That was in 1875. Now let us turn to the New Returns of 1913 and 1914. They will give us a pretty clear indication of what has been going on since 1875. In 1913 there were exported to foreign countries 544 stallions of the value of £100 and over, valued at £243, 398 and averaging, therefore, £447 apiece. Of these horses, 35 were taken by Germany at a cost of £75,065, and averaging £2,143 apiece.

It is said, I know not on what authority, that £27,000 was given by Germany for one horse alone. Assuming it is so, the remaining 34 would average £1,411 apiece, which makes it practically certain that the horses exported, according to this Return, to Germany in 1913 were high-class Thoroughbred stallions, exactly the sort that should have been kept in this country, where they are so terribly hard to find now. Again, I find this information as to stallions exported in the Returns of 1914, which I have tabulated as follows:

Country	Number	Value (£)	Average cost per head (£)
France	14	8,090	577
Japan	24	10,730	477
Brazil	12	4,305	350
Argentina	11	3,620	329
Germany	14	3,635	259

Thus in two years we find that 110 stallions, costing £95,280, have been taken abroad by five countries only in 1913 and 1914, and with regard to these horses from the prices which they have averaged, it is reasonable to suppose that the majority of them, at all events, would have been horses which should have remained in the country.

In view of what we know now, or rather what we do not know, of the stallion supply of this country, except that there is a terrible shortage of horses of the right class, I shall be pardoned, I hope, if I say that it seems to be very unfortunate that notwithstanding the very large sums of money which have been spent with the sanction of the Advisory Committee since the grant was bestowed in January, 1911, little or nothing has been even attempted by Government purchase to make sure of retaining more sires of the right class in the country.

This Committee, however, has happily taken a very different view, and recommends strongly the policy of the purchase of high class stallions by the Government, in a series of clauses which I cordially support. They also propose to extend the premium system, and assuming the funds at their disposal to be sufficient both for purchase and premium, and that the proposed extension will not be allowed to interfere with the system of purchase by the Government, again I entirely agree.

There are, however, two considerations connected with the premium system, and especially with regard to super-premiums, which must be borne in mind, and which in one respect should be carefully watched. It would seem in the first place to be a somewhat costly way of obtaining the object in view. In the case of super premium horses they may receive altogether over £500 for a single year.

In the Annual Report for 1912–13, we are told that in a few instances £523.5s. was earned. Five years' purchase would not be a very liberal calculation in the life of such a horse beginning at 6 years old nor do I think that even 10 years would be extravagant. Many of our best and most celebrated Thoroughbred horses have continued their services to the age of 25 years and upwards. The receipt of £500 by a premium winner for 5 years would be equivalent to a purchase price of £2,500, and for 10 years, of course, it would be doubled. A considerably larger sum in either case than the average price for which high-class country stallions could, on the whole, be bought.

There is another objection, and that is the blot on the premium system. It does not ensure their retention at home. Complaints are recorded in the Reports of the old Royal Commission of premium horses who were in this country most popular sires being taken abroad, and although in the case of super-premium stallions they are under contract to remain in the country for 2 years' service under penalty of forfeiting £100, we are advised of cases where, under the temptation of a high price from a foreign buyer, the contracts have been broken.

I am strongly of the opinion myself that no one breaking a contract of this kind should ever be allowed to compete for a premium again. On the other hand, I should be sorry to see the premium system abolished; the annual show of stallions fulfils a double purpose. It undoubtedly helps to maintain public interest in horse-breeding, and it offers the only opportunity we have of forming any opinion as to the character or the sufficiency of the stallion supply of the country.

In several European countries we know that they had, and undoubtedly still have, a very large number. I have quoted the case of Germany many years ago, who had then 1,700 stallions. Have we anything even approaching that number in our own country, and if not, how many suitable animals have we?

A census of stallions

What is really needed at present to my mind, more than anything else in connection with the improvement of the horse supply of the kingdom, is a reliable census of suitable Thoroughbred sires, and all Thoroughbred horses in training who give promise of becoming suitable sires, now in the country. I am greatly afraid that it will be found to be lamentably and even dangerously small, and I suggest that it should be undertaken without delay.

The sole information we have on the subject at present shows that only 205 Thoroughbred stallions (according to the Register of Stallions, 1914–15, of the Board of Agriculture and Fisheries) are registered in England and Wales. If that is all that we have, it is exceedingly serious, and more than sufficient to account for the precarious position of the horse supply of the country of which the War Office so rightly complain.

Brood mares

I concur in the proposal that the brood mare scheme be continued in eight or nine counties where it has proved successful, of which I know both from the Inspector's Reports as well as from private information that Northampton is one, and is doing well. But beyond that I am unable to go and for reasons which seem to me to be good. We learn from the papers relating to the brood mare scheme, which have been circulated to the Committee (and they are most important) that the broad results of that scheme are as follows: 892 mares, 400 of which I learn from the annual reports of the Administration of the Grant were purchased in 1911–12, 139 in 1912–13, and 201 in 1913–14, for 37 County Committees, at a cost of £37,765. What is the number of foals bred in 1912–13–14–15 which there is to show as the result of that purchase? 857, according to the latest figures obtainable in 1915, that is to say, 35 less than the 892 mares, the majority of which were purchased before 1913–14.

It seems to me that it is much too poor a return from a most costly scheme. It would be wiser, in my humble judgement, and in the interests also of the eight or nine counties where they have been successful, to postpone any new proposals until an adequate organisation has been arranged for the effective conduct of any new scheme in the future, and is ready and able to deal with the mares that are to be repatriated by the War Office.

Finally, I must express my absolute conviction that if any real and substantial improvement is to be made in the horse supply of the country, it can only be made with the aid of Government funds on a liberal scale.

The provision of a suitable number of stallions for the the use of breeders is the first step, in my opinion, to be taken in that direction, and more essential than anything else. And if it is found, as I believe that it will be, that the number of suitable stallions that we possess at present is far too small for our requirements, drastic measures will have to be taken to increase them if any real good is to be done; and no animal of the right class should be allowed to leave the country in future without a licence from the Board of Agriculture; and unless and until they are satisfied that we have again a sufficient number for our own use at home, no licence for the export of any such stallion should be granted.

We are warned that continuity of policy is absolutely essential to the success of any horse-breeding scheme. When we see the position in which continuity of policy over a number of years has landed the horse supply of the country today, I must respectfully differ in that opinion, and it seems to me that in our present proposals we are sanctioning very important departures from that continuity.

With reference to the number of high-class Thoroughbred stallions which are exported annually, we are warned that it is the foreign demand that gives the best incentive to breeders to produce the best class of stock. I can only say from my own experience that in the case of the high-class stallions referred to, and they are the foundation on which the light horse breeding industry rests in this country, that the idea that the foreign market for Thoroughbred stallions affects the production of sires of that class in the United Kingdom is an absolute fallacy.

I have myself bred any number of them, and anyone with the same experience will say the same thing. These animals are all of them bred, with the rarest exceptions, if any, for one purpose and one alone, and that is for racing.

They are bred in the hope that they may become winners of big races, classic or otherwise, in which case the dam and her future produce becomes the source of a fortune greater or less to the owner, and whether the foreign market for stallions of this class is lost or not, so long as racing countinues they will be bred in the future exactly as they have been bred in the past, and independently of all other markets, except the market that is provided for them by racing.

What is a very serious matter, and may become more so, is the castration of a wholly abnormal number of Thoroughbred colts, old horses in training as well as yearlings, since racing in England was stopped except at Newmarket. This question is dealt with in the main report, but the paragraphs which appear upon that point and on the purchase of stallions by the Government were written by me for the use of my colleagues, but as some of them have been omitted, which I consider material, they must not be taken to represent fully my views upon those two questions.

There are some other matters referred to in the Report with which I do not altogether agree. But they are of minor importance and I have written already, I fear, at too considerable length.

On two other points, however, I desire to say a word. One of them is on the important question of Artillery horses. On that point I think the mares so well described sound as though they would cross admirably with a strong Thoroughbred sire. I do not know quite what sires are contemplated in other cases, but I hope it will not be forgotten that *where courage is needed, a Thoroughbred cross is essential.*

With reference to the reconstruction of existing authorities, I venture to make two suggestions:

Racing being the foundation upon which the light horse breeding industry rests, in the reconstruction of any existing central authority, or in the creation of any new one, in connection with the light horse industry, it would be an advantage if racing was represented upon it by more than one of the members: and it would also be well if British farmers, who comprise the largest number of breeders, should be represented upon it by one of their own class as well.

(*Signed*)
HENRY CHAPLIN

APPENDIX I

Extract from Speech delivered on April 27th, 1875, in the House of Commons, on the following Motion:

Mr Chaplin to call attention to the Report of Select Committee of the House of Lords in 1873 on Horses, and to move —

'That this House views with apprehension the large and continued export of the best and soundest stud horses and brood mares for general purposes from this country, and wishes to direct the attention of Her Majesty's Government to the national importance of taking such steps as may be desirable to prevent the deterioration of the stock which remains.'

Some three or four years ago there was a sale of some of the most celebrated stock of Thoroughbreds in the Kingdom, forming the stud of that most eminent breeder of horses, the late Mr Blenkiron, a most patriotic Englishman. In that stud there were two horses descended from a breed of the most famous we possessed, and each of them conspicuous for the merits which distinguished it. One of them was Blair Athol, at that time considered by some the best horse in the world, and priceless as a sire for the turf, and the other was his own brother, Breadalbane, of great value as a stud horse and country stallion, though greatly inferior to his brother as a racehorse. It might not be generally known that the late lamented Lord Ossington (formerly Speaker to the House of Commons, as Mr Dennison) to whom he had alluded, combined with those other admirable qualities which they had recognised so long in that House all the instincts of a sportsman and a knowledge and a love of horses second to none.

Recognising the unusual merits of those horses, the noble Lord commissioned him (Mr Chaplin) to attend the sale, and offer for one of them a price which, considering that he wanted a horse for the service of his tenants and neighbours in the county of Nottingham at a fee of £1 was liberal in the extreme...

Blair Athol was bought, and kept in this country, for the sum of £12,000, the Prussian agent having actually offered £11,500 for him. Breadalbane fetched £6,000 — three times the liberal sum he was commissioned to give for him — and was bought by the same foreign agent.

That was a simple explanation of the reason why such horses did not remain in this country. They were bought up at prices against which private enterprise could not compete and taken out of this country. He would lay before the House some particulars as to the manner in which those studs were managed in foreign countries, and more especially as to the system adopted in Germany, for his information about which he was greatly indebted to the Ambassador, who provided him with the figures, and he took that opportunity of expressing his sense of the kindness and courtesy he had received from his Excellency.

He found that in the Austrian, in the Italian and in the French studs there were something like 5,000 stallions altogether, and they were distributed in this way. In Italy there were 350; in France there were 1,500 at this moment, which were to be raised at the rate of 200 a year until they reached a total of 2,500; in Austria and Hungary combined there were 3,400; and all those horses were kept at establishments which were maintained in order to improve the breed by the respective Governments of those countries. Again, in Prussia there were three principal breeding studs, which were originally intended for supplying the royal stud. In addition there were 11 depots containing about 1,450 stallions.

From those depots, at the proper season of the year, those horses were distributed in numbers varying from one to six, under the charge of Government servants; and they were located at 540 different stations throughout the country, where accommodation was usually provided for them by the landed proprietors, who took an interest in the matter. Now, the whole cost of maintaining these studs was £170,000 per annum, of which there was received back in fees (about 10 guineas per mare) £70 thousand; and the animal results of those establishments was a produce of something like 50,000 foals, at a gross cost to the State of about £100,000, or an average of £2 a head. Those were the results of that system, and they were surely worth our careful attention ... But the most serious part of that question as affecting us was that all those 1,700 horses in Germany were of English extraction, that was to say, were bred either from English horses or English mares, and one-third of the whole had been imported straight from this country.

The Great War was still dragging on when Volume VIII of the *Hunter Stud Book* was published in 1918, but it had nearly run its course. The Council determined that it was essential to the national industry of Horse-breeding that it should be published in normal rotation, although the prolongation of the conflict had naturally affected the breeding and registration of brood mares and young stock. Additionally adverse factors were the restrictions on racing and hunting, the rationing of young stock and the temporary extinction of the County Show. In all the discouraging circumstances, an entry of 550 for Volume VIII was satisfactory, as was the acknowledged success of the London Shows of 1916 and 1917, despite increased difficulties of transit.

The 1916 show was remarkable for the record entry received for the Thoroughbred section, no fewer than 174 stallions competing for 60 King's premiums and 12 super-premiums. Following the dual success of Captain Wickham-Boynton's King's Courtship in 1912 and 1913, his magnificent chesnut Rathurde brought off a hat trick in 1917, 1918 and 1919, winning the King George V Gold Cup outright for the first time.

In 1916 the hunter judges were Mr J. P. Arkwright, Master of the North Warwickshire for some 30 years, and Captain Geoffrey Phipps-Hornby. They awarded the young horse championship to the 3-year-old hunter-bred Blacksmith, GSB, by Matchmaker, dam by Avington, bred at Sudbury, Derbyshire by C. Mynors and owned by John Brown of Kirby Moorside, York. In 1917, Thomas Hudson and C. W. Tindall presented the led championship to George Dickinson of Cark-in-Cartmel for the 3-year-old Cark Marquis, by King's Courtship out of Duchess XII by Tacitus, bred by Sir William Cooke, Bart.

The stallions were judged in 1916 by Sir Gilbert Greenall, Bart., CVO, Mr

R. G. Carden and the Earl of Orkney, who awarded the King's Cup to Captain T. L. Wickham-Boynton's Birk Gill.

In 1917, when the Captain achieved his first of three victories with Rathurde, the judges were Sir Gilbert Greenall, the Hon. Alexander Parker and J. W. A. Harris. Rathurde was a 16.1 chestnut by Tredennis ex a mare by Berrill.

There follows a report of the proceedings at the Deputation by the Hunters' Improvement and NLHB Society to the Earl of Derby, KG, and the Right Hon. R. E. Prothero, MVO, at the War Office on Tuesday 20 February 1917. The deputation was formed by Mr Cecil Aldin, Mr A. S. Bowlby, Major Sir Merrik R. Burrell, Bart., Colonel the Hon. Charles Byng, the Hon. E. A. Fitzroy, MP, Lt.-Col. R. S. Forestier-Walker, DSO, Sir Walter Gilbey, Bart., Mr R. H. Gosling, Sir Gilbert Greenall, Bart. (also representing the War Emergency Committee of the Royal Agricultural Society of England), Lt.-Col. W. Raymond Greene, DSO, MP, Mr W. A. Hartford, Sir R. T. Hermon-Hodge, Bart., Sir Henry Hoare, Bart., Lt.-Col. J. McKie, Sir Gerald Mildmay, Bart., Earl of Orkney, The Hon. Alexander Parker, Lord Penrhyn, the Hon. Claud B. Portman, Major W. H. Rawnsley, Brig.-Gen. Lord Saltoun, GMG, Lord Stalbridge, Mr A. H. Straker, Mr Romer Williams, Major Clive Wilson.

LORD DERBY: Gentlemen, you have asked me to receive a deputation with Mr Prothero, with regard to horse breeding for the future, and I am glad to do so, because probably a deputation, especially when one is able, as I hope to be, to give a satisfactory answer, is always a good thing to have. I do not know whether you have settled upon whom you would like to be your spokesmen, but I should think that two or three would be sufficient.

COL. THE HON. CHARLES BYNG: Lord Derby and Mr Prothero; in the unavoidable absence of Lord Middleton through ill-health the Council of the Hunters' Improvement and National Light Horse Breeding Society have selected me to introduce this deputation to you and to thank you and Mr Prothero for consenting to receive us in continuation of the letter which was addressed to you a few days ago. If it is your pleasure, Mr Parker, who was the Vice-Chairman of the Advisory Committee on Horse Breeding to the Board of Agriculture, will lay before you the views of the Council. Sir Merrik Burrell and Sir Henry Hoare would also like to express some other views, and Sir Gilbert Greenall, who represents the Royal Agricultural Society of England, would like also to convey to you the views of that Society.

With your permission I would ask if Mr Parker may lay before you the views of the Council of the Hunters' Improvement Society.

THE HON. ALEXANDER PARKER: I will read my statement if I may because it expresses not only my own but other people's opinions. The council of the HIS desired you to receive this deputation in consequence of the very grave alarm with which it views the future prospects of the breeders of light horses and the horse supply of the country. The Society, while encouraging the breeding of the highest class of hunter, has always felt that by so doing it was indirectly assisting to produce a large number of horses necessary for the Army. It was undoubtedly in the hope of obtaining the high prices that good hunters commanded, that the majority of breeders of light horses were induced to continue breeding. The Society, however, has long felt that the industry required considerable Government help to raise the standard of the horses that were being bred, so that there might be a sounder and more useful class of horse in the country in case of emergency. The Council fully realise that the supply of horses of the

Artillery type is dangerously deficient, and it is anxious and ready to co-operate in any scheme whereby this state of affairs may be rectified.

In June 1910, the Horse Supply Committee under Lord Feversham's chairmanship issued an important report, containing numerous suggestions, and I would point out that these recommendations were adopted almost in their entirety by the Board of Agriculture and Fisheries. We consider that, in view of the limited amount of money at their disposal, the Board have done a vast amount towards putting new life into an industry which was rapidly crumbling away.

In August, 1915, Lord Selborne, then President of the Board of A & F in consequence of the very urgent representations of the War Office as to the serious position of the horse supply of the country, appointed a Committee under Lord Middleton's chairmanship 'To consider and advise the Board as to what steps should be taken to secure the production and maintenance in England and Wales of a supply of horses suitable and sufficient for military purposes, especially on mobilisation'. We would respectfully beg your perusal of that report which clearly sets forth the position of horse breeding in this country, and at the same time offers some valuable suggestions whereby the industry might be put on a sound footing. The conclusions arrived at by the Committee are summarised at the end of the report under 14 heads, nine of which apply to the Board and five to the War Office.

We cordially approve of these conclusions and recommendations, but much regret that all the labour of the Committee, which was considerable, appears to have been in vain inasmuch as in no single instance has its recommendations been followed with the exception that the Board are seriously considering the compulsory registration of stallions.

This Council feel that were the Government to guarantee adequate annual funds so that an advance might be made on the lines suggested in the Report, light horse breeding might be put on a highly satisfactory and sound basis. The crux of the matter is that the breeder has no remunerative market to look forward to. Before the war he could rely on a market, circumscribed though it might be. There was the hunter market and the foreign market, these were the only two that it paid to breed for. Both these are gone. All he can now hope for is the totally inadequate price that he may expect from the War Office, added to which he has no one to break his young horses, and the cost of fodder is prohibitive. Fewer mares were sent to the horse last year compared with 1915, and it is our firm conviction that fewer still will be sent this year. The position is indeed deplorable.

It appears to us therefore that unless something is done, and done quickly, to guarantee to the breeder a fair price for his stock, not only will the breeding of light horses decline to a minimum but that the interest which has been kindled in the industry will dwindle away, and that will take a generation and a very heavy expenditure to resuscitate it. To create this market they realise that money must be forthcoming from the Treasury not only to enable the remount department to pay more for their horses, but also to enable them to buy unbroken horses at 3 years old and so relieve the breeder of young stock, the keeping of which he now finds to be a burden, and one which is very general throughout the country. In order, however, to get the best results from the money spent on breeding horses we consider that, as recommended in the Report of Lord Middleton's Committee, an expert and adequate staff is essential inasmuch as the success of any National Horse-Breeding Scheme must depend on proper supervision and continuity of policy.

In conclusion I might say that our object in coming before you today is, if possible, to obtain some definite statement as to what breeders may look forward to from the Government so that they may clearly understand their position and formulate their plans for the future accordingly, as on this depends the question as to whether the country will be in a position to produce and maintain a supply of horses suitable and sufficient for military purposes. We have been able during this war to import vast numbers of horses from overseas, but it would be madness to rely on being able to accomplish this with such comparative ease again.

The Council of the HIS having duly considered the matter are of opinion that they would be failing in their duty did they not bring to your notice the serious position of the horse supply of the country.

Sir Merrik Burrell: Lord Digby and Mr Prothero. I fully endorse Mr Parker's remarks, but I would like if I may to bring to your notice a few other points, and to emphasise some of those which Mr Parker has already put forward. I speak not so much on behalf of the Society but merely as one who has for many years past been interested in this industry, and has kept stallions for the benefit of farmers in my part of the world, and has tried in other ways to encourage them to produce the horses which we require for national purposes.

I think that what those who are interested in this industry would like to have made clear to them today is whether the Government means to rely on imported horses in any national emergency in the future, or whether it means to foster and encourage private enterprise in this country until the Army can rely on not only being able to mobilise but to do so without draining the country to such an extent that no further suitable horses would be forthcoming to make up wastage.

If, in spite of the probable development of submarines and aircraft, and the possibility of the American horses not being available, the Government feel quite certain and would guarantee that we should always be in a position to import horses, the problem is of course simplified to a great extent, but even then we must be sure that we have a sufficiency of suitable and fit horses in this country for immediate mobilisation purposes. If the Government wishes to make itself as far as possible independent of imported horses, the Council of the HIS and all the rest of us throughout the country interested would like to be told what the Government wishes us to do and what the Government will do in order to assist us. In 1914 there was a sufficient number of horses available for mobilisation, but according—

Lord Derby: Mobilisation on what scale?

Sir Merrik Burrell: On the then scale, sir; but according to the evidence of the Director of Remounts given before Lord Middleton's Committee in August, 1915, he told us that many were of too inferior type, to use his own words, 'many very bad animals were bought for the Territorial Army especially', that is to say, sir, that even then we were very badly deficient in the light draught type of horse. But since then warfare has become largely that of artillery, and the proportion of artillery to the other arms has increased. If the proportion in 1914 had been then what it is now, I venture to suggest that the Director of Remounts would have had almost an impossibility before him to mobilise the Army. All through 1914, as came out before Lord Middleton's Committee, the War Office was urging the Board of Agriculture to take some steps, and they were urging the Board before the war was even thought of; so that the position even then was bad. But the war has hit the industry very hard indeed, and as Mr Parker has pointed out, the market for the high-class hunter for the time being has gone; the price of fodder is up, and owing to the scarcity of men, those of us who have got young horses cannot break them, and we cannot make them saleable. The foreign market is for the time being also gone. Both of these we hope will in due course be revived, but the trade for the horse not good enough for light draught purposes will get less and less as the cheap motor gets more and more used. For years people like myself have been urging the farmers to breed horses so that there might be a sufficiency in the event of war, and now when the war has come the farmer finds that he can only sell his horses at a price less than cost, and many he cannot sell at all because he cannot break them. I would venture to suggest that it is most important that farmers who have got 5 and 6-year-old horses running about on their farms unbroken should be relieved of those horses at a fair price in order that they may be encouraged to put their mares to the horse again this year. We are afraid, sir, that many farmers will not put their mares to the horse this season, and we have grounds for our fears because many of the farmers who took Government mares are already asking to return them, even in those counties where the Board of Agriculture Brood Mare Scheme has been thriving best up to now.

The Army in the past has never fostered this industry; and when I say in the past, sir, I mean before 1914. It has always bought what few horses it did buy with a view to buying them as cheaply as possible, and if the industry is to be encouraged one hopes that the policy will be abolished, and that in future the Army buyer will be in close contact with the expert staff which Mr Parker has urged should be instituted, and that through them he should buy horses in England as much as possible direct from the breeder. It is all a matter of organisation. But England up till now has hardly ever had a chance of selling horses to the Army although, when it came to mobilisation, a great many more than half of the horses bought were bought in England; they were bought on impressment, whereas Ireland, which has always profited by the Army market, only had impressment in force I believe in a few of the large cities.

There is another point, my lord, I would like to bring to your attention, and it is this, that I believe I am right in saying that in the past something like a quarter of a million pounds was spent annually in the hiring of horses for the training of the Territorial Forces. Many of those horses were merely the riff-raff of the country. They not only did one training but they did two or three trainings, and a lot of those horses when it came to mobilisation were not fit or suitable to be bought and go and do Army work; so that all that money was spent every year, and it was no encouragement for breeders to breed the right class of horse that the Army wants. (*Hear, hear.*) All of us who are interested in this industry hope that that policy shall be abandoned, and that money shall be spent in a direction that will really encourage the breeder of the right type of horse. I will not say as much as that, but money. I will give an instance —

LORD DERBY: What money are you referring to?

SIR MERRIK BURRELL: The money which was paid in hiring horses for the Territorial trainings. It amounted to a very large sum, and in my opinion it was to a very large extent thrown away.

LORD DERBY: The money paid for hiring horses for the Territorial Forces could not possibly buy the horses that we should require for the Territorial training, nor have the Territorials the men to look after the horses for 50 weeks in the year when they are not training. How are you going to make that up?

SIR MERRIK BURRELL: It is not for me, sir, to enter into the elements of a scheme.

LORD DERBY: But if you make a proposition, be prepared to justify it.

SIR MERRIK BURRELL: It would certainly have to be done on the principle of buying horses and boarding them out, as is done in foreign countries.

LORD DERBY: Do you think that £250,000 would go any distance towards buying all the horses which would be required for Territorial purposes, and which would only be used for a fortnight out of the 52 weeks in the year?

SIR MERRIK BURRELL: That sum was spent annually; you would not want to buy them every year.

LORD DERBY: Do you think you could possibly enter into such a scheme as that? Have you ever had anything to do with Territorial Associations or the organisation of them?

SIR MERRIK BURRELL: I have not, and I do not want to.

LORD DERBY: I have, and I say that I know that would be an absolute impossibility.

SIR MERRIK BURRELL: Well, sir, all I venture to say is that it is a very large sum of money to spend annually, and at the present moment it is only encouraging a very poor type of horse instead of the class of horse we want. I can give you an instance; a man where I was buying horses not very long ago for the Army, showed me a little horse with very worn joints, and when I looked in his mouth he was a 4-year-old. I said, 'I cannot buy this one, he is a 4-year-old', and he said: 'I assure you he cannot be 4; he has for 2 years done 3 trainings a year.' The money is annually spent.

Another most important reason I think why the Government scheme should be propounded as soon as possible is that when it comes to demobilisation there will be a very large number of very excellent mares to be distributed, and unless there is a sound Government policy and scheme, and an expert staff already established, I fail to see how those mares are going to be made the best possible use of. It is a chance to re-establish this industry which will never return to the country, and my personal opinion is that if this chance is allowed to go by it will be one of the greatest pities that has ever happened to us. I hope that when demobilisation occurs we shall see these mares put out in those districts to which they are principally suited, especially mares suitable to breed the light draught horse, and that then steps will be taken to put stallions into those districts suited to those mares, and the farmers encouraged to breed the light draught type of animal as much as possible. The Shire horse is neither able to be bred nor necessary in all districts, and it is in those districts where I think the industry of breeding lighter, more active and more economical horses might be built up.

I am quite sure that all of us, this Society and its individual members, are only too ready to be under any scheme that the Government will put forward, but in years past we have suffered a great many disappointments; schemes have been propounded and then nothing further has come of them. The Board of Agriculture (Mr Prothero will forgive my saying so) has in the past years shown great apathy in this matter. I have been connected with the schemes for some years now owing to being a member of the Advisory Committee, and there was at the Board first of all Mr Arthur Anstruther, and later Mr Shine, who have always tried to do their very utmost to forward things, but as far as we have ever been able to tell on the Advisory Committee, things never got very much further than their offices, and unless there is a really good man who understands this subject put at the head of it with an adequate staff under him, I fear no Government scheme will ever go forward as it should.

SIR HENRY HOARE: Lord Derby and Mr Prothero. I think there is nothing more for me to add about the general aspect of horse breeding, but I should like to say a few words about it in our own local district of Wiltshire with which I am intimately acquainted, and the first thing I propose to do is to read the Report of Mr Taylor, the Secretary of the Wiltshire Brood Mare Society, which I asked him to draw up, and which is quite independent of anything I may have to say.

LORD DERBY: I hope it bears generally on the scheme, because I really cannot go into the details of certain localities.

SIR HENRY HOARE: No, it bears generally on the scheme — as far as the horse breeding scheme is concerned. It is very short. 'In Wiltshire there has been a great increase in the interest taken in light horse breeding during the last 7 years, due to a great extent to the work of the County Committee in addition to the free nominations given by the Board of Agriculture. Sixty-three brood mares have been placed out by the Committee since 1914. Up to 1914 the applications for those mares were too numerous for the Committee to satisfy owing to the difficulty of finding suitable mares. The demand then began to fall off, and the majority of the farmers who had them could not find a market for their young stock, and if they kept them until they were 4 years old they had not the men to break them properly, and so it did not pay to breed them. The consequence is that many mares have been returned to the Committee, and great difficulty has been experienced in finding new custodians for them — in fact, some of the mares had to be sold as it was not found possible to place them out again. Thus unless some scheme can be devised to provide a market for young horses at prices which will pay the breeder, it seems probable that in Wiltshire, as in many other counties, light horse breeding will gradually be abandoned.'

In addition to that, in Wiltshire and all over the country motor traction is interfering very much with horses. I have been buying horses for the Government in Wiltshire for about two years, and I am also the military representative on the local committee, and in close touch with labour. The following trades are now practically doing without horses, that is the bakers, posting, and the grocers; the timber merchants are using motor tractors considerably, and in almost every other trade motors are largely used. I should say that the horses in my immediate vicinity have diminished by about 25% compared to the time when I began purchasing during the war. I think this is a very important factor in the matter, because motor traction is going to increase, and if horse breeding is not encouraged there is no doubt the horses will not be there when they are wanted for the Army. One of the principal reasons for the increase in motor traction at the present moment is the shortage of labour, but then after the war labour will be more expensive — there is no doubt about that — and that I think will tend very largely to the increase of motor traction.

I think this is one of the most important factors with regard to horse breeding — in fact, I look upon it as one of the greatest possible dangers to horse breeding — this increase of motor traction in every small way. I must say that the markets I have been alluding to are very unremunerative, but on the other hand, wherever you breed there must be misfits, and there is a ready market for the misfits. From these markets I have bought very useful horses for the Army, but these markets no longer exist. Also with regard to the breeder, there is no doubt that at the present moment he is very badly hit through the shortage of labour. The Government have encouraged him to produce young horses, and he has got yearlings, 2-year-olds and 3-year-olds, and no market for them. You have got a lot of practical men breeding at the moment, but if you do nothing to encourage them and to give them some hope for the future, there is no doubt that they will cut their losses and chuck it. Well, if they do, you will have to foot the bill very much more heavily before you get horse breeders to begin again.

SIR GILBERT GREENALL: I do not think that I need add anything to what has been said. I can only say that I am quite sure the Council of the Royal Agricultural Society will endorse everything that Mr Parker has said; they feel that there are lots of difficulties with which we have to contend, but one thing they are very certain of, and that is that if anything is to be done it should be done at once before the season starts. (*Hear, hear.*) When they discussed the matter the other day, they sent a resolution to you, my lord, I believe.

LORD DERBY: Did they?

SIR GILBERT GREENALL: Shall I read it?

LORD DERBY: Please do.

SIR GILBERT GREENALL: It also went to Mr Prothero and the Director of Remounts: 'That the Board of Agriculture and the War Office be requested to state their policy for stimulating the production of light horses suitable for military purposes. At the present time the raising of these horses is unremunerative as hunting is practically abandoned, and unless something is done by the Government to give confidence to breeders a very serious state of affairs will inevitably arise.' That was sent to you, I think, my lord. The chief thing I would impress upon you is the importance of doing something now before the season commences. I am sure the Council will endorse everything that Mr Parker has said.

MR PROTHERO: I should like to say that the Board of Agriculture appreciates very warmly the valuable assistance they have had from the HIS not only in preparing their scheme originally, but in giving effect to it. I think I noticed that all the five speakers today are members of the Advisory Committee of the Board of Agriculture.

The Board's scheme has been a very considerable success in the past. Since its conception the number of Thoroughbred stallions has been increased, and they are much better than they used to be (hear, hear) and I think that is a very strong point. Then, also, the voluntary scheme for the registration of stallions has been very successful, remarkably so. It shows, I think, that the Board's registration has a commercial value, which promises well for the future.

Now, I think both Sir Merrik Burrell and Sir Henry Hoare insisted — or at least, Sir Henry Hoare did — that the market for the misfit had disappeared. The aim of the Board now, as it always has been, has been really to grade up and improve the horses bred, and they have thought that improvement in quality is really more important than improvement in quantity; and although the misfit must always come every now and then, I think it is more than ever necessary that breeders should take the greatest care in the selection of the mares, in the choice of stallions and in the care of the young stock. In all those points I am sure we may rely on the Society to do their utmost with the farmers in their different localities.

I think it was Mr Parker who said that the crux of the whole situation is having a remunerative market, and there is no doubt that is so. If breeders saw their way to produce horses at a reasonable profit, there would be plenty of horses bred (hear, hear), but in order to do this they must aim at really very high-class horses. Horses of that class will, I hope, be wanted again for hunting which, after all, is the backbone of the light horse breeding industry. (Hear, hear.) Without it we could not hope to revive the industry. But we do hope that the War Office will be able to give some assurance today that the Army will become a larger and more remunerative market than heretofore, and that the farmer will be in that way encouraged to produce horses which, if they miss the hunter market, can yet be sold at a profit for Army purposes.

So far as the Board is concerned, we propose to carry out the first conclusion of Lord Middleton's Committee's Report, to protect the farmer from unsound stallions by compulsory annual registration of all stallions that are travelling for a service fee or publicly exhibited for stud purposes. (Hear, hear and applause.) In the next place, we propose to arrange for the inspection of stallions recommended for the Board's premium by the Board's officers. We should also be prepared, if and when we get the Treasury sanction, to purchase a few stallions every year, not of course in substitution of those provided by private enterprise, which we should not wish for a moment to attempt, but to supplement those that are so provided.

We do not contemplate taking any action at the present moment in regard to brood mare schemes, or the award of prizes to mares and foals. But it is quite obvious that if we are going to buy stallions, if we are going to run stallions of our own as well as to subsidise stallions we must have an additional expert staff, and we must reconstitute the Board's Advisory and County Committees if any comprehensive national breeding scheme is to be adopted; and again, subject to Treasury sanction (which is not always easy to obtain) I may say that we propose to make that part of the policy of the Board.

There is one question I should like to add to those that have been asked of Lord Derby, and that is whether he will authorise the exemption or release from military service of stallion leaders from being compelled to serve, who are specially needed at this present time, during the breeding season. (Hear, hear.)

LORD DERBY: Gentlemen, I have written down some notes to give you, but I would like to add one or two words in answer to some of the matters that have been brought up. I would like first of all to express to you on behalf of the War Office my deep sense of the HIS's patriotic and helpful action in the early days of the war, when they took over several hundreds of 4-year-old Cavalry remounts, kept them free of cost for a year or more, and returned them broken and in such condition that the majority of them could be issued as officers' chargers — a most patriotic action on their part. This is not the only debt that we owe to the Society, for among those gentlemen who have helped us to purchase and care for the many thousands of horses we have collected in this country and in America, the majority are members of your Society, and not a few serve on your Council.

The provision of horses, especially light draught horses, for the mobilisation of the Army is a subject which has given cause for anxiety to my predecessors in office ever since the advance of motor traction began to run the light-horsed vehicle off the road, and even before that, because in the year 1901, when I was Financial Secretary to the War Office, I was chairman of the Committee which was appointed to try and see whether anything could not be done to increase the number of horses from which we had to draw in this country, and I do not think that the conclusions at which I arrived were altogether acceptable.

I think it might interest you at this moment if I told you something of what the War Office has done in the way of buying horses in this country. In the United Kingdom we have bought during the war well over 400,000 horses, and the total paid for them has been well over (I have not the exact figure) twenty millions. The prices paid, I think, were prices that could be fairly said to be remunerative. Now, the Army needs three classes of horse — the light draught, the riding and the heavy draught, and that is the order of importance.

Now, as regards the light draught horses, the situation before the war was that for passenger vehicles the motor had superseded the horse, while for the delivery of goods the horse still held its own, but only on short journeys. This move in the direction of motor traction must assuredly grow. Sir Henry Hoare alluded to it in his contribution to the proceedings, and there is not the least doubt that motor tractors are coming in more and more every day, and will continue to come in more and more every day. There is no doubt that we have to face that. We are therefore up against the fact that the demand for the light draught horse, or the gunner as we call him, must diminish in civil life, while he still remains very necessary for the Army. As to how necessary he may become I think it is impossible at present for us to say. The war, as you know, is changing the whole condition of affairs, and to my mind the future will lie far more with the big heavy gun than it will with the light gun, but I am speaking as a layman, and it may be that the military authorities would not agree with me. I think that the big gun will eventually oust the lighter gun, and if I am correct it will be drawn by a motor tractor.

Now, as regards the riding horses, as long as racing, hunting and polo continue — and speaking for myself, and I think I can speak for the Army also, I should view with the gravest concern anything which threatened permanently to interfere with these three sports (*Hear, hear and applause.*) As far as I am concerned I shall always support all three because I believe that they make in this country the industry of horse breeding, which is a great one, absolutely the first in the whole of the world. (*Hear, hear.*) I believe those three sports are necessary to keep up that supremacy. Now, having said that, I think as long as they do continue, the demand for high-class riding horses will insure their production in sufficient numbers; and for heavy draught, cart horses will always be required for farm work.

As to these three classes of horse — light and heavy draught and riding — it is difficult to say what will be the requirements of the Army, but it may interest you to know that of the animals now serving with the Army in France, 54% are light draught, 30% are riding horses and 16% heavy draught. Of the total riding horses, only one quarter belong to Cavalry Divisions, and of the whole number of horses of all kinds, only 10% belong to Cavalry Divisions. This gives you some idea of the proportion of horses required for the Army at war strength, and that brings me to another important factor. The peace strength is but a small proportion of the war strength (mind you, I am talking of the past, one does not in the least know what the future will bring forth) and the difference has to be suddenly made good from the resources of the country. On 4 August 1914, the peace strength of our Army included 26,000 horses; a fortnight later it stood at 140,000, the increase having been obtained by impressment of horses working in civil life. What the peace strength of the Army will be after the war it is, as I have already said, impossible to forecast, and what its relative position to the war strength will be is impossible to define, but the broad situation will always remain the same, that the number of horses maintained in peace must be comparatively small, and that the annual purchase by the Army will be comparatively small, but to ensure rapid and efficient mobilisation the general horse stock of the country must be sufficient in quantity and suitable in quality for the immediate military needs. I think Sir Merrik Burrell must have had that in his mind when he talked about our having enough horses in this country for the mobilisation of the Army.

SIR MERRIK BURRELL: Quite so.

LORD DERBY: 'I think that to ask anybody, either the Board of Agriculture or the War Office, to have in this country enough horses for the mobilisation of a huge Army on the scale we have now would be practically impossible. Sir John Cowan tells me that we and our Colonies have bought over a million horses altogether, that is 600,000 outside the United Kingdom, and it is therefore quite impossible to think, as God forbid, we should ever have to have an Army again on the strength of the present one, that we should be able to rely entirely on our own production at home for our horses.

In our own scheme of Government, as well as among the great military nations of the Continent, the duty of maintaining the horse stock of the country at a suitable level is always assigned to a civil department. It is not for the War Office to venture to interfere in the business of the Agricultural Department, but merely to say what it wants and to give all the help it can on the lines agreed by the two departments. Mr Prothero is perhaps newer in office than I am, but he has got some of the tricks of the trade — the old tricks — when he says that he wants the War Office to become a remunerative purchaser of horses — he will run the show and we will pay for it. As you know, I have engaged in a certain form of horse breeding myself, and I am only too ready to help in any way I can the Board of Agriculture, and from what I know it is very difficult work. I am sure that Mr Prothero can rely on the active co-operation of the War Office.

Now, it is the light draught horse which is to be the great difficulty, and the solution appears to me to lie first of all in so grading up the quality of horses of all classes that misfits are the exception, and that as numbers diminish (as they may do) the proportion suitable for the Army becomes greater; and, secondly, in the development for farm work of some breed with less bulk, greater activity and altogether tougher fibre than our present farm breeds, that is, a horse that will eat less, endure more, and is quick enough for Field Artillery — really a carthorse that will trot. (*Hear, hear.*) That is what we want.

In August 1915, Lord Selborne appointed a Committee, of which Lord Middleton, whose absence today we all regret, was Chairman, to consider the problem we are now discussing, and their Report, which was presented to Parliament, is sound and instructive. In it they made certain recommendations as to the future action of the War Office as regards their method of buying horses, and though I shall not be in this office when peace methods are decided, and therefore cannot pledge my successor, I am now prepared to recommend to my successor the adoption of the Committee's suggestions. A larger portion of the annual purchase will, I trust, be made in Great Britain, and we shall, I hope, after the war buy what we can from breeders direct at $3\frac{1}{2}$ years old at a fair price; indeed, in some ways I would go further than Lord Middleton's Committee recommended.

I will now deal with the question of mares after the war. We have under consideration the outline of a scheme by which we hope to take advantage of the opportunities which the conclusion of peace will present for aiding the light horse breeding industry. This scheme contemplates a distribution on easy terms of surplus mares approved by the Board's inspectors to breeders approved by the Board, with the liability that they should be covered yearly by an approved stallion. That latter condition is really due to the fact that we brought back 250 mares that had been cast from work in France by the Board of Agriculture, they were sold at the time for the breeding of horses, and only 45% of them were so used. I admit at once that it is perhaps not right to judge what may happen after the war from what happens now, when you have a shortage of labour and a high cost of fodder. It is impossible to say how many mares will be available, but it may be many thousands; they will be of all breeds, but only the best of each will be brought home. It will be possible for the Board of Agriculture, by judiciously grouping them in suitable districts where suitable stallions are available, to give a great and lasting impetus to the production of the classes of horses required for war.

I would like to mention here — I should have dealt with it before — as Sir Merrik Burrell referred to the question of the Territorials, that I think it is just as well that you should recognise the difficulty that exists there. Supposing we were back in the old days of peace, with the Territorials trained in relays from 1 January to 31 December, it might be possible to do something in the way suggested, but all the Territorials go out practically within one month, and therefore while you are able to do a certain amount of exchange between them, and especially in the Yeomanry, it would be quite impossible to attempt to board out horses in such quantities that they would do for your Territorials for two weeks in the year, leaving them for 50 weeks doing, as far as the Army is concerned, nothing.

Horse breeding should be reasonably profitable with a mare that can earn her living on the farm, with premium or State-owned stallions provided at nominal fees and possibly a market for the produce at $3\frac{1}{2}$ years old. As regards the market, it is quite impossible to make any forecast of what the future strength of the Army may be, but I think I should probably be within the mark if I said that the number of horses bought annually for the Army after the war will not be less than those bought before the war. We shall certainly (speaking with regard to the Territorials) see whether we cannot do something in the way of boarding out in order to help both in the training and in the horse breeding industry.

Now there is the question of the foreign market, which will return when things have settled down. That is one thing that is absolutely settled; do what they like, they have always come back to England to replenish their stock with all kinds of horses. There is no soil or climate in the world equal to ours for breeding horses, and therefore I am not in the least despondent as to the foreign purchases. That will remain. My only hope is that we shall be able to come to some such arrangement as will prevent our best from going abroad (*hear, hear*).

There is only one further thing, if I may say so, that I think will appeal to all horse breeders, and that is, it will never pay you to breed inferior stock (*hear, hear*) whatever it is, whether it is for racing, light draught or heavy draught — it is only the best that will ever pay, and it is only the best horses that we can ever encourage. I am bound to speak to you very much in the dark as to what will happen in the future. You will quite realise that it is impossible for me to forecast what our requirements will be. The only thing I can tell you is that I hope first of all, by preparing some plan for demobilisation, to give you these mares to help the breeding of horses in the future; and secondly, by doing everything in my power to assist while in this office, or afterwards to help my successor in this office, to back up the Board in whatever they may do for the benefit of horse breeding. I am afraid that is all I can say to you today, and I hope you will realise that what I have said is said with a thoroughly sympathetic feeling to you.

There is one question Mr Prothero asked me as to stallion leaders. I agree with you that stud grooms and stallion leaders, especially at this time of the year, until the breeding season is over, are practically indispensible, and I will do my best to secure that they shall be left with the various studs. I cannot promise in the case of what we call the 'A' men; we want all the 'A' men we can get, but in regard to the other classes than 'A', I think we can safely promise you that they shall be left with you until the close of the breeding season.

Unless there is any other question you would like to ask, those are all the views I have to put forward.

COLONEL BYNG: May I ask a favour of you, my lord, and that is that we may have copies of your speech and of Mr Prothero's, in order to give them full publicity and encourage breeders?

LORD DERBY: If what Mr Prothero and I have said will encourage breeders, I should be only too glad that you should have copies.

LORD PENRHYN: As the senior member of the HIS present, I have the honour to tender our very best thanks and the thanks of the Council to you, Lord Derby, and to Mr Prothero for having received us this afternoon. That we should receive a sympathetic hearing from you, my lord, is only what one would imagine and expect from so well known and successful a breeder as yourself. I think, besides having received a sympathetic greeting here, we must also be satisfied and pleased to hear that Mr Prothero and the Board of Agriculture propose to do what has been advocated by the Society for many years past, and that is to endeavour to see that we have sound stallions travelling throughout the country. That is a very excellent step in the right direction, and I think we also would be very glad to hear from Lord Derby that although he is unable to pledge the War Office to buy the number of horses that doubtless we would like them to buy, anyhow he is prepared to do what he can during his term of office to help and encourage the horse breeding industry in every possible way. The question of misfits will always be the trouble. Good stuff will always sell; the trouble is the misfit, and the only way we can help is by endeavouring to see that the new stock of brood mares and the stock in general is improved in every possible way, so that there may be as few misfits as possible.

On behalf of the Hunters' Improvement Society, I tender you my very best thanks for the kind way in which you have received us.

LORD DERBY: Thank you very much indeed, Lord Penrhyn, and you can be quite sure that I shall do everything I possibly can to carry out what I have said, and if at any time your Society sees that there is any way in which I can help you, and you care to come to me, I am perfectly certain if I am here (and I think I can speak for Mr Prothero as well as myself) I shall always be ready to meet you, and as far as possible not only give a sympathetic hearing to your views, but to endeavour to carry out any suggestions you may choose to make to us. (*Hear, hear and applause.*)

The Board of Agriculture's statement concerning the hunting field in their Report for the first year of the war is worthy of preservation. 'Mobilisation and the impressment of horses have proved — if indeed any proof was needed — that the hunting field is a national asset of the greatest value, providing, as it has done, a reservoir from which the Army has been able to draw a large supply of horses that are eminently suitable for military purposes.'

The encouragement and improvement of light horse breeding

The outstanding feature of the horse breeding operations of the Board of Agriculture from 1 November 1915, to 31 October 1916, was the acquisition of Colonel Hall Walker's stud at Tully, in Ireland, and his training establishment at Sussley in Wiltshire. They were purchased by the Government, but the valuable stud of high-class horses and mares, together with a large head of cattle, provender, stores, farm furniture, etc., were very generously presented to the Government by Colonel Hall Walker, so that the stud could be taken over, as it was on 1 January, 1916, as a well-equipped going concern. At Lord Selborne's invitation Captain H. Greer was good enough to undertake, for the period of the war, the honorary directorship of the National Stud, as it is now called, and the Board are greatly indebted to him for the valuable services he is rendering.

The number of horses which were made over to the nation as a gift was 3 stallions, 52 mares, 19 yearlings and 9 horses in training (3 of which will be returned after their racing career) and, as they included such well known stallions as White Eagle, Royal Realm and Great Sport, and mares such as Flaming Vixen, Burnt Almond and Countess Zia, the value of Colonel Hall Walker's gift will be realised.

The National Stud was established for military considerations, as have been all the state studs on the Continent. It is intended that it shall be carried on as an establishment for breeding high-class Thoroughbreds, as they are the foundation stock of the breed of light horses, the reservoir from which the small trickle of Army remounts flows annually in time of peace, but which can be drawn upon to a very large extent in times of emergency, as happened on mobilisation in 1914.

The essential qualifications for cavalry horses and hunters are constitution, courage and stamina, and for the transmission of these hidden but all-important characteristics we must look to the Thoroughbred horse, that has proved a success, or at any rate a trier, on the race-course. The unseen qualifications of heart, brain and nerve constitute the value of the Thoroughbred in the general scheme of horse breeding, and the possession of them can be determined in one way, and one way only — on the race-course.

Thoroughbred horses have to pass this test before they can be regarded as suitable sires; but it does not follow that State ownership of a bloodstock breeding establishment imposes any necessity on the State to race the horses bred by them, or renders them any more directly associated with racing than they are at present in awarding premiums annually to stallions whose soundness, stamina and constitution have been proved by their ability to stand the test of training and racing.

The Board do not intend to race the horses bred by the National Stud. They propose to follow the practice of many private breeders of bloodstock, and sell as yearlings the majority of the horses bred, retaining only the very few of them which will be leased for their racing career, and subsequently returned to the stud.

In this connection it may be of interest to record that during the year under review two lots of yearlings have been sold from the National Stud at the Newmarket Sales. The first lot of six averaged £505, and the second lot of 10 averaged £596, prices which may be considered as satisfactory in these abnormal times. Seven 2-year-olds have been leased for training and racing, and will be returned to the Stud in due course.

In spite of the many difficulties under which the breeding of bloodstock is being carried on during the war, it is hoped that the National Stud will not be a serious charge, if it is a charge at all, on the Public Exchequer during its first year of existence, but as the balance sheet cannot be completed for two months after the period covered by this report, it is not possible to make any definite statement at present as to the financial aspect of the enterprise.

So far as the training establishment at Russley is concerned, it is intended to use it as a Government stallion depot when purchases of entires are made by the Board to supplement those provided by private owners under the existing scheme. For the present it is being used by the War Office as a remount depot.

Apart from the establishment of the National Stud, the horse breeding operations of the Board do not call for comment in any special direction for the year under review. Reference must be made, however, to the increasing difficulties experienced by breeders in carrying on their establishments. The depletion of their staffs owing to the needs of the Army, the increased cost of feeding stuffs, the curtailment of hunting and the absence of the foreign buyer are factors which adversely affect the Light Horse Breeding industry at the present time. Fortunately, during the past year the Army were buyers of all classes of horses that were suitable for their purposes, and though the prices paid were not very remunerative they enabled breeders to dispose of stock for which otherwise they would probably have not found a market.

In another direction also the Army came to the rescue of breeders, and from their remount depots supplied for the Service Season, 1916, a number of men for employment as stallion leaders, of whom there was a shortage. The assistance of the Remount Department was very opportune and much appreciated, as it enabled many stallions to be travelled who would otherwise have remained at home or been castrated.

When account is taken of the abnormal conditions that prevailed, and the apprehension as to the future that existed, it was not surprising that the number of mares sent to the premium stallions was fewer in 1916 than in the preceding three years. It averaged, however, 69 mares per stallion for 100 stallions, and this number cannot be considered altogether unsatisfactory. In this connection it may be of interest to show in tabular form the number of premiums awarded, and the results of the Service Seasons during the last seven years.

| | King's Premiums | | | Board's Premiums | | |
Year	No.	Mares served	Mares per Stallion	No.	Mares served	Mares per Stallion
1910	28	1540	55	—	—	—
1911	50	3245	65	10	552	55
1912	50	3438	69	25	1655	66
1913	44	3280	75	25	1581	63
1914	50	3820	76	28	1756	63
1915	50	4317	86	40	3067	77
1916	60	4360	73	40	2542	64

CHAPTER 8

Between the wars

THE YEARS 1918–20 are covered in Volume IX of the *Stud Book*, published in 1921 when the war had been over for 3 years. In 1918 the Journal of the Board of Agriculture told its readers:

Light horse breeding even in normal times is a somewhat speculative business, and it is not a branch of farming that can be regarded as a remunerative one as a general rule, or as one that appeals to the majority of farmers. But it is absolutely essential to hunting and to the provision of cavalry and other horses for the Army, and on this account it is hoped that farmers and other breeders of light horses will carry on.

A year later the same source observed:

The adverse conditions under which the Light Horse Industry was carried on were even more marked than in the previous years of the war. There was practically only one market, the Army, for the riding horse, which is not sufficiently remunerative to encourage breeding. Owing to the raising of military age there was a further withdrawal from civil life of stud employees, shoeing smiths and so on, and no little difficulty was experienced in the feeding of horses owing to shortage of forage and the Horse Rationing Orders.

The very restricted supply of petrol for commercial motor traction, the ploughing of thousands of acres of grass land and the purchase of draught horses for the Army brought about a demand for heavy horses in excess of the supply, with the result that prices soared high above the normal and many farmers, whose custom in past years had been to put their mares to Thoroughbred stallions, sent them to heavy sires. In view of these circumstances it is not unsatisfactory that Premium stallions in 1918 averaged 59 mares apiece.

The war had shown how important was the production of good, active horses of strong constitution, and the Board had it from Field-Marshal Earl Haig himself that the Cavalry had been, was and would continue to be indispensable in modern warfare, however great the development of the Air Force in the future. In an advance, he said, mounted troops were essential, and rear-guard actions their use had proved invaluable. They could be moved quickly to threatened areas and were not dependent on roads or railways, and traffic control, which is all important in the rear of the battle zone, cannot be carried out satisfactorily in the absence of mounted men. In open country, moreover, such as the theatre of war in which Lord Allenby's troops had been operating, Cavalry played a most important part, and the use of them had a very decisive influence on the results obtained. In this connection the War

Office had furnished the Board with reports on the suitability for war purposes of the various types of horses in use in the Army, and in all of them there was unanimity of opinion that the well-bred hunter on short legs and of moderate height was the ideal riding horse for the army. Though the price which the War Office had hitherto been authorised to pay could not secure the ideal, it was the type that breeders should aim to produce. At its best it commanded a remunerative price in the hunter or foreign market, and even if it missed the ideal it was the type for Army purposes.

From the returns furnished to the board of the mares served by the 60 King's Premium Stallions the foaling percentage for the Service Season 1917 worked out at 54, the same figure as in 1915 though slightly below that of 1916. Stortford, the property of Major Faudel Phillips, proved to be the best foal-getter of the year, serving 82 mares with a foaling percentage of 78.

The 40 Board's Premium Stallions had an average foal-getting record of 53%, which was slightly below that for the 1916 season (56%). The worst record for any subsidised stallion was that of a Board's Premium horse which served 54 mares with a foaling percentage of 13. That stallion had been castrated.

The average amount paid by the Board for the 48 King's Premium horses was £277 and the maximum £348. With the addition of the service fee of £1, payable by mare owners, the average earnings became £340 and the maximum £438. The average payment for the 12 super-Premium Stallions was £399 and the maximum £464, and the average and maximum earnings £470 and £554 respectively.

It was a prophetic cast into the future, some 40 years ahead, when owing to the commandeering of the Agricultural Hall for War Purposes, the Annual Show was held at Park Paddocks, Newmarket, in 1918, which were kindly placed at the disposal of the Board and the HIS by Messrs Tattersall. The arrangements made for the stabling and exhibition of the horses were all that could be desired. The Show took place on 5 and 6 March and there were 156 entries, of which 36 were stallions which had not previously been shown. The judges, Mr J. W. A. Harris, Lt.-Col. J. McKie, DSO, and the Hon. Alexander Parker reported that the quality of the horses exhibited showed an improvement on 1917, when the standard was a very high one.

Sixty King's Premiums (including 12 Super-Premiums) were awarded, the King's Cup being won for the second time by Rathurde, owned by Capt T. L. Wickham-Boynton. The reserve horse was Gay Lally, the property of the Compton Stud. The 60 stallions served 3,662 mares — an average of 61 per stallion. Board's Premiums were awarded on the recommendations of the County Horse-Breeding Committees to 33 other stallions which served 1,836 mares, averaging 56 per stallion.

The National Stud, under the able Directorship of Captain Greer, continued to show a balance on the right side, in spite of the very adverse conditions that had affected the bloodstock industry during the year under review (1917–18). Fourteen yearlings were sold at an average of £460; eight mares were drafted and one purchased.

The circumstances surrounding the 1918 Spring Show were repeated a year later, when Newmarket was again gratefully accepted as a venue. Birmingham,

Peterborough and Crewe had also been considered and found wanting by the four Societies. The two desiderata — a permanent covered-in building and the requisite boxing accommodation — were not to be found in conjunction at any one place. The latter consideration was the most important in the choice of locale. When Messrs Tattersall made their generous offer it was ideal. The permanent stabling was naturally superior to the temporary accommodation provided annually at Islington. Two hundred excellent looseboxes, large and roomy (averaging 10 feet by 12) were available.

The possibility of covering the judging ring was found to be prohibitively expensive; moreover, it would have been practically impossible to obtain the timber and other building materials. It was resolved to leave the arena uncovered and to take the risk of bad weather. The attention of the committee was centred principally on the judging ring. The Paddocks are intersected by a gravel road, 160 feet long and $8\frac{1}{2}$ feet wide, bordered on one side by a permanent fence. Adjoining the road was a large grass space suitable for the laying out of a judging ring.

The gravel road was therefore utilised as one end of the judging arena with the track continued 9ft. wide through the level grass paddock — the shape being almost circular. This track was specially prepared, to ensure a ring that would withstand the wear and tear of 2 weeks' shows. It more than fulfilled the requirements demanded, especially in 1919, when the consistent heavy downpour would have turned it into a quagmire had the bottom not been most thoroughly prepared.

By this arrangement a special track of some 460 feet was provided, enclosing a judging area of 158 by 133 feet, amply sufficient for judging and parading the horses. The disposition of the various yards and paddocks lent themselves to the arrangements, providing suitable collecting rings. In the lower paddock, within easy reach of the judging ring, a Veterinary yard with lunging ring 36 feet in diameter was specially erected.

The convenience of members and the public was met by reserving a space behind the permanent rails bordering the gravel road. The whole was roofed over and provided a promenade with a raised platform to enable spectators to see the proceedings in the ring. A special stand for the Press with seating and desks was erected. Provision was made for every possible contingency, and with cold, dry weather the show of 1918 was a great success, but the climatic elements accompanying the second venture were highly unfavourable and the programme had to be carried through in the most inauspicious conditions. Apart from the discomfort and inevitable dislocation of the arrangements, the continued downpour necessitated continuous renewals of straw and fen litter, involving additional labour and increased costs in materials and organisation.

The Societies were deeply grateful to Mr E. Somerville Tattersall for his co-operation (he was treasurer of the HIS) through his family connections, which enabled them to maintain the continuity of their shows of stallions, and he was pleased to accept from the HIS, the Shire Horse Society, the Hackney Horse Society and the National Pony Society a memento of the two wartime shows at Park Paddocks.

In both years His Majesty the King presented his Cup to Capt. T. L. Wickham-Boynton's Rathurde.

The sequence of the Society's Spring Shows was resumed at the Royal Agricultural Hall on 2 to 4 March 1920. Entries fell short of previous London Shows, due to increased rates of railway transport without the previous concessions to horses and grooms, the high cost of keep and labour, all of which combined to reduce the usual support from members and exhibitors. But in respect of general receipts the public provided loyal support. The takings were well above those in 1914, and though the Society had to face increased charges in every department, the financial result worked down to the normal cost of a Spring Show at Islington.

Representations secured the renewal of pre-war travel concessions, with an increase in the value of King's Premiums, and the Society then developed a scheme at Country Shows for encouraging owners to retain their mares and fillies and put them to suitable stallions. The Ministry of Agriculture and Fisheries offered 60 King's Premiums of an approximate value of £345, and 12 Super-Premiums of an additional £100. The board of Agriculture for Scotland offered 6 King's Premiums of £298 for Thoroughbred stallions to travel Scotland. The Society gave £985 in 15 classes for Hunters, or a total of £24,650, at the 36th Spring Show of the Society.

Sir Gilbert Greenall, Bart., CVO, and James J. Maher, judged the Young Stock in 1920, when Stortford won the Produce Groups from Soft Answer, who sired three 3-year-olds from George Dickinson's Cark Stud in Lancashire. (Dickinson had 7 sons and the legendary National Hunt trainer in 1982, Michael Dickinson, is his grandson.) George Dickinson also won the Young Stock championship in 1920 with his 2-year-old chesnut filly, Cark Silver Pheasant, by Silver Grill. Col. Sir Merrik Burrell's 3-year-old filly Blood Ruby, by The Best, was reserve.

Only 3 ridden classes were held, judged by Ernest Bellaney and Major-General John Vaughan, CB, DSO, whose champion was Sir Edward D. Stern's 5-year-old brown heavyweight, Botha, by Dundreary.

The Stallions in 1920 were judged by Captain C. Fetherstonhaugh and The Earl of Orkney, and Rathurde finally met his match, going down in his District Class III (East and West Riding of Yorkshire) to his stable companions, Scarlet Rambler and King Edgar. The King's Cup went to Gay Lally (reserve to Rathurde the previous year) and the reserve to Scarlet Rambler, a 16-hand chesnut, foaled in 1913, by William Rufus ex Ramage by Ramapo, granddam Warble by Skylark.

Membership was slowly contracting, due to the abnormal condition of the times. The financial position remained satisfactory and the Council determined it to be essential to publish the Eighth Volume of the *Stud Book* in its normal rotation, maintaining the continuity of the valuable records and statistics of the previous issues.

The Society added its protest to the many other representations when it was proposed to stop racing, on the cardinal ground that the racecourse test is of the utmost value as guidance to breeders of halfbreds. The Council were also successful in securing favourable modifications of the Order affecting the rationing of brood mares and young stock. The vital necessity of conserving grass was also urged, as ploughing up pastures would be disastrous to breeding if carried out indiscriminately. The council also instituted an inquiry into the costs of production of light horses with a view to essential facts being laid before the War Office and the Ministry and the payment of an adequate price by the Government for horses reared and bred in this country, based on the actual cost of production, having regard to the present war prices, plus a reasonable profit.

At the Annual General Meeting of Members at Newmarket in 1919, it was stated that the Council had consistently pressed the question of the unrewarding nature of the breeding of remounts, but for the last 2 years, beyond their acceptance of the principle in abstract, no decision had been reached. The Council had always maintained that until an adequate price was paid by the Government the scheme of the Ministry was incomplete, breeders would not take advantage of the selected stallions placed at their disposal unless a definite prospect was presented whereby the resulting produce could be sold at an advantage. It was therefore essential that the War Office should co-operate and stimulate the industry by the payment of a price based on commercial principles.

The co-operation of members had been offically invited on two occasions — first on the outbreak of war when the War Office temporarily placed out with custodians a large number of 4-year-olds from the depots, and more recently by the Ministry in dealing with the repatriation of selected brood mares of hunter type. The Council emphasised the danger to the horse stock of the country by the return of Army horses, and sent to the Government a special and unanimous resolution, to the effect that: 'The Society views with considerable anxiety the introduction of diseases by the repatriation of Army horses, and urges that re-examination after adequate quarantine shall be made by veterinary surgeons in this country, thereby securing further assurance against contagious disease.'

With the return of peaceful conditions, when four years of war had seriously curtailed all its activities, the Society, who had been able to advise the Government on many matters relating to the horse during the conflict, was able to return to its customary regime. Volume X of the *Stud Book* did not appear until 1924, covering three years. In 1920 the Premiums had been raised by £50 each. The highest percentage of foals was obtained by Maitre Corbeau, belonging to Capt. T. L. Wickham-Boynton and Mr H. A. Cholmondeley, whose foal-getting percentage in 1918 was a record 85. In 1919 at Newmarket the judges, Lt.-Col. J. A. McKie and Mr J. W. A. Harris reported that the 25 new stallions shown for the first time were of good quality but in some instances there was a tendency to lightness of bone and to being somewhat high on the leg, though generally speaking they were in good condition, doing credit both to their owners and to the men in charge of them. The total of mares served was 3,491, an average of 58 per stallion. The Board's Premium horses totalled 32 and served 1,666 mares, averaging 52 apiece. The society's stallions, including Super-Premium winners, totalled 60 holders of King's Premiums.

When the Show returned to Islington in 1920 the entries dropped to 106, as against 133 in 1919 and 156 in 1918. The decrease was attributed to some extent to the resumption of racing after the war and to the shortage of race horses. Twelve new stallions, three of whom obtained premiums, including

Jutland, owned by The King, who was awarded a Super-Premium. The King's Cup was awarded by Capt. C. Fetherstonhaugh and Lord Orkney to Gay Lally, owned by the Compton Stud who were winning it for the first time after standing reserve each year since 1914. The runner-up was Scarlet Rambler, the property of Capt. T. L. Wickham-Boynton and Mr H. A. Cholmondeley.

The National Stud, whose Director, Captain Greer, was assisted by Mr Noble Johnson as Assistant Director, continued to pay its way. For the four years ended 31 December 1919, the average annual income exceeded the annual expenditure by approximately £5,000. In July, 1919, eight yearlings realised 11,150 guineas, an average of nearly 1,394 guineas. A bay colt (half brother to The Panther, by Spearmint out of Countess Zia) realised 4,500 guineas and a chesnut filly by White Eagle out of Canidia, 2,100 guineas. In October, three yearling fillies were sold for 3,010 guineas, an average of 1,003 guineas.

In light horse breeding in the year ending 31 March 1921, a considerable increase is reported in the number of mares served in 1920, which averaged 66 — ten higher than in 1919. The Horse Breeding Act of 1918 had been in operation for its first year and the number of stallions examined, as was to be expected, rose from 2,476 under the last year of the voluntary registration scheme to 4,153 under the first year of operation of the Act. The stallions examined represented approximately two-thirds of those in England and Wales. It was notable that the number of refusals under the Act was considerably higher, approximately 10% of the number examined against 6% under the voluntary scheme.

The indication from the second year's working of the Act was, however, that the proportion of refusals was considerably reduced, indicating that owners of unsound stallions were either castrating them or keeping them at home, being unable to travel them.

The introduction of the Agricultural Act resulted in the dissolution of the County Light Horse Breeding Committees which so ably assisted the Ministry in its schemes since their formation in 1911. In their stead a Sub-Committee of the County Agricultural Committee in each county was appointed to advise the Ministry. The transfer was effected in December 1920, and the new Committees would assist in the arrangements for the 1921 service season. As a consequence of their formation the executive duties of the old Committees in relation to brood mares were now discharged by the Ministry's Horse Breeding Officers, and the balances of the grants for purchase of mares had been recalled.

The foaling percentages of the 60 stallions awarded King's Premiums in 1919, calculated on the returns furnished to the Ministry by mare owners, worked out at an average of 52, an increase of 1% on the figure for 1918. The highest fertility rate was that of Ednam, belonging to Messrs T. and H. Ward. The average foaling percentage of the 32 Board's Premium Stallions was 44 as compared with 49% in 1918.

The average amount paid by the Ministry for the 48 King's Premium Stallions was £259, and the maximum £324, the corresponding figures for the 12 Super-Premium horses being £375 and £413. The average earnings of the stallions (including the service fees paid by the mare owners) were £316 for the King's Premium horses and £438 for the Super-Premium horses, the maximum earnings being £414 and £490 respectively.

The average payments by the Ministry for the Board's Premium Stallions was £123, and the maximum £184, the average earnings of the stallions being £175 and the maximum £274.

The 60 King's Premium stallions served 4,072 mares, averaging 68 per horse. On the recommendation of the County Light Horse Breeding Committees 26 Board's Premiums were awarded and these stallions served 1,635 mares, an average of 63 a stallion.

The Show of Thoroughbred stallions was held at the Royal Agricultural Hall on 22–24 February 1921. The number of entries was 97, a drop of nine on the previous year. Only eight new stallions were exhibited, none of them of sufficient merit to receive an award. The judges were Colonel J. McKie, DSO, and Mr James Maher, who reported that the general quality and substance of the horses shown was good and previous standards were maintained, but the eight new stallions proved very disappointing. Sixty premiums were awarded and the King's Cup went to Gay Lally for the second year, with Scarlet Rambler in reserve for the second time.

The National Stud showed an increased profit for the year ended 31 December, 1920, the net profit that year being approximately £12,400 as compared with £7,650 in 1919. The chief items which contributed towards the increase were (1) £24,000 realised by the sale of bloodstock, (2) £9,000 by the sale of cattle, sheep, pigs etc., and (3) £3,600 in respect of fees for the service of privately-owned mares sent to stallions at the Stud.

Enhanced prices were obtained from the sale of yearlings at Newmarket, 18 being sold for £25,200 gross, i.e. an average of £1,400. The highest price (£3,780) was obtained for a colt by white eagle, out of Jean's Folly. Three colts and two fillies of exceptional merit were retained for the Stud, four of these animals being leased to Lord Lonsdale and one to Lord Chaplin, for racing.

In 1921–2, as far as the Ministry's schemes during the 1921 season was concerned there was little to report in the way of change. Arrangements for the location of stallions, made in conjunction with the new sub-Committees of the County Agricultural Committees on lines similar to those which obtained when the original County Light Horse Breeding Committees were in existence.

It is interesting that although the average number of mares served by the King's and the Ministry's Premium Stallions combined was the same as in the previous year, the average number for a King's Premium Stallion increased by four, whereas the average number for a Ministry Premium Stallion decreased by ten.

With reference to the Horse Breeding Act of 1918, it was of course premature to expect any good results becoming noticeable from its operation, but the Ministry had evidence that owners of licensed stallions no longer suffered competition from the unsound travelling stallion whose chief qualification was a cheap fee. The clearance of such stallions from the road must in due course secure improvement in the horse breeding industry.

During the 1921 season Ministry Inspectors were instructed to stop stallions they met on the road and demand to see their licences. Only in comparatively few instances were they unaccompanied by their licences and in only seven were they unlicensed. Failure to comply with regulations was also reported to the Ministry by the police, who took proceedings for offences under the Act: in the great majority of cases, convictions were obtained. It is evident from the working of the Act during the second year of its operation that the necessity of having stallions licensed and of the licences being carried by the grooms when leading the stallions is now generally recognised, and the plea of ignorance which was so common in the first year was seldom made in 1921.

The foaling percentage of the 60 stallions awarded King's Premiums works out at an average of 49, a decrease of 3% on the figure for 1919. The highest percentage (67) was obtained by French Eagle, owned by the Llawes-y-Coed Stud. For the Board's Stallions the foaling percentage was 47, compared with 44% in 1919.

The average amount paid by the Ministry for the 48 King's Premium stallions was £324 and the maximum £404, the corresponding figures for the 12 Super-Premium horses being £455 and £500. The average earnings of the stallions (including the service fees paid by mare owners) were £390 for the King's Premium horses and £532 for the Super-Premium horses, maximum earnings being £494 and £590 respectively. For the Board's Premium Stallions the payments averaged £189 and the maximum was £244.

The number of mares served by the 60 stallions awarded King's Premiums was 4,348, an average of 72 per stallion. Twenty-six Ministry premiums were awarded, these stallions served 1,398 mares, an average of 53 per stallion.

The 1922 show of Thoroughbred stallions was judged at Islington by Sir Gilbert Greenall, Bt., cvo, and Lt.-Col. J. McKie, dso. The number of entries was 88 (97 and 106 in the two previous years). The drop in entries may have been due to the fact that uncertainty existed in the minds of exhibitors as to the continuance of the Premium system. Only eight new stallions were exhibited, none of sufficient merit to receive an award. Fifty-seven King's Premiums (including 12 Super-Premiums) were awarded, and for the third consecutive year the King's Cup went to the Compton Stud's Gay Lally, with Capt. T. L. Wickham-Boynton's Scarlet Rambler in reserve, also for the third year.

During the second year's working of the 1918 Horse Breeding Act, 3,816 stallions were licensed and 244 refused, 18 on appeal. There was a slight increase on the number of stallions licensed in the previous season, 1919–20, when the comparative figures were 3,749 and 404 respectively, while there was a marked decrease in the number for whom licences were refused.

The National Stud continued to show a satisfactory profit for the year ended 31 December 1921, the amount being approximately £8,300. During the year it was found necessary to purchase a sire in place of Royal Realm (dead). He was Silvern, by Polymelus, out of Silver Fowl by Wild Fowl, bred by Sir E. Hutton, Bt. It won five times as a 3-year-old and was placed second in the St. Leger and Eclipse Stakes. As a 4-year-old it won the Coronation Cup.

The chief items on the credit side of the account were (1) £30,000 realised by the sale of bloodstock, (2) £7,000 by the sale of cattle, and (3) £2,700 for service fees. Sixteen yearlings were sold in 1921, realising a gross sum of £31,200, an average of £1,950. The highest price was £8,400, obtained for a colt by Tracery out of Countess Zia. The Stud again occupied a prominent position in the list of winning breeders.

The operation of the Light Horse Breeding Scheme during the 1922–23 season followed the usual lines, except that for reasons of economy the number of Ministry's Premiums was limited to 15, and only 57 instead of the usual 60 King's Premiums were awarded at the show in 1922, owing to the lack of stallions of sufficient merit to justify the full number of awards.

In the 1922 season the 12 Super-Premium horses served 855 mares (averaging 71) and the 45 King's Premium horses 3,033 mares — average 67. The 15 with Ministry Premiums served 872, or 58 apiece. In the 1921 season, the 12 Super Premium horses served 941 mares (883 returns furnished to Ministry) for an average foaling percentage of 51, 48 King's Premium horses served 3,407 (3,154 returns) for an average of 54, and 26 Ministry Premiums served 1,398 mares for an average of 60 (1,228 returns). The highest percentage (71) was obtained by two stallions, Ednam and Cock-a-Hoop, owned respectively by Messrs T. and H. Ward and Lt.-Col. Sir Merrik R. Burrell, Bart., CBE.

The annual show of Thoroughbred Stallions at the Agricultural Hall in 1923 was judged by Messrs Ernest Bellaney and Romer Williams. There were 87 entries, one less than in 1922, but a satisfactory feature was the entry of 24 new stallions, of which 9 were considered to be of sufficient merit to receive an award. One of these, St David, the property of HM the King, took third place among the Super-Premium winners. The full number of premiums was awarded and the King's Cup was won for the fourth year in succession by Gay Lally, the Reserve horse, as in the previous 3 years, being Scarlet Rambler.

The operations of the National Stud during the year ended 31 December 1922 continued satisfactory under the able direction of Capt. Greer. The profit for the year amounted to some £3,000, bringing the accumulated Trading Profit up to £33,550 since the establishment of the Stud in 1916. It was very satisfactory to record that the National Stud headed the list of winning breeders for the year 1922, with 25 horses winning 42 races to a total value of £32,939.

During the year 1922, 15 yearlings were sold at an aggregate gross sum of £17,951, an average of £1,197, which in view of the general fall in prices could be deemed satisfactory. Both stallions, Silvern and White Eagle, had full subscription lists, and the performances of the stock of the mares at the stud, which numbered 37, during the racing season of 1922 testified to the excellence of the brood mares.

The London Shows from 1921 to 1923 emphasised one salient and satisfactory fact — that the show had regained its pre-war influence and importance. This applied especially to the Young Stock section, as progressive improvement was fully evidenced in 1923 by the increased entry and excellent quality of the exhibits. This success appropriately coincided with the Presidency of HRH the Prince of Wales, who received their Majesties the King and Queen upon their visit on the Wednesday afternoon. Presiding at the Annual General Meeting of Members that forenoon, His Royal Highness, in response to the vote of thanks for the honour bestowed on the Society by his occupation of the chair during the current Show and past year which was associated with a record addition to its membership, said:—

'I need not tell you how very proud I am to be your President this year, and what a great pleasure it is to associate myself with the activities of a Society which, from my own experience, I know to be of tremendous value, not only to hunting men, but also to the State, activities which were largely responsible for the fact that we had an adequate supply of quality horses as remounts at the outbreak of the Great War.

'We all sincerely hope we shall not have another Great War, and to encourage this aspiration the strength of the cavalry regiments has been reduced, but so long as we have a standing Army we shall always want remounts, and hence the necessity for ensuring a Society which ever strives to see that the supply of remounts of well-bred horses of hunting type, on short legs and of moderate height, is kept up.

'So much about the State and the reduction of cavalry. May I say a word about foxhunting. I would say that the popularity of foxhunting, far from being reduced, has been increased. Anybody who has hunted since the war must have been greatly struck and delighted to find the numbers of fellows who manage to hunt. It is often a great struggle for them to do so, but it means they are very keen.

'May I also say a word, though perhaps it is rather irrelevant, about the wonderful co-operation of the farmers at the present time. They cannot, many of them, hunt themselves, but without them and their help we could not hunt. I think the farmers are to be congratulated. We cannot say too much about them.

'I have hunted with ten packs this season, and I have certainly come across very little wire. We are grateful to them for the help they have given us to keep a sport going without which this country would not be the same as it is today.'

His Royal Highness then went on to express his pleasure at the success which his appeal for increased membership had achieved, and also at the fact that the continuity of the grants made in the past in regard to King's Premiums had not been broken. He knew, he said, that His Majesty had always been keen on such grants being continued. He also expressed gratification at the success of the Show, remarking that all of them knew how difficult it was at the present time to find horses, and the appeal of the Society in stimulating the production of suitable hunters made a call to every hunting man and woman.

At the London Show in 1921, the Young Stock were judged by H. S. Brenchley, MFH (Heythrop) and the Hon. Alexander Parker, with Major Denis St G. Daly as referee. The championship went for the second time to George Dickinson's outstanding homebred filly Cark Silver Pheasant, now 3, by Silver Grill, and the reserve to her male contemporary, Mark Fenwick's chesnut gelding Air Raid, by Gilgandra ex Aeroplane by Aquamarine. Lt.-Col. R. S. Forestier-Walker, DSO, judged the ridden classes with Mr Romer Williams, who made an Irish under 14 stone horse champion — Mrs Eustace Mansfield from Co. Kildare's chesnut 7-year-old Northants, by Oriolus ex Lady Cerasus, bred in Blessington, Co. Wicklow by Mrs Panton. Reserve was Sir Edward Stern's former champion, Botha.

In 1922 the young entry were assessed by Mr J. P. Arkwright and Major Denis St G. Daly, with the Hon. Alexander Parker as referee. Their champion was the 3-year-old Golden Crest, by Cookhill, owned and bred by McMorran Brothers near Nantwich in Cheshire, a brown. Reserve was the filly Santa Gertrudis, by Santair from a mare by Ormondale, owned and bred by E. Guy Fenwick of North Luffenham Hall, Stamford.

Lt.-Col. Forestier-Walker and Mr Romer Williams judged the ridden classes for the second successive year. Their champion was the 7-year-old Goldfinder II, by Devolution, dam Joan of Arc, bred by N. Preston at Silverstream, Co. Meath, and shown by an exhibitor from Rotterdam, J. Hoboken. Reserve was a grey 7-year-old lightweight, Dawn, owned by B. Giles Bishop of Winslow.

In 1923 the Young Stock judges were Mr H. W. (Herbert) Nell and Lord Willoughby de Broke, MFH (Warwickshire). As champion, their choice fell upon Major and Mrs E. A. Dodd's 2-year-old chesnut filly Elsenham Dawn (GSB), from Essex. By My Prince out of Tyraness, by Oppressor, she was bred by T. L. Plunket, and she received the Prince of Wales's Cup which was offered for the first time. In reserve the 3-year-old chesnut gelding The Tory, also from Essex, shown here a year earlier as Pantomime, by Political, dam Prudence IV by Puro Caster, a winner for his then breeder-exhibitor, the Rev. E. T. Murray from Bourton-on-the-Hill, Gloucestershire, who sold him to Mr Arthur S. Bowlby.

The ridden champion was Goldfinder, for the second consecutive year, and the reserve the lightweight Best Man, another black 5-year-old, bred near Cirencester and shown by J. Kenneth Stevenson of Upper Welland, Malvern Wells, for whom Harry Bonner rode as a young man. Best Man was by The Best.

At the Annual General Meeting of 1921 it was announced that the supply of Thoroughbred stallions had been arranged through the grant to their owners administered by the Ministry. The Council were anxious that similar advantages (secured by the initiation of their original scheme of Service Premiums for Thoroughbred Stallions) should be extended to the owners and breeders of mares and fillies.

A scheme had been formulated for 1921 whereby 50 premiums of £20 each would be awarded at selected shows throughout England and Wales, open to brood mares and 3-year-old fillies (suitable for breeding hunters), and the conditions under which they would be awarded had been made as elastic as possible. The Council simply required compliance with three essential conditions:

(1) The retention of the brood mares and fillies in the hands of their owners.
(2) The soundness of a selected mare.
(3) The production of a living foal to a Thoroughbred horse or registered hunter sire.

This scheme was to be in addition to the normal activities of the Society at the Affiliated Shows, with the two provisos:

(1) No affiliated Society can claim a gold medal for brood mares if it elects to offer a £20 Premium, and vice versa.
(2) No owner can take more than one of these Premiums in all in 1921, and no mare can take more than one Premium.

'The grant of 1,000 guineas must obviously throw a severe strain on the financial resources of the Society, and the Council would solicit the support of all hunting men and of those who have at heart the future of our Light Horses, and ask them to help by becoming members of the Society. Members can individually co-operate by bringing the claims of the Society to the notice of their friends and thereby secure their support as new subscribers. The programme for the current year will necessitate an outlay of £2,860, as follows:

London Show	£1,090
Country shows	£350
Mare and Filly Scheme	£1,000
Stud Book	£420.'

Little of moment was revealed at the 37th AGM in 1922, but the following year Lord Mildmay of Flete, the Acting President, reiterated the deep debt of gratitude owed by council and Members to HRH the Prince of Wales, who as President not only had taken a keen interest in the work of the society, but had further honoured it by presenting a perpetual challenge cup for the best Young Hunter exhibited at the Spring Shows, to be held annually by the owner, to whom the Society would present a gold medal as a memento of his success.

Lord Mildmay was further authorised to issue the following letter with his appeal, sent to all interested in the breeding of hunters:

As President of this Society, I share the grave anxieties of the Council as regards the future of Light Horse Breeding, especially interested as I am in the breeding of Hunters.

The Society was the pioneer in establishing the system of placing sound and suitable Thoroughbred Sires at the disposal of breeders at low fees; and it has been due to its persistent representations that the scheme has been in being since 1887, and its continuance quite recently guaranteed on grounds of national necessity.

Our work demands the support of every hunting man and woman, and, at our next General Meeting, I hope to report a large accession of Members during the year of my Presidency.

I trust that subscribers to all hunts in the country will help by becoming members of the Society.

Believe me,
Yours very truly,
EDWARD P.'

'The Council feel that this appeal will have the very hearty support of existing members. In no more appropriate way could they — collectively and individually — acknowledge the special and practical interest taken by His Royal Highness in the breeding of Hunters and the honour conferred upon the Society by his acceptance of its Presidency than by proposing each a new member.

The Council have to record the loss of a staunch supporter by the death of Lord Middleton, elected a member in 1885, and twice President, in 1891 and 1912. Lord Middleton was Chairman of the Light Horse Breeding Committee. He owned the most typical Hunter Stud in England, which had been in existence for over a hundred years. He bred many high-class Hunter Brood Mares and fillies, and exhibited several Thoroughbred stallions, which won King's Premiums at the London Spring Show, while practically all the horses in his Hunt stables had been bred, reared and broken on the Stud farm at Birdsall.

The Council are able to report that after persistent representations to the Government they were enabled to obtain an authoritative statement that the continuance of the encouragement to Light Horse Breeding was of such national importance that the Army Council would take over the scheme and provide the funds. The management of the 1923 show will be undertaken by the Ministry of Agriculture and Fisheries (acting on behalf of the War Office). Sixty King's Premiums will be provided, together with 12 Super-Premiums.

A list of Hunter Judges — for the Breeding and Riding classes respectively — has been drawn up and will be at the disposal of all shows providing classes for hunters.

Three delegates have been appointed as the society's representatives on the council of the National Horse Association [newly incepted; after World War II it amalgamated with the Institute of the Horse to become the British Horse Society].

The audited balance sheet indicates that in 1922 the receipts exceeded expenditure by £223.6s.11d. Adjustment of liabilities and assets indicated that the balance in favour of the Society was £6,423, as compared with £5,817.14s.1d. the previous year. Membership rose from 2,154 to 2,459.'

The administration of the Light Horse Breeding Scheme was transferred to the War Office on 1 April, 1924. Thus the report on the year 1923-4 marks the termination of the Ministry of Agriculture's active interest in the scheme which was inaugurated in 1910 and had been in existence for 14 years.

The service season of 1923 showed considerable improvement on that of 1922, the average number of mares served both by King's Premium and Ministry stallions showing a marked increase.

12 Super Premiums served 966 mares — an average of 81 per stallion
48 King's Premiums served 3,437 — averaging 72
15 Ministry's Premiums served 886 — averaging 59

The foaling results for 1922 showed a slight increase on 1921 — 56% for the Super-Premiums, 53% for the King's Premiums and 54% for the Ministry Premiums. The highest percentage (73) was obtained by Ballyvodock, now owned by Mr Terry O'Brien of Midleton, Co. Cork.

At the request of the War Office the Ministry made the usual arrangements for the Thoroughbred Stallion Show in 1924 in conjunction with the HIS, for the purpose of awarding premiums for the 1924 service season. The Judges were Mr Ernest Bellaney from Lucan, Dublin, and the Hon. Alexander Parker. The number of entries, 94, was an increase of seven on 1923. The full number of 60 premiums was awarded, and the King's Cup was won by Scarlet Rambler, the reserve horse being Gay Lally — a reversal of the prevailing order for the previous four years.

Mr T. A. Hudson and Major J. W. Perry, the Young Stock judges, awarded the Prince of Wales's Cup to the 3-year-old chesnut filly Artful, by Sir Harry, out of Easthorpe Gladeye by Wales, owned and bred by Philip Burnett from Malton in Yorkshire. In reserve was the contemporary gelding Golden Gate, by Kirwan Gate, dam by Maccana, owned and bred by McMorran Bros. of Nantwich.

Ridden judges were Col. C. E. G. Norton and Romer Williams, whose champion was Bullace, a heavyweight 7-year-old owned by W. E. Stokes of

Market Harborough, purchased from R. Bullard from Norwich — no breeding given. In reserve was John Darby of Hillmorton, Rugby's 6-year-old Sorso, a lightweight also of unknown ancestry.

In 1925 the judges of Young Stock were Major W. P. Cantrell-Hubbersty and the Hon. Justice Wylie, later to become the legendary Judge Wylie, benevolent dictator of the Dublin Horse Show. They awarded the Prince of Wales Cup to the bay 2-year-old, Tarpaulin, owned and bred by Major W. H. Rawnsley of Alford in Lincolnshire, by Top Covert out of Mermaid VIII by Ocean Wave. The same owner was reserve with his chesnut 3-year-old Top-o'-the-Vale, also by Top Covert, bred by Edmund Davy of Spilsby, Lincs. The ridden judges, Lt.-Col. Sir Percy Laurie, CBE, DSO., and Mr Romer Williams, selected as their champion Red Fox III, by Kilmuklin, owned by the Reading dealer, Oliver Dixon and bred in Co. Waterford by Matt Fitzgerald of Ardmore. Reserve was the second in the heavyweight class, Frank Buckenham from Essex's grey Buckingham, bred at Bishop's Lydeard, near Taunton.

The King's Cup in 1925 was awarded by Major Denis St G. Daly and Mr J. W. A. Harris of the Ballykisteen Stud, Limerick Junction, Co. Tipperary, to Capt. T. L. Wickham-Boynton and H. A. Cholmondeley's Ardavon, by Ardoon. The 4-times champion Gay Lally was reserve. In 1926 Sir Gilbert Greenall, Bart., judged with P. Fitzgerald of Adare, Co. Limerick and Ardoon won the King's Cup for the second time, with His Majesty the King's London Cry, by Call o' the Wild, as runner-up.

The Young Stock were assessed by Capt. J. Bailward and Ernest Bellaney, who awarded Tarpaulin the Prince of Wales's Cup he had won the previous year. Reserve was the 2-year-old Romeo, by King's Prize, owned and bred by R. P. Cawsey of Torrington, North Devon. Judging the ridden classes on his own, Captain Wickham-Boynton made Captain C. Scott-Hopkins' 5-year-old brown lightweight, Ptarmigan by Primary out of Heather III by Scotch Sign his champion. He was bred in Yorkshire by Major Clive Behrens. Reserve was the runner-up in the class, John Darby's chesnut Skylark, by Birk Gill.

In 1924 a new class was introduced, for 4-year-old mares or geldings in hand, affording breeders an opportunity of bringing their unbroken horses to the notice of prospective buyers. The Council also allocated the sum of £400 to be offered and awarded to 3-year-old fillies stinted to a Thoroughbred or Registered Hunter Sire. The selected shows were: Bath Horse; Border Union; Devon County; East Berks; Essex; Hertfordshire; Lincolnshire; Monmouthshire; Northamptonshire; Peterborough; Royal Norfolk; Royal Welsh; Rutland; Shropshire and West Midlands; Thame; Three Counties; United Counties; Warwickshire Hunt; Yeovil and Yorkshire.

At the 40th AGM in 1924, it was said that the 40th Spring Show, honoured by the visit of their Royal Highnesses the Duke and Duchess of York, was successful from every aspect. The entry in the Young Stock section was practically back to pre-war level while the quality of the exhibits, especially as disclosed in the Group Class, yielded confirmatory proof of the soundness of the Light Horse Breeding Scheme.

This result — the consummation of successful association in 14 shows — heralded the termination of the joint activities of the Ministry of Agriculture and the Society in the furtherance of Light Horse Breeding. Reciprocal acknowledgements coupled with mutual regrets testified to beneficial and cordial co-operation. To Mr E. B. Shine the Council had conveyed their expression of sincere appreciation for his invaluable assistance rendered during these years, and conferred on him the Honorary Life Membership of the Society.

The 1925 Show — the first to take place under the auspices of the War Office — in addition to the King's and Super Premiums which the War Office would provide, also would identify themselves still further with the work of the Society by the provision of an increased number of prizes for Groups of Young Hunters. The sum of £90 would be available for award to the first three Groups by a Thoroughbred or Registered Hunter Stallion, with gold, silver and bronze medals to the respective owners of the successful sires.

The attention of the council was constantly being drawn by members resident in every part of the country to the numerous accidents, in many cases fatal, consequent upon the slippery condition of the roads. With great frequency they are informed of definite cases involving losses to owners of valuable hunters, cattle and livestock generally. Many farmers and small owners have been handicapped in business by injury to their horses running milk carts, etc., through inability to keep their feet on the roads. In particular, there have been frequent losses of cows about to calve.

Hitherto, attempts to remedy this evil have been thwarted by the difficulty of providing a foothold on a road, the surface of which must of necessity be waterproofed. But of late, results beneficial in this sense have most certainly accrued from the treatment applied to certain roads in definite districts through the use, after tar-spraying, of a larger size of grit, spread in a thicker layer, than is at present customary. Experience has undoubtedly proved that this method has a double advantage — a better foothold for horses and stock is provided and the life of the road is materially extended.

The representations made by the President to the County and Rural District councils elicited sympathetic replies. They appear fully to realise the vital importance of the matter to all users of horses on the roads, and it is hoped that practical steps will be taken by them to lessen the danger to horses and live stock arising from the slippery road surfaces.

Investigations were being carried out by the Animal Breeding Research Department, Edinburgh, into breeding problems, and they declared themselves anxious to work in close co-operation with breeders. There are many problems which face stock breeders; some have been solved by genetical science, others remain unsolved, especially the question of sterility. The Department has undertaken a very complete investigation of all the causes contributing to this condition, but their essential requirement is material, and the Council were using the medium of this report to appeal to Members to co-operate in work which is really of practical value to all, by placing themselves in direct touch with the Director of the Department, High School Yards, Edinburgh, for full details. In the particular instance quoted, the reproductive organs of any sterile animal that may die or be slaughtered should be sent to him, together with a very complete history of the case.

The actual receipts for 1924, were £5,320.19s.7d. and expenditure £4,813.16s., and the funded property account had been strengthened by a further investment of £300 in Treasury Bonds. Its value on 31 December 1924 was £7,100 as compared with £6,732 on the same date in 1923. The amount received in annual subscriptions and life compositions, £2,375.16s., was the largest amount received under this heading in any one year.

Nine mares had been presented to the society and lodged with suitable custodians by District Representatives. Reports lodged with the Council testify to the care and health of each mare, and periodic inspection ensures that they are being used only for work that they can reasonably be expected to perform so as not to impair their usefulness as brood mares. They must not be hunted or ridden with Yeomanry. In every case the mares had been served by a qualified sire and were believed to be in foal.

The scheme could be greatly extended if more gift mares were forthcoming, and a further appeal was again addressed to Masters of Hounds and owners to present mares for which they had no further use. No mare should be destroyed which was likely to make a suitable matron.

Substantiated cases of condition of roads dangerous to horse traffic had been taken up (in conjunction with the National Horse Association) with the local or county authority, and carried further to the Ministry of Transport where circumstances dictated. Biassed publicity propaganda designed to drive the horse off the streets has been met by reference to hard facts. It has been pertinently urged that the problem of traffic congestion would not be solved if every horse was banished from the Metropolis, while reacting most unfavourably and unfairly on their breeders and users. National interests would, moreover, be seriously endangered by any action tending to diminish material sources of supply in times of emergency.

At the 1926 (41st) AGM the Council drew attention to the large addition of new subscribers in 1925, due to the efforts of the President, the Hon. Alexander Parker, who during his second term of office had personally nominated 293 candidates. To Mr Parker was due the sincere acknowledgements of members for his untiring zeal in the welfare of the Society.

The official figures were annually verified on 1 January and on that date the total number of members was 2,635 as compared with 2,542 on the corresponding date in 1925. At the February meeting a further list of 109 were admitted to membership, making a total of 2,744 on the books of the Society.

As a token of their deep esteem and with sincere appreciation of invaluable service rendered since his admission to membership in 1888, the Council unanimously conferred upon Mr Romer Williams the Honorary Membership of the Society.

The inflow of new members had favourably influenced the financial position. Adjustments of assets and liabilities showed a credit balance of £7,918 in favour of the Society.

Fifteen mares presented to the society had been placed out by the District Representatives, who reported that seven foaled; two were barren; five placed out too late to be served and one was sent to the kennels. Nine had again been sold. Applications for mares from suitable custodians far exceeded the supply, and the scope of the scheme could be extended if more gift mares were forthcoming.

The condition of the roads as affecting their use by horses and live stock continued to engage the serious consideration of the Council. Local Authorities had been asked to instruct their Surveyors to take note of the three essential points to which the society attached special importance:

(1) That the roads should be made with a non-slippery surface, suitable for the use of Horses and Cattle as well as for Motors.
(2) That where grips are cut in the roadside waste for draining, they should be piped and covered in.
(3) That in laying out new roads, room should be allowed for grass verges of sufficient width to allow for Horses to be ridden and Cattle to be driven along them.

A record was established with the publication of the XIIth Volume of the *Hunter Stud Book* covering the years 1927–9, as with a total of 1,162 stallions, mares and geldings it exceeded by 301 entries the then largest number of pedigrees recorded — 859 received for Volume XI.

At the London Show in 1927, Major Gordon B. Foster, MFH (Sinnington) judged the young stock with Mr R. W. Wilson, awarding the Prince of Wales's cup to Miss Violet Wellesley for her brown 3-year-old gelding Eiffel, by The Tower, ex Bright Eyes by Red Prince, bred by Harold Worrall in Somerset. Reserve in this ladies' year was Mrs C. W. Sofer Whitburn with her 2-year-old chesnut filly Translucent, by Political out of Glass Doll, home-bred near Andover. Lt-Col. John McKie gave the ridden championship to the previous year's winner, Ptarmigan, now 6. John Drage's heavyweight Brandy III, bought near Ipswich but with neither age nor breeding given, was reserve.

The King's Cup resulted in a walk-over for Captain Wickham-Boynton and Mr H. A. Cholmondeley, who won it with Hector, by St Amant, and were reserve with their former champion, Ardavon. The judges were Major W. Gore Lambarde and W. P. Hanly from Thurles, Co. Tipperary.

In 1928, Lt-Col. G. C. Birdwood, CBE, and Sir Henry Greer of Curragh Grange, Co. Kildare, with Lord Southampton, OBE, awarded the King's Cup to Brigand, by Lemburg, owned by Stephen Mumford, Junior, and Captain D. Blew-Jones. In reserve was the defending champion, Hector, the property of Capt. T. L. Wickham-Boynton.

In 1929 Brigand became a dual winner of the King's Cup. In reserve was Orthos, by Orby, owned by H. C. Callaby of King's Lynn. The judges were Major Denis St G. Daly, MFH (Heythrop) and Lt-Col. John McKie, CBE, DSO, from Scotland.

At the London Show of 1928 Major W. Gore Lambarde and Mr Fred Unwin awarded the Prince of Wales Cup to the 3-year-old bay filly Snail III, by Gay Lally, owned by Mrs L. M. Smith-Ryland from Barford Hill, Warwick, out of Snail II by Kilmarnock. Reserve was the contemporary bay gelding Kingfish, by King Midas out of New Star by Travelling Lad, owned by Miss R. M. Harrison of Newcastle-under-Lyme. Under Lt.-Col. Sir Merrik Burrell, the ridden champion was Richard Bullard's brown 4-year-old Lord Rowland, by Sir Rowland, bred in Northern Ireland by Lewis Aston. The Reserve was another Irish-bred horse, Lady Dennis's chesnut 7-year-old heavyweight The General III, by The Boss, dam by Oppressor, bred by J. Reid of Navan, Co. Meath.

In 1929 Lord Daresbury (formerly Sir Gilbert Greenall, Bart.) and Sir

Merrik Burrell judged the Young Stock and awarded the Prince of Wales's Cup to the 3-year-old chesnut filly Gorse Bush, GSB by Rathdennis ex Bush by Thorn Lane, shown by Mrs Harry Frank of Wootton-under-Edge, Glos., and bred by P. O'Neill of Moate, Co. Westmeath. Reserve was the contemporary chesnut gelding Gold Standard, by Political out of Exchange II by Barabbas, owned and bred by Dudley W. J. North of Chipping Warden, Banbury. Major Gordon B. Foster judged the riding classes, awarding the championship to Lt-Col. F. D. Alexander's 7-year-old bay heavyweight Director, by Sunningdale, bred by Mr Gilmour from Crossmaglen, Co. Antrim, N. Ireland. In reserve was Miss Diana Russell Allen from Northwich with Trespasser, a lightweight bay 5-year-old bred by Mr Ryan of Naas, Co. Kildare, by The Jabberwock out of a mare by Grebe, and bought from T. and H. Ward of Guisborough, Yorkshire.

At the 42nd Annual General Meeting in 1927 the Council announced that His Royal Highness the Duke of York (later King George VI) had graciously consented to accept the Presidency of the Society in 1928–9 in succession to Sir Gilbert Greenall, Bart., CVO (Lord Daresbury).

The encouragement of the younger horse had been the consistent policy of the Society since its inauguration. In the earlier shows classes for fillies were an integral part of the London schedule. Systematic extension of this encouragement now covered not only the comprehensive schedule of each Spring Show but its ramifications embraced those of the Country Shows affiliated to the Society.

The desirability for uniformity of classification had been pressed upon the Council. The question was referred for examination and report to a special committee, who were invited to suggest any further practical steps whereby the co-operation existing between the Society and its allied bodies could be strengthened.

The Council were of the opinion of the committee, that this desirable object could be best achieved:

(a) By the issue of a copy of the London Show Schedule to each affiliated Society.
(b) By financial support of their Young Hunter Classes.

A covering letter emphasised the view of the Council that the schedule was submitted without any desire to dictate, but with one object — the encouragement of Light Horse Breeding, fortified by offers of a practical nature. The London schedule was selected as providing a comprehensive and yet elastic medium. Component parts could be used to meet local requirements without detriment to its structure. It was suggested that where a schedule was restricted by financial considerations, preference should be given to Fillies.

The advantage to young hunters under saddle by the restriction of ages in the Riding classes was also emphasised.

One of the most instructive and successful of the 15 classes provided in London had been the Produce Group class, and its institution in their schedules was strongly urged on each local society.

The offer of special prizes for foals testified the desire of the Council further to strengthen the local support of Young Hunter Classes. In November the

Council allocated — preferentially to the smaller Societies — the necessary funds for initiating the two schemes in 1927:

The Produce Group Class: The offer of three Premiums of £1 to the owners of the best three Young Hunters.

Hunter Foals: The offer of a first prize of £5, for the best Foal exhibited with its dam, if the Affiliated Society provides a further sum for second and third prizes.

Affiliated Shows: The normal schemes of gold, Silver and Bronze medals, with prizes to breeders, were to be maintained and would include the offer of Champion Gold Medals at the Royal and Highland Shows.

Group Class at the Royal Show: The Council had invited the RASE to institute a Group Class for Young Hunters at their meeting at Newport on the same lines as those operating at the Society's Spring Show. The Council had offered three premiums for the Group, with Gold and Silver Medals to the owners of the Stallions siring the Young Hunters in the selected Group.

During 1926, awards had been made as follows:

National Shows: 3 Gold Medals.
Affiliated Shows:
    Brood mares: 28 Gold Medals.
    Fillies: 50 Silver Medals and 24 Breeders' Prizes.
    Saddle Classes: 56 Silver Medals.
Shows outside British Isles: 5 Silver Medals (Canada — Calgary and Edmonton) India (Imperial Delhi) and South Africa (Bloemfontein).

The 42nd London Spring Show, 1926, was held in conjunction with the War Office. The innovation of not keeping any exhibit in the Hall for more than two days was much appreciated. Its success ensured its maintenance at the 1927 show (from 1–3 March).

In this connection it is interesting to note the offical view of the American Military authorities as to the continued utility of the Cavalry branch. After recapitulating the important roles adopted — in reconnaissance — at night, and under all weather conditions, over thickly wooded or badly broken country, etc., the advantages are summarized thus:

'Cavalry is an indispensable part of the army because of the importance of those services that it alone can render, or that it can perform better than any other troops. Modern inventions and appliances affecting the conditions of War have added to the power and scope of cavalry.'

Under the Brood Mare scheme 35 mares had been placed out with suitable custodians. Twenty-one were presented to the society, while 14 were purchased from the grant authorised by the Council in 1925. Twenty-seven of these mares were served in 1926 by Premium Stallions. The Council allocated a sum of £300 towards the maintenance of the scheme in 1927, and desired to place on record their appreciation of the valued assistance of the District Remount Officers in the organisation of the scheme and the acquisition and location of mares with suitable custodians.

The credit balance in favour of the Society was £8,420.

At the 43rd AGM of Members on 28 February 1928, it was announced that His Royal Highness the Duke of York, KG, had honoured the Society by graciously consenting to be its President during the year. The Council ventured to hope that Members would co-operate with them in assuring His Royal Highness a most successful year of office.

The revised list of Hunter Judges would be available to all applicants. In conjunction with the Shire Horse Society, negotiations took place with the Royal Agricultural Hall Company, and it was arranged to continue to hold the shows at Islington from 1929–35 inclusive.

A further sum of £200 — making a total of £700 since the inauguration of the scheme — was devoted to the purchase of suitable brood mares to be located with responsible custodians. Since its inception, 58 brood mares had been acquired for the scheme by gift or purchase. Thirteen foals resulted from 24 services in 1926, and 46 mares were served in 1927 by 25 approved stallions.

An influential deputation, organised by the Society and representative of the horse-breeding interest, was received in the Spring of 1927 by the Chancellor of the Exchequer. In response to their considered representations that a considerable proportion of the proceeds of the betting tax should be returned, either directly or indirectly, to the National Industry of Horse-Breeding in its various branches, the Chancellor intimated that 'if at any time the Totalisator were legalised and became an important feature in this country, that would be the moment for those who are interested in the breeding of bloodstock to press their claims for a share in whatever was left over after the Government had taken what no doubt would be regarded as its prior due'.

The deputation as constituted remains in being to deal with any future eventualities arising from projected legislation in this direction.

The Council had also countered by reference to facts, anonymous allegations in the Press as to the decline of Hunter entries at representative shows, and of the ill measure of success attendant on the services of the Premium Stallion in specified districts.

'From its constitution in 1885 the society had enjoyed throughout the interest and support of the Royal Family. His Majesty the King had perpetuated this valued association with annual visits to each of the Spring Shows. The council and Members had followed with deep concern the fluctuations of his illness, and they joined in the universal expression of hope that he would soon regain good health.'

This preamble to the 44th AGM in 1929 was followed by the sincere appreciation of Members being expressed to HRH the Duke of York for the whole-hearted interest this second of the three Royal Princes had graciously extended to the work of the Society as its president during the past year. During 1928 the Society had greatly extended its sphere of operations, by the development of the scheme for the location of suitable brood mares with responsible custodians; by the increased recognition of the value of registration in the *Hunter Stud Book*; and by the practical application of the auxiliary schemes for Foals and Produce Groups, which have received a cordial reception from the Affiliated Country Shows.

During 1928 24 Mares — donated and purchased — had been located. Funds amounting to over £180 had been applied to the organisation of the scheme. Reports from the District Representatives indicated that the percentage of foals from the 1927 service was 62%, while during 1928 55 mares had been served by 33 stallions.

Closer co-operation with the War Office was envisaged in 1929, when increased opportunities would be offered to the Society to acquire by purchase mares cast from the Army, but recommended for sale as brood mares. The assistance of the District Remount Officers would be available in the periodical inspection of located mares.

The terms of the agreement under which each mare was placed out had been revised to bring the conditions of loan into line with the increased scope of the scheme. The council had authorised a grant of £300 towards the expenditure involved by its development during 1929. Gifts of suitable mares would be welcomed by those desirous of co-operating in the location of the mares with responsible custodians for breeding purposes.

Regular and systematic application for registration had been received and the entry for Volume XII of the *Stud Book* already numbered over 650 Hunter-bred stock. The results were undoubtedly influenced by an improved market, and by the demand from the United States of America for horses registered in the *Hunter Stud Book*. Prizes gained at Hunter Trials by registered hunters would be recorded, and the advisability of offering the Society's medals for Hunter Trial Winners was under discussion.

One hundred and sixty-nine foals were entered for the 16 prizes of £5 provided by the Society and 45 Groups (with an aggregate entry of 245 Young Hunters) were exhibited for the 12 premiums of £2 and 30 premiums of £1 at the 10 shows selected by the Council.

The success of the 44th Spring Show was assured by the entry of 117 Thoroughbred Stallions competing for the King's Premiums. An entry of 199 Hunters — an increase of 42 — brought together a representative exhibition of Thoroughbred and Hunter Stock. The Produce Groups numbered 11, with an aggregate of 46 entries.

Their Majesties the King and Queen were present on the Wednesday to witness the selection of Brigand for His Majesty's Champion Challenge Cup. His Royal Highness the Duke of York presented on Thursday the Prince of Wales's Challenge Cup for Young Hunters, won by Snail III.

The schedule for the next show would be the same as that for 1928. Sixty King's Premiums and 6 Super-Premiums would be offered by the Army Council in the Thoroughbred section, while the Society provided fourteen prizes for Hunter Stock and prizes value £1,300. Details from the Remount Depots would be on exhibition and paraded on the Wednesday afternoon.

Receipts during 1928 totalled £5,389.16s.3d. and expenditure £4,480.18s.1d., and allowing for outstanding liabilities the balance in favour of the Society on 31 December 1928 was £9,210.15s.6d.

Heavier commitments had to be met in the current year, due to the extension of the Brood Mare Scheme and the encouragement to the Affiliated Societies, the increased financial quota under the new agreement for the London Shows and the publication of the next volume of the *Hunter Stud Book*.

The total number of members on the books of the society was 2,678, and 73 further new members were elected at the first Council Meeting in 1929.

Lieut.-Col. Viscount Lascelles, KG, DSO, MFH (Bramham Moor) would be President in 1929, and as Vice-President (President in 1930) the Council begged to nominate Col. C. Spence-Colby, CMG, DSO.

*   *   *

Unfortunately for the historian, with Volume XI the old familiar format of the *Hunter Stud Book* changed, probably in the interests of economy. It became quite literally a *Stud Book*, full of facts and figures concerning pedigrees and honours won in the show ring or the racecourse but no longer containing articles, reports of Annual General Meetings nor of meetings with Ministry of Agriculture officials which were so productive of background material. The 1930s were a fruitful time for the Society, until 1939, when World War II closed the horse world down again, horses were requisitioned and sent abroad but happily replaced on the battlefield by tanks and armoured cars. The Army horse was used largely for transport except in ceremonial regiments, and the HIS shut up shop until peace reigned again in 1946.

Part II

The people who made the Society

CHAPTER 9

The Viscount Knutsford

LORD KNUTSFORD's mother, who came from Cumberland, inspired her son, Thurstan, who was born in 1888, with her love of hunting. He was not in his early years particularly keen, and on one occasion when a small boy he fell off his pony and burst into tears, and his mother was heard to say: 'You'll never be any good.' She hunted all her life, first with the Cumberland, of which her brother was Master for many years and then, after her marriage, with the OBH, Hertfordshire and Whaddon Chase.

Lord Knutsford's lifelong love of hunting showed itself when he was at Cambridge, reading law. There he whipped-in to M. E. Barclay when he hunted the Trinity Foot Beagles, and took them on for the season 1911/12, during which he killed 67½ brace of hares — which was then a record, and may still be.

He married in 1912, and served in the First World War, first in the Hertfordshire Yeomanry and later, having recovered from dysentery at Gallipoli, transferred to the Royal Scots Greys.

After the war he joined Sir Robert Green-Price as joint Master of the Teme Valley, which he hunted for one season, and then went to the Avon Vale, where he was Master and huntsman from 1924 to 1933. During these years he developed his interest in hound breeding and got to know Henry Robinson — Lord Roundway's butler — who was a fanatical student of the *Foxhound Kennel Stud Book* and a remarkable character.

While at the Avon Vale he realised a long-standing ambition by winning at Peterborough in 1930 with a dog he had bred called Ragtime.

In 1935 he went to the V. W. H. Bathurst as joint Master with the 7th Earl Bathurst and hunted the hounds until 1939. There he had a bitch called Lawful with a wonderful nose, undefeated on any road, a characteristic she passed on to her progeny.

In 1945 the Duke of Beaufort asked him to hunt his dog hounds, which he did for one season.

In 1948 he moved to his ancestral home, Munden, in Hertfordshire, where his son and daughter still live, and from where he hunted with the Whaddon Chase until he was 83, when he was forced by arthritis to stop riding. At the end of the First World War he bought out his charger, Hinnegan, and won £300 show jumping on him, which in those days of £5 first prizes was a considerable achievement.

Known to his friends as 'T', Lord Knutsford had a great reputation as a raconteur and after-dinner speaker. The following account of his experiences both breeding and judging hunters was written by him in his later years.

Breeding, horse shows and judging
by
THE VISCOUNT KNUTSFORD

The gift from my mother of a mare, Ranee by Red Sahib, first interested me in showing, although I had previously bred several hunter foals. I should think that my experience was just about typical of the luck attached to breeding hunters. A short-tailed grey mare which my mother heard about at Stamford started me off as a breeder. I was told I could go and see her and find out for myself if I liked her.

Clad in a dreadful light grey riding coat and breeches, and white canvas gaiters, (which ensemble I considered to be wonderfully horsey,) I went to Stamford. The dealer and I rode out into the country. 'Go on, sir,' he said encouragingly. 'Have a jump.' The first road-side fence had sheep-netting in it, which we got over well. He then said: 'Come on, Sir — in and out the road.' She did it well in spite of the other horse, and I was so pleased with *myself* that I could not help being pleased with the mare, and in due course she was bought. She turned out well, and now I come to think of it I asked her some pretty stiff questions with the Whaddon.

One double into the big field at the bottom of Wing Park I can well remember. I rode at it anyhow, and owing to that and rabbit holes I took a proper toss. This was made worse because Lady Orkney laughed at the fall, but due to her short sight this bad bit of horsemanship was attributed to Clive Burn, who also had a short-tailed grey.

One foggy day the Meet was at Marston Gate. After a delay it was decided to go to Aston Abbots, on higher ground. We found and, jumping a fence near Oxley's farm, I had a fall into a ditch beyond and she never recovered from a shoulder injury.

I sent her to E. W. Robinson's Riverstown, by Ascetic, and bred a colt which we called Stream. He turned out to be one of the best horses I ever rode, and I had over 250 days on him before an incompetent second horseman allowed him to shy over a heap of stones and he injured his back. The mare went next to Red Sahib (by Red Prince) and bred a filly. She grew into a fine mare but got a cold and her wind went, so we sold her at Tattersalls before she ever even hunted. We had a foal from her which was found dead in the field with a twisted gut. The post-mortem proved that she was full of coarse grass, so no doubt she had colic and rolled.

Next the grey mare went to The Tower, and bred a colt which we called Special Leave. He did very well as a whipper-in's horse when I had the Teme Valley, but got pneumonia and was touched in the wind thereafter so we sold him — a well made little big one.

The next foal, a filly, was also by The Tower. She was a very good example of the extraordinary difficulty that attends the breeding of hunters. She grew to 17 hands, up in the air and not much bone — the exact opposite of the previous colt, although bred in just the same way. Her only resemblance to her full brother was that, like him, she turned a toe out, which indeed was characteristic of The Tower's offspring. This mare could never really move herself and had little go about her. She was sold at Tattersalls as a 5-year-old and I had a good idea that she would become a whistler.

The next colt broke his pelvis in his box, and had to be destroyed, as a 2-year-old. Then the grey mare died, having produced one exceptional horse out of 6 foals. But, nothing daunted, we started again with the mare my mother had given me. She was a good hunter but not very well balanced, and had moderate hocks. However, she won a great many local brood mare classes and bred two real good 'uns out of the four she had. The first, Indian Red, was by Red Hand — a wonderful looking foal who won many prizes before he suddenly shot up into the air and grew to 17 hands. He was never balanced and had his mother's hocks, went in the wind, and we gave him away to a farmer. In a farmer's race in the Avon Vale country, with a tube in him, he ran quite well.

The next, Lloyney, was by Darigal. We never managed to get her balanced but she carried my daughter in a whole-hearted way for seven seasons and won a Ladies' race. A splendid jumper and absolutely untiring, she eventually broke down and we gave her to a farmer to breed from, with rather a poor foal at foot by Cheerful Abbot. The farmer used to hunt with us in the Cirencester country.

The third foal, Aspirin, was a colt by Vertigo. Aspirin should be written in red ink. Sensible, cheerful, and terribly fond of hunting, there was nowhere you could not go. He knew the whole thing. He was painted by Lionel Edwards and it is good to be reminded of him because he came to a sad end; he either ricked his back in a field full of little half-filled-in ditches or else was struck by lightning, and he had to be destroyed.

Ranee, the mare, then went to stud again and we sold her in foal to Mrs Lopes, of Sandridge. The resulting filly, Vicereine, was very hot but ran well in several point-to-points.

So, out of 12 foals we bred three really good ones. We certainly never did the foals nearly well enough but that was not entirely responsible for the failures, and in spite of a rough and ready young life the three successes were horses of a lifetime. The outstanding features of my experience are that you never know in the least what you are going to get but the better bred the mare, the more certainty there is that you will get the good characteristics that will outweigh the bad ones; but an underbred mare with faults will reproduce those faults, and when they come out in the progeny they outweigh anything that may be good. Also it is foolish to breed hunters from a mare with bad hocks or a poor shoulder. I remember one mare of a friend's who never bred anything without reproducing her own bad shoulders, which was just a waste of everyone's time.

The three good ones we did manage to breed were a continual source of joy to us, although of course if you put their value in money in order to buy them they would have cost at least £500, and that sum cannot be said to cover the expenses of the foals we bred.

We did a great deal of showing, also of children's ponies, and had many successes with my daughter riding; notably with a short-tailed pony called Greylight, who was a wonderful hunter, but the showing of children's ponies got to be very high class, and when the 'High School' riding came in one had to be more or less of a specialist to do any good. We bred three foals from Greylight, much against my will, and sold them all. I believe someone made some money out of them by careful placing, but it is an unprofitable job breeding ponies, and only dealers have the opportunity to place them satisfactorily.

I did a good deal of show jumping just after the First World War, before it had got to such heights of proficiency. My first effort was in France, where I won the Officers' jumping on my charger, Hinnegan. I had little idea of the art of it and just rode round, hitting him at the right time by intuition rather than knowledge.

A brother officer, Joe Dudgeon, had a waler called Inky who could jump. Joe went on leave and gave me the ride on Inky at the Cavalry Corps Horse Show at St Pol. We all stood waiting in the broiling sun and the horses got drowsy. My number was called. The turf had been cut in front of the first jump, for some reason. Inky, only half awake, took off at the scar in the grass, and the first thing that hit the grass was my cap badge. This was the start of the many falls I had, which always ended up with my neck being hurt.

When the war was over, Hinnegan (named after my groom) was booked for me to buy out. I got news that he would come up at Tattersalls on a certain date. I went up. The officer's name, when he had received permission to buy his horse out, was clipped on the horse, but was supposed to be erased before the sale. My servant had carefully clipped 'Lt T. Holland-Hibbert, Scots Greys' on both sides of mine and although an attempt had been made to erase it, it was quite clear and he looked like a zebra.

Anyhow, there was quite brisk bidding, but I eventually got him for 60 gns. A man called Aspenal bid against me and I was stupid not to have told him quietly what he was doing. I remember our stud groom, Hobman, came down to Luton Station to meet him. Out of the box came poor Hinnie — pot-bellied, dry in his coat, cat hairs all over him and these clipping marks, dirty, tired and forlorn. Hobman obviously thought nothing of him, and caused me to say that I would bet him that the next morning I would jump the rails near the laundry at home, and that Hobman on Stream, whom he had been schooling all through the war, would not be able to get over them at all. Hobman took the bet but would not compete when the time came, and Hinnegan sailed over the rails unchallenged.

This old horse won eight cups and £300 for me. At Richmond, the first summer after the war, he was left in with six others in a class of 69, but knocked a slat off the gate with his tail in the elimination. He was doubtful at the water and would sometimes take charge and refuse to be helped. At Watford one year terrific rain came on. Nobody had gloves, and they began tying their reins in knots, and other dodges. My father called out from the top of the stands 'Borrow a policeman's gloves!' This I did. Hinnegan was in one of his worse moods but I managed to hold him, and we roared round and did a clear round ... the prize was £20.

He also won several handy hunter classes, and on days when he had been in the jumping classes as well he showed his versatility; one moment he was asked to go on and jump a gate, and shortly afterwards to go up to it and let me open it. I won a prize or two jumping other people's horses, but that was not much of a game as you never knew the horse well enough to do much good. There was tremendous satisfaction in being called in to get a prize and Hinnegan used to show off, smashing his teeth on the double snaffle I rode him in and shaking it. However, it is a disappointing game; so little robs you of the prize.

One of my companions on those show jumping jaunts from Leighton Buzzard was Gerry Wilson, who was afterwards champion steeplechase jockey for many years in succession.

An amusing incident occurred once at Knighton when, as MFH of Teme Valley, I entered Hinnegan in the Riding Horse class. Every other competitor was a hackney or half-bred hackney who had been shown in carts in the previous class. We kept on walking round and were then asked to trot. Off went the others, stepping up to their chins, urged on by be-trousered riders with sharp cries. Round and round we went, with the judges and stewards in a huddle in the middle. I saw their dilemma and pulled up by one steward to say: 'Why don't you ask us to canter?', knowing full well that the others would hardly be able to do that at all. No response. Presently: 'Young man, will you come in here, please,' said the chief steward. He then said: 'Will you please take your horse out of the ring. We have not seen a horse like that before and if we give you the prize we shall not get the class filled again. We will return your entrance fee to you.'

I replied: 'If I was not Master of the local hounds, nothing would induce me to leave the ring as mine is the only real riding horse here, but I will go in order not to cause difficulties.' Off I went, and jumped the gate on the way out!

I won the local jumping class two years running at the Bedfordshire show and hoped to do it again at Ampthill the third year, but the old horse jumped disgracefully and I rode home to Leighton very disappointed. When I got back Fred, our groom, said: 'I've put the bar up to the top, try him over it, sir.' I thought it stupid but was so cross with him that I did. It was fixed and over 4 ft. 6 in., but he popped over it with no difficulty at all. They get too clever at the job, and if they are not feeling in form they simply do not bother. A horse has really to have no temperament at all if he is to be a consistent show jumper.

I remember once at Olympia, in the High Jump, Tommy Glencross coming in, and to everybody's amazement — and obviously to his also, his horse failed very early on. When it was over and the prizes awarded, Mrs Glencross came marching it. She was an imposing-looking lady with a swinging walk. Olympia in those days was much more of a party than it became later after Lord Lonsdale's personality had gone. She marched up to the judges and stewards and said something, they seemed to acquiesce, and the pole was put up higher than the winner had cleared. Mrs Glencross then ran a bit of red ribbon along the pole. In came her husband and the horse cocked one ear at Mrs G, who was standing near the jump with her hand on the pole, and cleared the lot!

In the competition that I was in at Olympia that time, all the first 20 or so competitors had difficulty with a jump at the top of the ring that was placed at the apex of the oval. When my turn came, we cleared everything up one side, I pulled him back into the flowers and set him off again at the jump instead of, as the others had done, trying to take it all as it came. I got over, the first to do it, and all went well down the other side. It remained to do the criss cross. My Uncle Arthur, seated in the roof somewhere, then took it into his head to blow a horn. My old horse put one ear back, one forward, and went up the jumps rooting them all as he went. That was the end of me. I met Uncle A afterwards and he was quite unmoved. He said he had a wreath in the cloakroom which he wanted to put on my grandfather's statue on the Embankment, and that he had not got much time. The crowd were all leaving their seats. 'Come on, T, I'll show you the way to get through this lot!' and he touched the man in front of him on the shoulder. 'Have you seen the hounds, sir?' The man turned in astonishment and we hopped past him. At the next block he did the same, except this time he said: 'Have you seen my second horse?' and so we got out very quickly!

While on the subject of Olympia, it started as the International Horse Show in 1907 when I was 19, and it had tremendous glamour for me and really was a wonderful sight, with its wonderful display of flowers, ringmen in red coats, top hats and boots. Lord Lonsdale was there every day smoking a cigar and with a gardenia in his buttonhole. There were marvellous driving classes, with all the horses decorated, the glass roof was hidden by thousands of yards of muslin, bands played and there were shops and stalls displaying and selling everything appertaining to the horse world.

One year I was in London, supposed to be doing a 'season', but as soon as a dinner party was over one night I crept away to Olympia and had the luck, by chance, to sit next to John Swire, who was MFH of the Essex, a great driving expert. It was really an Olympia for me, and remained so. Imagine my pleasure when I was asked to judge. I had by that time a good deal of judging experience, but Olympia — ! I judged with Eddie Griffith, who was a *persona grata* in The Hunters' Improvement Society although I did not know much about him, coming as he did from North Wales. I don't think we made any bloomers and certainly picked on a very good novice for the championship, owned by Hindley, which was pretty daring. He was a good hunter too and was subsequently bought to hunt by Beckwith Smith.

Brand new dress clothes had to be bought — and not before they were needed! My wedding coat did all right for the afternoons — new jack boots necessary and also some cloth-topped brown laced ankle boots. It was an expensive outing as my wife wanted to be there most days, and the journeying backwards and forwards had to be done. They were very good about free tickets for meals in the Pillar Restaurant. Cigars and all were available free. It was a difficult place to gallop a horse as directly you got him going you reached the end of the oval ring and had to pull up a bit to turn.

The next time I judged there was with Harry Cotterill; this was very different, for he was rather deaf and much more a racing man than a hunter man. He knew none of the horses or exhibitors, which was a help to fairness in one way. Impossible to make any 'asides' to him, so we said little and had a discussion afterwards as to how we were eventually going to place them. One incident gave me an example of why some people were bothered about Lord Lonsdale's autocratic behaviour; we were judging the top weight class and Lady Helen McCalmont's Handley Cross was stripped and standing for our contemplation before the Royal Box. I knew the horse well and all about him, how he had never surmounted any obstacle and was a real bad hunter. Cotterill was a small man and not much in love with such an enormous horse, although he was a remarkable ride for one of that sort. There was a pause as Cotterill contemplated the horse. Lonsdale evidently thought we were in difficulties, and as the horse was a well known winner, no doubt expected that we were about to make a bloomer. So he came up and said: 'That's Lady Helen McCalmont's Handley Cross, a well known winner and winner of many point-to-points.' Not bad, was it, as I knew what I did?

A new class introduced that year was a Hunt Competition, for three members of any hunt, marks to be given for turn-out, etc. I really enjoyed judging that. Three Bicester ladies were by far the best — Mrs Philip Fleming and two others, all in black coats, matching breeches and riding chestnut horses. After examination for turn-out they had a few fences to jump in single file, then joined up at the top and jumped one fence abreast. Their drill was excellent and they were easy winners. After it was over they asked me if there was anything wrong with their turn-out, thinking, I knew, that they were perfect. I said I did not like ornamental tie-pins — one had a diamond fox and another a coloured fighting cock — and that one had patent leather garters with ordinary leather boots.

The Old Berkeley Hunt had two teams in, one of ladies in beautiful blue habits and on three of Major Stanley Barratt's (MFH) perfect and well known show-horses. Their jumping and drill, however, was awful, and afterwards Mrs Barratt sent him up to ask me if I had taken any marks off for turn-out. I said 'Did she really want to know,' and when he said 'yes' I said I had taken marks off for their hunting ties, which were not tied but were just pulled over. Whereupon, when this had been relayed to her, Mrs Barratt came bouncing up. She had been to a shop, she said, where she was specially taught the correct way to tie a hunting tie, so I said that I would go with her if she liked and show the shop how to tie it properly! Somehow or other, people nowadays seem to think that all that is necessary is to simply fold a hunting tie over and there you are, as long as you have enough safety pins to keep it all in place. If you haven't, well, that's too bad and you let it come out anyway it likes.

I also remember on another occasion taking off marks from the men's OBM team because the Master had his horn tucked into his coat all the time, and no couples on his saddle. I say he should have had his horn in its case, although not everybody agreed with me about a huntsman wearing couples. I say they made an extra pair and who knows when they might be needed. This team had taken tremendous trouble, even to having yellow woollen gloves tucked into the girths, and yellow crackers on their whips. In the judges' box a discussion arose about couples or no couples; later I heard a lady say to a newcomer: 'Do you know, Barratt has no *couplings* on his saddle!' How few people really know ...

The third time I judged at Olympia I was with Harold Nutting, MFH Quorn. He was not very enthusiastic over the job. The Hunt Teams again produced the Bicester ladies; easy winners. The brightest-eyed member, Mrs Holden, asked: 'Are we all right *this* time?'. I saw they had all bought new gold pins, on which I complimented them, but added that they should have been put in horizontally, not perpendicular, and also that hers was only through her tie, not pinned down through her shirt to her vest. She said: 'I haven't got a vest on.' So I added that I was afraid I could make no use of that information in the middle of a show ring!

I always watched carefully each rider in a hunter class to see if he was employing any particular dodge in riding his horse. I noticed in the novice class the last time I judged that one chap was having a job to hold his horse (Francis), so when I was getting on I asked: 'Is this a puller?'. He said it was keen but that I'd be all right. I walked, trotted and then shook him up into a canter and off he went — absolutely dead mouth. One has no time at Olympia to try more than one dodge to stop a horse, and if that fails you find yourself on one wheel going round the corner. Two corners we negotiated, then I put him at some empty seats and he stopped dead, but was off again until he almost came down at the next corner, where I was able to stop him, and get off.

I contemplated saying nothing to Nutting so that he would get bolted with too, and show the spectators that it was not my bad horsemanship, but then I thought Nutting was a valuable MFH and not a strong man, so if I had said nothing his death would have been in my hands. So I warned him, and he did not ride the brute. I heard afterwards that this horse had bolted three times round Richmond show with Wallis.

There was one dreadfully awkward affair in the Ladies' class. Two horses had been temporarily and probably placed after riding first and second by Mrs Stevens and Mrs Campbell. Number 2 had given a bad show owing to a bad rider, and a fresh rider was put up in the evening, when the horse went so well that one judge wanted to alter the morning decision. But the other judge did not agree, saying that they had placed them from the 'good ride' point of view and that misbehaviour in the morning must count. Neither would give in and the spectators became restive. At last a third lady judge was produced and by then the horse that had misbehaved in the morning was at it again, so the order was confirmed.

There is no doubt that the method adopted for Olympia is much the best — the prolonged riding and looking to be done in the morning if possible, and just a show for the public and the prize-giving when the house is full.

I had found these judging expeditions expensive, especially when free lunch tickets became harder to get, so that when asked a third time to judge I said I should like to but really it cost too much for anybody like me with no home in London. I also pointed out that although I realised the honour to be asked, even the very smallest show at least offered to pay a judge's expenses. As a result we were given 10 guineas, which was certainly a help. It was great fun being in that atmosphere and the jumping classes were always worth watching, I found, just to see the different styles and faults. Also the High Jump never ceased to thrill me and to see the winner standing with the rider's head hardly reaching the top bar never ceased to surprise me. I also saw a vanner type win it, and a tall, leggy horse with bad hocks.

The French riders were really the most striking, with their method of coming in at full gallop on a loose rein, and everything given to the horse as he jumped. When timing was introduced it certainly sharpened things up but I think it unbalanced the spectacle and made it all much less finished. We had some wonderful spectacles — the Cadre Noir, Spahis, Hanoverians, and trick riding at its best by some chaps under Mike Ansell as show pieces, but the introduction of police motor bicycles and a police musical ride indicated the beginning of the end. One night the London Casino gave a free invitation to Horse Show personnel and we had a good evening. The Lambeth Walk was the dance 'of the moment' and a lot of fun was had by introducing the foreign officers to that manœuvre.

There was also a horse show dinner at the Dorchester when Lord Digby was president. He made the best all-embracing speech I have heard, and was rightly described by the American harness class judge as 'tops'.

The first time I was asked to judge at Richmond I replied that I should be pleased to, but asked with whom. I always did this for any big show because there were one or two people about, whom I knew I did not get on with. I was glad that I had asked on that occasion because I was told that a very well known judge of hacks was to be my partner, and I knew him to be old and frail and a *persona grata* at that show. Accordingly I regretted that I could not accept as I knew full well he would not listen to me, he would not really be able to try a keen horse, and that if there were a really bad decision he would put all the blame on me. I thought my refusal would mean I should never be asked there again but I was, and had a very pleasant day with Guy Lucas as co-judge.

There were lots of stories about him, and how a man that sold as many horses as he did should not be allowed to judge, but all I can say is that one day when we were together, I think at the Royal Counties show, we had two horses that there was nothing much between. He said: 'Go on, Tom' (there are about half a dozen people who always called me Tom, for some reason) 'You do it because I sold one of these horses to his present owner'.

Richmond is a grand big ring, but is sometimes very hard and slippery, and wherever you are it's a good tip to make certain a horse has studs in before you get up. There were two horses during the years I judged that caused some judges trouble. One was Goldfinder, a great, slashing, over 14 stone horse, rather of the charger type. It was like being on the deck of a sailing ship in full rig to ride him, and he wanted plenty of room. Terrific stride — some of the older judges were frightened of him and he got the reputation of being doped. There was another horse called Ballymonis who made off with one or two judges and the dope story was on about him too. It has always pleased me that I did not have any difficulty at all with either of them, although I was not by any means alone. However, it is curious to note that some very excellent horsemen *did* have trouble with both.

I should really have started this with my first-ever judging experience on a Bank Holiday at Colchester in Essex. I was very surprised to be asked, and found out that I was to be with Arthur Sowler. I knew I would be safe with him, but wondered how he would feel about it, so wrote, and also asked him why he thought I had been asked. He said to come along, that new blood was wanted. Presumably what successes we have had as exhibitors and also show jumping had got my name put forward.

All I remember was that I got a tremendous thrill out of finding myself where I had so often watched 'celebrities', and also to ride Goldfinder and absolutely fly round the ring was a terrific experience.

It took me a long time to overcome my soft-hearted feelings for the exhibitor with an obviously useless horse, and even up to the end I rode every exhibit unless we were behind time or had an enormous class. The worse the horse and the more ignorant the rider, the more earnest the rider was — always.

Exford show was one of the hardest. The ring was on the side of a hill and also ridge and furrow. The farmers' class was always full of colts caught off the hill that morning, with saddles on their ears and bridles that did not fit. The secret was to walk them downhill and give them a try-out uphill. It was also a good tip to keep the gallop round going until those with their backs up had got settled, and let their owners have the rough riding instead of yourself. I also think it quite fair to refuse to take much trouble with a horse that is obviously green and misbehaves, because even in the youngest saddle classes they should surely be sufficiently schooled for a judge to get a proper ride. I also used to take trouble to show the 'clever' ones that I was not in the least impressed by their tricks, and knew the tricks just as well as they did: all that rot about fighting to lead the way round, and also racing.

I made a point, too, of shutting them up if they started to tell me about the horse as I got on.

The greatest ordeal was the first time I judged at the Royal. In those days the judge was alone, as he still is. The show was held at Wolverhampton, and it was a very exhausting experience and a great responsibility, but I got through it somehow, although there were occasions when I wished I were underground! The worst trouble I ever got into was at Oakham: open classes first, three prizes and several cards. 'Squeak' Thompson and I got that done — brood mares, foals and young stock. He then went on with the riding classes and I was taken into another ring to judge the local young stock. Not having bothered much in the open classes over the cards, which carried no money, I found myself unwittingly altering the previous placings. A steward came to the rescue with his book and we sorted it out. The situation was serious because since the winners in the open classes were not in the local class, those who had only had cards now came into money prizes.

It was always a help to make descriptive notes in your book, and also the 'crabs' you saw, so that afterwards, when questioned by interested spectators or disgruntled exhibitors you had your reasons, although of course there was no need to give them to anybody.

I stayed with James Baird for Oakham show. He insisted on taking me to the station, and when we got to the motor park he could not find the car. The AA scout came and asked what sort of car it was and was told it was a 'bloody awful Austin'! I was also interested when staying with him to be told that nothing in his father's smoking room had been moved since his father's death, even to an opened envelope lying on a table. He was an excellent host, and when he came into my bedroom to see if I 'had everything' even looked under the bed to see if that was there! Excellent valet too, who spotted I had no button hook (I always had one on my knife) and also no tooth powder (never used it) and provided both in the morning.

It was a curious thing that all the time I was judging regularly I only had one really wet day. That was at Shepton Mallet with Major Wallis, and it rained so hard that we stood in the stand while they went round. It must have been an awful job for judges on a wet day, getting on and off wet saddles, with wet feet, mud and wet, slippery reins.

I very nearly made a fool of myself once, judging alone at Tunbridge Wells. In one class there were two horses that I could not separate — they were so different. One was a well-made half-bred, the other obviously clean-bred; both good sorts in their ways. Anyhow, I had to do something so I made the awards. I wasn't certain, even then, and had a stroll round the boxes afterwards to try and set my mind at rest. The rider of the winner, whom I knew well, said: 'What kept you so long, m'Lord?' I told him how difficult I found it to divide two good horses of such different type. He listened, then said: 'What about the other horse's dropped hip?' I had never noticed it!

Herbert Nell, who judged more than most people, told me he always started by standing in front of a horse and looking at his eyes, as he once gave a blind horse a prize! He also said he then looked between the forelegs to see if the hocks were free of spavins and a pair, at that. A very good method. Curbs, or perhaps one curb, are sometimes a difficulty. That lateral bone can look like a curb to anybody but a first-class vet. Wind is always a difficulty; a fat pulling horse makes a noise not at all unlike a whistle. A horse with a cold or sore throat from standing in a show box can easily sound like a whistle. The best plan was to say nothing until the other judge had had his ride, and then say: 'Did you notice anything about Number so-and-so?' But whatever you do, don't say: 'Did you think Number so-and-so made a noise?'

I only disagreed sufficiently once to have to call in a referee, and then, to my utmost satisfaction, the die was cast my way. Your attention cannot be diverted for a moment, or lessened in any degree. Even if you give a horse a prize of any sort the day before you see him again in another class, you are not safe and cannot say: 'Oh, that's So-and-So again'. He may be sore on a hidden splint or an old leg may have given. There was a glorious horse called Danno that I gave champion to at Wolverhampton. If there ever was a horse that made you feel for the horn in your case, that was the one. Two years afterwards he came up before me again at the Royal at Windsor. I took him for granted, having ridden him several times meanwhile. However, whilst watching the ladies' class in the collecting ring I noticed Danno had an obvious 'leg', with the bandage mark visible, and sure enough, when he came up for us to judge, I felt some sort of dressing on my hand. He had rather 'curved' forelegs, not really back at the knee but his forelegs seemed to curve from the shoulder if you looked carefully, broadside on. Really, I suppose he should therefore not have been made champion, but nobody would ever have been able to convince me I was not right when I set him alight — perfectly glorious.

Although of course I could not help feeling pleased that I was thought capable of judging at important shows, I never forgot that not everybody would want to, and that judges are not easy to get hold of.

The worst I ever judged with was a man who used to write round and ask to be invited. I looked a horse over one day and said I thought he had a curb. He went and looked at the horse's hocks as he had seen me do, through its forelegs, and said: 'Yes'! In fact, there was one worse, only he was certainly a stop-gap, at Chippenham. One horse he could not get on at all, and he had the tabs of his boots *stitched* on and no slit to his coat, but it did not matter as I took no notice of him!

Shows must have great trouble getting judges, they much too often ask to a repertoire year after year. There should be somebody to intimate when a judge gets too old. I was once with a very well-known judge, Gore Lambarde, and he was absolutely gasping every time he got off a horse, and his hand was shaking too much to write down the numbers. There is also the old judge who has been at it so long that he can't be bothered to take the trouble he should and has no care at all for public opinion or other people's feelings.

The Royal at Windsor was most enjoyable and I was with Wickham-Boynton, who I knew would get any blame there was. We also had an obvious champion in Drage's horse, although we got into an unavoidable position over the reserve champion. Perhaps not unavoidable, though, had we looked far enough ahead. The reserve was a very common novice of Oliver Dixon's. We had Drage's horse, Dixon's novice and a middleweight to decide between. The lightweight was very small and not much, the middleweight had a bad neck, so Dixon's novice had to be reserve, and it was awful to see it blundering round after Drage's beautiful mover. So it was not really avoidable unless we had forgiven the middleweight its neck, and I think we should have. This is just to show what you have to bear in mind.

I was fearfully pleased when I was asked to judge at Dublin. They stick to their judges year after year but Hope Johnson was ill and I was paired with Bert Davies to judge heavyweights. The first morning I was struck flat when about 35 horses came in for the first class. The ring was very small but this is the *only* crab about judging there. However, the method employed is excellent. The judges are asked to pick out about 10% of the best without riding them. You put those 10% apart, then look over the rest and perhaps add one or two, and dismiss the others for good. Those set apart go out to be vetted, thus taking all the onus off the judges for wind, curbs, spavins etc, and those that pass come back for you to ride in the afternoon. Thus the 35 were reduced to about eight to be ridden and placed — a splendid method. The stewards are very good at their job and you are looked after marvellously. For the championship your best horse goes into the big ring and is judged by the three senior judges again the best middle and lightweights.

Two years later I was asked again, this time as senior judge with Bill Jaffray. I had a bit of luck that time because he happened to get on one that went mad. How he kept on him I don't know, I should have burst apart. Apart from the championship, there was also a cup for the seven senior judges to award to the best horse in hand or saddle, bred in Ireland. Very difficult, as they were all ages. I was with Wickham-Boynton and Guy Lucas, and the former was in some hurry and would not take the trouble I felt should be taken. However, I could not do much. I think we got No. 1 right, but am certain we did not Nos. 2 and 3. *Such* rot, as the eyes of all the breeders in Ireland were upon us. A championship really does fill one with awe. As the time approaches for the moment of truth, one sees every soul going into the stands.

Such a wonderful ring, both for size and for going, it must be the best in the world. There stand the champion and reserve of the three weight divisions, and one is really unlikely to be bothered with any but the first prizes in each weight. We were confronted by 'my' heavyweight, a strong built chesnut, strong all over and perhaps more quality needed. The middleweight was nothing more than a 'trade horse', I thought, although a good goer. The lightweight was *Beautiful,* only very small indeed, although with good bone, and clean-bred.

Boynton and Lucas, both tiny men, didn't care about the big horses, and it was decided against me to give the lightweight champion, which had hardly ever — if ever — been done before. That may have been right, but I'm perfectly certain it was wrong to give the second lightweight reserve. However, Boynton was again in an old-man, 'don't care' hurry, and I did not get a word in, while Guy Lucas could not be bothered to argue although he agreed with me. My word, I *did* have a ride round on the lightweight, one of the best I ever had, so smooth, fast, head up exactly right, mouth and all.

The jumping was such fun, everybody so keen and wrapped up. The Germans did very well — I never saw a better recovery than one made from right around the horse's neck, and get back in place before the next fence.

De Valera's bodyguard I shall never forget. It followed him in on his arrival in a delapidated Rolls: some trotting, some galloping, two hands on the reins, one hand, talking, laughing, and their turn-out! — filthy boots that almost looked as though they had been dubbined, baggy, shapeless breeches, blue jackets with yellow frogging, and on top of all this, hussar hats that must have been made of the back parts of a Highland cow's hide! More like musical comedy military chorus. Beautiful horses, apparently all 5 years old or younger!

They have a pack of hounds in front of the display of competitors in the jumping — the first pack I saw gave a good show; the Master put his hounds almost unattended in one corner, then went away and blew for them and then went out blowing 'home'. The next pack I saw had a lady Master — great rumours about her and the mess she would make. She did very well, though, went round the ring absolutely flat out with her hounds all going it too, none messing about.

I went to Dublin show shortly after the First World War and saw a mare belonging to Flossie Garth win the jumping with a foal in her stall. A mare called Motor Car, owner up. Also Mrs Marshall who rode horse after horse for all sorts of owners over the jumps, and I've never seen any woman so down in the saddle and holding the reins each side of the saddle, like a man does.

Last time I was over there I went to Joe Dudgeon's riding school and saw a man arrive with a head-in-the-air brute that he intended jumping next day at the show. Joe told him to go over some jumps and he rooted the lot. He then got on himself and also put his daughter up and the horse dropped his head, ceased fighting and cleared everything — best example I've ever seen of the immediate effect of good riding.

Never shall I forget when Joe had to jump off for the *Daily Mail* Cup at Olympia on Goblet, a little grey mare he bought as a 5-year-old in Northern Ireland. I gave the best holloa of my life when he cleared the gate in the jump-off after the other chap had only had half a fault at the gate. I think the proudest moment of any show person's career must have been to come in at

Olympia and receive the cup from the King, and to stand there with the National Anthem playing.

Another Olympia memory was when Miss Stella Pearce won the *Daily Mail* Cup, a wonderful performance for a girl, against the whole world. She was chaired by the crowd. I am always glad to have seen Geoffrey Brooke in the days just after the First World War on Combined Training. He was a perfect example of balanced, taped down to an inch riding — I have never seen anybody ride quite like him: hands on one hip ready to 'shoot' everything when the horse wanted it, stirrups on toes and if he lost one they used to fly right up in the air; slow canter, and at exactly the right moment he told his horse to do it.

I once at Richmond asked Colonel MacTaggart, who wrote books about riding, and rode a wonderful mare called Ozone, if you could tell a horse when to take off when going flat out at the water. He said it *was* possible, then soon after not only rooted the water fence but went into the water as well! A lot of his stuff was rot. He had short, thick legs and said long legs and flat thighs were not an advantage, adding that if you wanted to crack a nut you put it at the top of the cracker, not the bottom. I told him that when you crack a nut you apply pressure from the bottom of the crackers, when you ride a horse you don't grip from your ankles. He also said in his book that it was wrong to pull a tail, and that you had to 'pursue every offending hair to its root with the scissors'. Quite impossible, of course. And he put 'Yoicks' in his glossary of hunting expressions.

I pointed out all these mistakes but all I got was that 'Yoicks' would be deleted from the second edition! No one has ever been able to tell me what 'Yoicks' is intended to convey, or when if ever it is used.

Another Olympia memory was a funny little man who used to pay Glencross £100, it was said, to ride one of his horses in the High Jump. He only had a brave heart, no idea of real riding, but in he used to come, all anyhow, fall off, lose his hat, his glasses and all, but always got over the first two heights. Of course, one of the most overpowering events ever staged was the parade of old Grand National winners, one or two of the oldest all gaunt and sunken-eyed, but one and all, be they long-bodied or short, they all had wonderful fronts and depth through the heart. Every night as they went out to 'Auld Lang Syne' we were all reduced to tears.

It became a great vogue to have a pack of hounds at shows, and at Olympia it was most impressive. The Horse Show sent a van for whatever pack it was and Horace Smith provided the horses on most occasions. The huntsmen differed in their performances but all sent a whipper-in to the exit doors to give a hollos at the end, and then the huntsman came galloping from the other end with the pack, blowing the horn. It was a wonderful sight to see the whipper-in framed in the double doors with his hat up, and the building adding to the thrill of a holloa.

At Richmond I saw Stanley Barker with the Pytchley give a very good show. He cantered round and then suddenly have a 'Ter-rum-tum-tum' on his horn and turned straight back. The pack stopped at once and flew back to him. A thing for anyone showing hounds to remember is to give them a drink before they come in; if you do not, they all dive into the water jump.

The worst show I ever saw was at the Royal at Windsor; great fat huntsman, first whipper-in like a frightened footman — the huntsman rode in, pulled up almost with his face in the Royal Box, then set off with no warning at full gallop, *blasting* on the horn; the frightened footman riding for his life, looking over his shoulder, ready to be trodden into the ground at any moment, hounds scattered all over the ring. The huntsman then decided to pull up, which he did, again with his horse's head stuck over the front of the Royal Box, then went out still blasting his horn. Awful, and everybody laughing.

I always Hated having to judge hacks, and more so when it got so full of *haute école*. A well-trained hack, or indeed nearly any hack, has been trained by one man. Even if the aids employed are recognised, every man applies them a little differently. These highly-trained hacks are suddenly mounted by a complete stranger and expected to make a good show. I say (and also did) this; make each exhibitor give a display of certain stated movements, then get on each one and only do the simplest movements like changing legs at an obvious moment, then pull up, see if they stand still and also allow you to mount without moving.

I suppose Captain Hance's Radiant was one of the best hacks when I was judging, produced for his owner, Sir Archibald Weigall. Whenever I got on Radiant he practically said: 'I'll do anything, even write my name, if you tell me, in words I understand.'

No, hack judging is a job for hack or hunter judges who have been through that sort of school. I also hated being asked to judge driving. I once had to at Great Somerton with Mrs Aubrey Hastings. We decided on a spanking little pony. One competitor drove straight out when he saw what had happened. When I asked what was wrong I was told he was the Richmond champion!

Two-day shows should be avoided unless you can get an invitation to stay with somebody. It can be pretty grim in an hotel for two nights, which is almost certain to be necessary as your first class is almost always at 9.00 a.m. on the first morning.

Stewards vary very much. I have been practically ignored, and on one occasion was left alone in the ring at 1.30 while the president's house party loaded up into Rolls's and went to the 'Castle' for lunch. Dublin is easily the best for hospitality. The best steward I came across elsewhere was Marples at Olympia; untiring and watchful.

I can say that I judged at all the chief South Country shows but I always had to refuse Peterborough because I was more interested in the hounds.

CHAPTER 10

——❋——

The Judges

THE JUDGES of hunters, both led and ridden, are of tremendous importance to the scheme of things, for they set the standard — or hopefully, follow the old standards set by our forefathers, permitting no deviation from the accepted make and shape of the hunting horse. If a horse stands over ground on four good limbs, is deep through the heart and loin, well ribbed-up, has bone, substance and quality, he will be up to weight, high-couraged, able to pull out in his turn and gallop and jump through the deep, muddy going of an English or Irish winter — in short, a workman. Hunting is very hard work and it finds out a horse's weakest points and exposes them mercilessly. Thus, although individual judges have slightly different priorities, they all agree on the basics — which is why a consensus of opinion of different judges usually put the same handful of horses at the top throughout each season.

Limbs and feet are, of course, the top priorities. A good hind leg is a necessity, as the old saying goes, and a good shoulder is a luxury.

There were, in the old order of things, two top categories of hunter judge — the cavalry officer, and the dealer; and Dublin always made it a point to combine the two in each ring. Sadly, the cavalry officer, except for the Household Brigade, is no longer horsed, though he is still encouraged to ride and hunt; the only remaining horse gunners are in the King's Troop and even the big dealers with a yardful of horses are a thing of the past.

Thus the Society asked Mr E. G. E. Griffith to compile an excellent booklet *Notes on the responsibilities of Judges and Stewards*, to which His Grace the Duke of Beaufort wrote in his Foreword: 'How I wish that when I first accepted to judge, I had been able to study something of the sort, instead of relying on a few words of advice from a more experienced friend. Never was it more important than it is today to observe the suggestions and rules in this pamphlet, both in and out of the ring. We live in an age of ever increasing competition and criticism; much of the latter is often unjustified, because the man in the centre must see more than the spectator outside. But if shows are to continue in a happy atmosphere, there must be confidence among competitors that the Judges are doing the right thing in the right way. Our thanks are due to Mr Griffith, therefore, for the care and trouble that he has taken over this pamphlet'. (See Appendix IV, p. 266.)

In 1978 the Society asked Michael Gibson, a well known hunting veterinary surgeon from Leicestershire and the son and grandson of equally celebrated practitioners, to prepare a *Guide to Conformation in the Horse* as a guide to young judges. He says: 'Of course there will be variations between individuals in the assessment and importance that they give to different points of conformation.'

In 1938 the HIS published a list of their panel judges. It carried, after each name, the number of major shows at which they had officiated during that season, and it makes interesting reading, for many of these men are still household names, even though some, alas, are no longer with us.

Mr Eddie Griffith heads the list with 10 shows, followed by Captain Guy Lucas with 8, a total and placing he shares with Captain James Lethbridge. Col. Brian Robinson was third with 7, jointly with Major Chase Meredith. Captain Tom Wickham-Boynton, Herbert Sutton and Jack Bletsoe did 5 shows apiece, Major Ken Wallis 4 and Harry Bonner 3; more often, he was exhibiting.

Edward Griffith

Edward (E. G. E.) Griffith (Eddie to his intimates) was the son of Colonel Edward Wynne Griffith, Master of the Flint and Denbigh Hounds from 1912 to 1927, and brother of the first Lady Daresbury, mother of the present Lord Daresbury. Eddie was an outstanding judge of horses, ponies and indeed of cattle as well. He was also the most frequently invited judge of ridden hunters in England during the years between the wars, and a Council member of the HIS for many years, in addition to being its president in 1967. He and his wife bred some outstanding children's ponies. I am indebted to his brother, Major Humphrey Griffith, for the following information:

'Edward joined the Royal Field Artillery via Eton and Woolwich as a 2nd Lieutenant stationed at Colchester.

You were allowed to hunt your charger in those days, and also draw rations for a horse of your own. There were some beautiful horsemen in the Regiment, but none of them could afford to buy a horse of their own, so Edward started a Horse Coping business and drew all the other officers' rations and had a civilian stud groom, Mew by name, and very good he was too.

My father used to find him the horses and Edward used to get his brother officers to help school and hunt them. One of the first was a 16.2 chesnut called Bubbly, a real good horse. This horse was sold to his Colonel, Colonel Vicary, who was delighted with his purchase and actually won a point-to-point with him.

So the young "Dealer" not only made his name, but got all the encouragement as well.

After about two years the Regiment was posted to Quetta in North-West India. The Garrison had a pack of hounds and hunted jackal. Edward, being the son of an MFH, became whipper-in, and wrote home to say that they were very short of decent hounds, but had a few good bitches. Father, being Master of the Flint and Denbigh, sent to India a couple of first-class dog hounds. They were both great grandsons of some of the Belvoir hounds that Father brought with him when he gave up being Field Master, and his brother-in-law Sir Gilbert Greenall, afterwards Lord Daresbury, gave up the Belvoir Mastership. Father picked these hounds so that they would not only show sport, but would act as stallion hounds as well. I remember one was called Racer, but I cannot remember the name of the other one, although I remember them both well and can see them now.

Colonel Vicary had served in Quetta before, and knew everybody. One day the Prime Minister of Kalat State rushed down to see him and said that they were in a mess as HH's private trainer, an Englishman, had died in the night and that they had no one to carry on, and could the Colonel help? As it was vital for the British Government to keep in with the people of the N.W. Frontier, the Prime Minister was told that 2nd Lieutenant Griffith could certainly do the job and also look after the State Stud, as he knew the breeding of every horse in the *Stud Book*.

So 2nd Lieutenant Griffith was more or less seconded from regimental duties and became HH's trainer, and was also made responsible for his Stud.

In addition to the Kalat horses, Edward took others owned by his brother officers and a few private people. He had two professional flat race jockeys attached to him, the best of whom, Doug Balfour, I met as one of the leading jockeys in Calcutta when I went out there in 1928. Balfour was a beautiful horseman and a first-rate jockey. He had served his apprenticeship in this country and would not come home, as he was doing so well in India.

Poor Edward broke his neck out hunting and was invalided home. HH The Khan presented him with a huge plain cigarette box in recognition of his services to the Kalat State.

The RAF had a squadron in Quetta and the Squadron-Leader was Wynne Eyton, son of a Welsh landowner and a family friend of ours. Sandy Wynne Eyton was a topper to go out hunting, and a real good chase jockey who could ride at about 10 stone. Sandy rode a lot of jump winners for Edward; the other jump runners were ridden by his brother officers. Edward did very well with these horses and actually became leading trainer in North-West India. After his bad fall, he was not allowed to jump fences for some three years, so he took to judging at shows. The finest judges of horses in Great Britain at that time, and probably of all time, were Tom Wickham-Boynton and Ernest Bellaney; as they were both old friends of my father's, they more or less adopted Edward and took him with them as assistant judge to all the big shows. After two sessions with them, Edward was judging on his own.'

James Lethbridge

Major James (J. C. B.) Lethbridge started hunting with his father's hounds in Cornwall at the age of eight. The pack consisted of three couple of Stud Book Harriers, hunting hare and fox in the Lamerton, Tetcott and East Cornwall countries, sometimes having to ride as far as St Breward, a distance of 14 miles, with his father and the pack. After his first pony, bought from a colt-breaker on Bodmin Moor, which he outgrew at the same time as his governess, he was promoted to a 14.1 hand pony bred near Trebartha when he came home from Eagle Lodge near Camberley. Thereafter he and his brother Jack — later MFH Lamerton and Eggesford — rode their father's hunters, of which there were always 9 in stable, in addition to a pair of carriage horses.

After leaving Marlborough he passed into Oxford and was then going to stay at home and farm, but the Great War changed all that and he joined up as a horse dispatch rider and in August, 1914, was given a commission in the Royal First Devon Yeomanry, Cornish squadron. After serving in the desert during the Senussi campaign he was transferred as a regular officer in 1916 to the 20th Hussars, serving in France for the rest of the war.

After the armistice he went to Col. 'Peach' Borwick's French Cavalry School at Cayeux-sur-Mer for Cavalry officers and horse gunners, where the instructors included Brig. 'Bogey' Bowden-Smith, Col. Trevor Horn and Jock Swire and the chief vet was J. B. Walker, whose daughter, Mrs David Bourne, is herself a well-known judge.

In 1919 the 20th Hussars were posted to Egypt and then to Turkey, where they fought in the Kemalist campaign. When they were disbanded in 1921 he remained in Turkey with the 3rd Hussars under Col. Kelly until 1923, when he was posted to a remount depot in Turkey. It was manned by Cossacks of the Don — 'Wrangel's White Army' officers, who presented him with one of his most treasured possessions, a bronze equestrian figure. He then accompanied all the horses to a depot on the Suez Canal before being posted to the 14th/20th Hussars, with whom he served at Tidworth and York as equitation officer. During part of this time he was at Weedon under Gen. Lucas in Brig. 'Dolly' de Fonblanque's ride. Among the instructors was Brig. Keith Dunn, much later the society's corresponding member for Gloucestershire.

During these four years he started riding racing, both in point-to-points and under NH Rules. While stationed in the Cavalry Barracks at York he won a 'chase at Wetherby and races at the Bramham Moor, York and Ainstey, Retford steeplechases and Market Rasen. He also won a number of races in the West Country on his own and other people's horses.

In 1928 he went out to Egypt for four years in a big remount depot in Cairo, going into Syria to buy Arabs for the infantry officers stationed in Cairo. They were all entires, but were gelded without any setback.

In 1932 he returned home and served under the War Office as remount officer for South Devon. He did two or three police beats a day, meeting the constable and accompanying him to all the farms in the area where horses were kept, and to the bakers' and butchers' stables in Plymouth and Exeter where the horses were light enough to be used in the event of mobilisation by gunners and Cavalry. He maintained close contact with all the blacksmiths, and in time 'I knew every horse in South Devon, even if it did not know me! I had to inspect the foals and write reports on them in a district which extended from Honiton to the Tamar, with Okehampton as the Western boundary.'

In 1937 he was elected to the Council of the Society and became chief steward at the National Stallion Show and National Hunter Show, a position formerly held by his uncle, Colonel Alexander King, who lived in Aberdeenshire and allotted all the Scottish premiums. He retained this task, which he loved, for forty years. In 1937 the War Office dispensed with a large number of remount officers and he was given an even bigger area — Dorset, Somerset and the whole of Devon and Cornwall. He was then able to live at home, where he was often visited by Brig. Bowden-Smith and Gen. Lucas, whom he took to see chargers and cavalry horses. They were bought as 2-year-olds and the farmers kept them until they were 4 for the princely sum of £15 a year.

Part of his job was to see that they were looked after properly during this time. Arthur Brake found many horses for him, including black horses for the Household Cavalry, officers' chargers commanding a top price of £120, cavalry troop horses and gunners (£60 to £80).

An exceptionally fine horseman with a wealth of experience, Major Lethbridge was initiated into the judging field of operations in 1932. The late Captain 'Tiddley' Lucas took him under his wing. By 1937 he was a Council member of the HIS and chief steward at the Spring Show, which he remained at Newmarket and Shrewsbury until the 1970s.

When the Second World War broke out he went up to Sir Ian Walker-Okeover's place, Osmaston, near Ashbourne in Derbyshire, and in command of a remount squadron took out 200 horses via Dunkirk and Marseilles to Haifa, having sent a similar number on ahead. Then he went to Syria with reinforcement horses, and did quite a lot of mule purchasing in Cyprus for transport. At the end of 1943 he returned to England and went to various Royal Armoured Corps training regiments, ending up at Catterick Camp with Col. Gordon Cox-Cox, whence, already over age, he was demobilised when the war ended. He started judging again in 1945 and in 1963 confined himself to the led classes.

He shared his beautiful home, Tregeare, near Launceston, with his sister Dorothy, and they were wonderful hosts. The big white house could be seen for miles and there was always a warm welcome there. To stay at Tregeare, which had its own little village and church and was surrounded by rhododendrons in glorious profusion was to travel back in time to a more gracious era. With utmost delicacy, two bedrooms were placed at the disposal of married couples, with twin beds in the larger and a single bed in the smaller, lest they preferred separate rooms.

Jim hunted with some 40 packs of hounds throughout his life and in 1953 took over the East Cornwall for 5 seasons as Master and huntsman, continuing until 1966 with Joint Masters. He chose the premium stallions for Devon and South-East Cornwall and judged at Dublin regularly. Comparing horses of the past with those of the present day, he found that there were not so many bad hocks, weak legs and long cannon bones in the old days, because the stallions were bigger, had more bone and substance and their stock were consequently stronger. The old type of stallion was stronger and more robust than those of the present day.

Herbert Sutton

I am indebted to Captain John Macdonald-Buchanan, MC, for the following notes on Herbert J. Sutton, whom I remember judging hunter classes annually in Dublin after the Second World War:

'Herbert Sutton was born about 1885 in Yorkshire and remained for the whole of his life a Yorkshireman through and through. His father was a yeoman farmer but centred his interests more upon horse-dealing than agriculture, in which he was joined by his son. In his early years Herbert was a first-rate boxer and although he was not tall, yet to the end of his life he was made very spare — nevertheless he had the largest hands I have ever seen! (I have noticed that, even with women, those who from the riding point of view are considered to have "good hands", often possess very large ones!) He was a very dapper person and invariably immaculately turned out, although some of his riding and hunting kit was somewhat idiosyncratic. He was most observant and therefore fussy about other people's and their horses' turn-out.

He was a beautiful horseman and a bold rider and continued to be so right into his seventies. Before the first war he rode in and won a lot of point-to-points in the North. He was also a fine polo player, playing mainly at Toulston with the Riley-Smith family. At his best he played off a 7-goal handicap but I think this was mainly at Rugby after the war, with such stalwarts as the Baldings, Nickalls's, Riches and Millers.

During the Great War he joined the Remounts and attained the rank of Captain. Just prior to the war he married his wife Florrie who came from a well-to-do Leeds family. After the war he moved to Market Harborough where he set up as and became an extremely successful horse dealer, although not on the same scale as the Drages, Hames's, MacIlwaine etc. During this period and virtually without a gap he judged annually at Dublin, and this continued again after the Second World War. At this time, when I was a small boy, my mother often took me over to his yard, and my greatest thrill was to see him putting horses round the loose school, which was of a unique design of his own.

At about the same time Mr Victor Emanuel, the American, took over the Masterships in turn of the Woodland Pytchley, Fernie and finally the Pytchley, although he took very little part in hunting affairs. Herbert Sutton bought and supervised his horses for him, and also his National Hunt racehorses, including Royal Arch—a 17 hands black horse who got round Liverpool I think on four occasions and was subsequently hunted by Mother side-saddle!

When my father took over the Pytchley with Colonel Jack Lowther early in the 1930s, Herbert came to him and looked after the horses in the same manner, including all the hunt horses as well. In 1936 he moved to a house at Cottesbrooke and continued there until the end of his life in about 1965. Over the period of the war he acted as agent for my father's estate and at the same time he commanded the Cottesbrooke Home Guard with my father's stud groom, George Smith, as his Sergeant. The Company Commander was George Middleton, a famous "white collar" man and a nephew of Bay Middleton. The Cottesbrooke Platoon as a result was the epitome of Fred Karno's army—all were ex-cavalrymen and all the commands for broom sticks, pikes, rifles etc consisted of "slope swords", "trot march" etc. Herbert was a wonderful stableman and a natural veterinarian; he virtually never had to call upon the services of a vet.

I recollect that there were about 80 geldings turned out in one huge field in 1939 when the Remount Officers commandeered most of them for the Household Cavalry. These were all assembled at the Old Etonian Country Club on the Thames, and as a boy at Eton I was taken round them by Sir Rupert Hardy, who was in charge—he still rides round Cottesbrooke although he is well over 80. Alas, all these horses were lost when torpedoed *en route* for Palestine.

Herbert was certainly not a great farmer but the fences at Cottesbrooke were beautifully cut and laid, the timber sound and the hunting gates opened and shut like clockwork.

Apart from his equestrian achievements and knowledge he had a superb sense of humour, was a great gossip, a wonderful raconteur and the very best of company. He used to make a terrifying cocktail on Sundays which he never allowed anyone to see in the making, and on one memorable occasion an elderly and well-known Pytchley hunting lady reversed all the way home to the next village, about 2 miles away! It was a great privilege to have been all but brought up by Herbert Sutton, and any knowledge of horses that I may ever have had came from him, with the notable exception of Fred Darling. During my teens I used to spend most Easter holidays with him at Beck-hampton.

Herbert's horse "knowhow" really *was* encyclopedic and it was certainly a by-word. His friends and acquaintances in the whole world of horses were legion. He had an anecdote about every one of them, yet he was both univ-ersally loved and also respected for his judgement and knowledge of horses in their every aspect. It is most improbable that we shall see his like again.

His wife Florrie died about five years after he himself. They are both buried at Cottesbrooke.

(I write these notes at Herbert's old desk, which his wife thoughtfully left to me.)'

Kenneth Wallis

Of more or less the same vintage was Major Kenneth (K.P.) Wallis, who earned the sobriquet of 'The galloping Major' during the 40-odd years he spent judging hunters, hacks, cobs and ponies. Although first and foremost a foxhunter, who served the South and West Wilts as Honorary Secretary for 41 seasons, he was also an able administrator on the Councils of the HIS and the National Pony Society, where he spoke his mind but never gave offence. He judged ridden classes without fear or favour until well on in his seventies, then confined his activities to breeding classes. Even when his wife, Winifred, died he threw himself even more deeply into the life he enjoyed — 'I really go to the shows for the free lunches!' he remarked to me once. 'That lovely chicken and ham, and all those lettuce leaves!'

Distinguishable by his bristling white moustache and boots with black patent tops, Ken was born in Monmouthshire where his father, who commanded the Yeomanry, drove horses until he died in 1918 and never owned a motor car. Ken's first pony was a chesnut Welsh Mountain gelding who was so strong-willed that his young rider never knew which friend he was going to visit until he actually arrived. Later some sort of working partnership was established, and they had their first hunt together when he was 8, with Lord Tredegar's (of Light Brigade fame) private pack. Tiny also took his young master to school, remaining there in the stable for the homeward journey.

In those days it was possible to hunt six days a week in Monmouthshire, and every Saturday a special train, sponsored by Sir Edward Curre of Itton, went from Newport, with horseboxes attached, into the Fitzhardinge country, where hounds met at Berkeley Road Station. When he was 15, his father gave him the best horse he ever owned — Dick II, who was jet black, 16.1, by a premium stallion out of a Pembrokeshire pack mare. Dick carried him for 14 seasons, and accompanied him into the Army, with only one fall: 'And he gave me prior notice of that one. A wattle fence, uphill, and hounds weren't running. He refused the first time and turned upside down the second — served me right for playing the fool'.

Dick won the Monmouthshire Hunt Club's open race in 1908 and lasted until he bought his next really good one in 1919, paying £60 for him when the surplus cavalry horses were sold. A 16.3 chesnut with a docked tail, who had seen foreign service, he was the worst possible stumbler when hacking and fell at least 10 times, though he never chipped his knees; but the moment he was hunting he never put a foot wrong and was quite brilliant.

In the Army he gained a lot of experience with cavalry horses, including some very good ones bought by Colonel Wood, one of the best judges ever. Then he went ranching in the Argentine for 3 years and had a wonderful troop of horses at the time when Frank Balfour, Al Watt and Frank Bradney were just starting to grade up the Criollo ponies with polo pony stallions and small thoroughbred stallions imported from England. Ken bought the early progeny, got them handy to swing a stick on and sold them to the English buyers. Then he went to Brazil for 18 months, where the ponies were so bad that he asked for some to be sent up from the Argentine. A troop of 20 duly arrived by road, having spent 3 months on the journey in the care of a man who wished to leave his native land, where he had shot someone in a pub. He was a wonderful horse-master and delivered his charges in beautiful condition, losing only one *en route*. Such a man was clearly an asset and Ken took him on.

On his return to England he acted as whipper-in to Colonel Dealtry Part's Harriers in Hertfordshire, recreating old Parson Milne's country. Here he was mounted on Edward Christie Miller's Captain Dreyfus, winner of numerous chases. 'I have never ridden such a frightening horse. He never left the ground, yet he always seemed to find an extra leg and never fell. When I asked Jack Anthony, who had ridden him, how the horse jumped, the jockey replied: 'He goes straight through the lot — thank God it wasn't Aintree!'

After 2 or 3 seasons in the Home Counties a chance meeting in the street with Ikey Bell, with whom he had hunted from Craven Lodge, changed the course of his life. The latter had just given up the Kilkenny hounds and taken on the South and West Wilts, and he suggested that Ken should go down there to live. Within the year he had taken over as joint Honorary Secretary — a unique appointment, for in 40 seasons there were then only two Masters, Ikey Bell and Major John Morrison (now Lord Margadale of Islay); both wonderful men in every way. Ken was mounted by the latter during nearly all his Mastership on very high-class horses.

Ikey Bell was, of course, one of the most famous Masters of Foxhounds ever, having started his career at the age of 19 when he was sent down from Cambridge and his mother gave him the Galway Blazers. One of the founders, with Teddy Curre, of what was then known as the 'new' type of foxhound, he was a great huntsman and hound man, and used horses merely as bicycles, leaving all that side to his daughter, Di. When he had the Blazers he hunted them seven days a week and had two lots of servants. He was also a great sailor until arthritis forced him to give up, and had three yachts built for him at Cowes and won the Fastnet race in Bloodhound, later sailed for the Queen by Prince Philip. Towards the end of his life he went back to Ireland and managed the West Waterford for Mrs Tom Morgan.

Ken held a starter's licence under National Hunt rules for 17 seasons and thoroughly enjoyed the close contact with 'that gallant band of warriors, the National Hunt jockeys. Come sun, come hail, on going hard or deep, they are still the same. Riding good or indifferent horses, they remain cheery optimists!'

All of his summers were occupied in judging, and three or four horses stood out in his memory. The first was Don Bradman, by the premium stallion Irawaddy. He had a formidable record, both showing and racing. He started his career in point-to-points in 1933, winning two open races and second in another on his only three outings. That summer he was a consistent winner in the show ring, and in the autumn he won five hunter trials including the South Oxfordshire championship, in four outings. The following year he won the Grand National trial at Towcester and three hunter 'chases, and in 1936 the Foxhunters' Chase at Aintree, which was then run over the full Grand National course.

Don Bradman was owned by George Jackson of Wychbold, and by odd coincidence the best middleweight Ken ever saw or judged was owned by another resident of this Worcestershire village, Hugh Sumner. This was Blarney Stone, of post-war vintage. 'He was a great galloper, it would have been interesting to see what he did on the racecourse. I only let him go twice in my life, at Henley and at Cheltenham. We certainly arrived at the corners very quickly! He was beautifully produced by Jack Gittins, senior.'

Bernard Selby's Ballymonis was the best lightweight he ever saw — 'But when you put him in top gear you never knew whether you were the boss or not. He ran away with Lady Fortescue, who said that she would never ride him again and asked that he should not be shown in front of her; and with Mrs James Baird.

'Mighty Atom, Dublin champion in 1949 and then bought by Horace Cooper, was certainly the best heavyweight. The most curious thing about him was that he was an extraordinarily light mover, which made him a beautiful ride; if you sat by the ringside you could hardly hear him galloping past.'

At one Richmond show, Ken and his co-judge pulled in a well-known showman at the top of a huge class of novices, and when he went over to ride the horse he followed his usual practice of looking at the bit to see what sort of ride he might expect. This time it was a little Tom Thumb with a slack chain, though he was less reassured by the exhibitor's: 'It's all right, Major' — which almost certainly meant that he was not.

They walked, trotted, cantered and were gone — six times around the perimeter of the ring. The thoughts uppermost in the judge's mind concerned the necessity to retain his hat and his stick, and to avoid coming back puffing, blowing and red in the face. Geoff Phipps-Hornby and Andrew MacIlwaine were standing on the rails, and kept saying as he galloped past in full flight: 'It's all right, Ken, he's sure to stop next time round.' His wife, who always told him that he galloped too much, was also standing near and said: 'Oh, I do wish he wouldn't gallop that horse so much!'

'Don't you realise, my dear, he can't stop!' came the reply — hardly conducive to setting a wife's mind at rest.

Lord Knutsford rode the horse later at Olympia, thinking that it would not try to take charge indoors. When asked later how he had managed to stop him, he confessed: 'Only by taking my feet out of the irons and riding him into the hydrangeas in the corner!'

After the Second World War, Ken was made a member of the Army Buying Commission which was responsible for buying horses for the Household Cavalry and the King's Troop, RHA, at St John's Wood. This entailed a visit to Ireland every 3 months.

Letters of protest were being written to the papers declaring that horses for the British Army should be bought in England, not in Ireland, and the War Office therefore decreed that some should be bought at home. But it was very soon proved to be a waste of money to take a vet, and motor 100 miles to look at one horse, when the Irish dealers could produce anything from 20 to 60 horses in one day.

Colonel 'Priest' Alexander had made all the original contacts with the Irish dealers, and in following on, Ken got to know some of the biggest ones who were household names — men such as Rog Shanahan, Charlie Webster (Marshall Parkhill's father-in-law, whom he followed on in the business), Dan Murphy, and in the North that great judge of a horse, Willie McAldin — to learn *some* of the mysteries of horse dealing in Ireland.

In the course of time they all became friends, in particular Rog Shanahan who, for all his burly exterior, had a very soft heart and would sit on his sofa beside Ken and hold his hand as he talked. On one occasion when food was short in England he said: 'Now tell me, Major, would Colonel Alexander be a poor man?'

'Well, not exactly,' Ken replied, wondering where this was leading.

'He'd have a bit of money, would he? And would he have plenty to eat? Perhaps you would take him back a bit of butter with my compliments.'

A staff car with a veterinary surgeon from Belfast would be sent to meet Ken off the boat and to drive the commission around Ireland for a week. Sometimes friends in England would ask him to find them a nice horse after his official business was done, and once he asked Charlie Webster to find a good-looking horse for a lady to ride side-saddle, with the stipulation that it must have manners and be a real performer.

On his next visit, Webster said: 'I've got that horse for the lady, sir', so up they went to the field where customers were shown their potential purchases, and the dealer's nagsman gave them a show. Then Webster asked if the Major would like to ride him. 'No — he's no use unless he performs.' So: 'Go on then, Mick, show the Major how he can lep.'

So the man faced the horse at a big, hairy bank leading out of the field. The horse lost his feet taking off, and in a split second all that could be seen of him was his stomach. 'Are ye all right, Mick?' bellowed his employer. When the reply was in the affirmative he went on: 'Then come back and ride him properly and show the Major the horse lepping.'

Mick came back and re-enacted the identical scene, whereupon Charlie Webster turned, shaking his head, and said: 'Major, we've been deceived!'

Once a second-rate dealer who had a yard just outside Northampton got in touch with the War Office and said that he had eight black horses to show to buyers for the Household Cavalry. Ken and the vet went over from Melton on a bright, sunny day, and when the first horse was led out Ken thought that he must have suddenly developed a migraine, for its face and legs were shining with a dazzling light. Murmuring to his companion 'Have I gone mad?,' he stepped closer to investigate and discovered that the dealer, who had imagined that horses with any white about them would be unacceptable (although in fact the Household Cavalry do not object to a bit of white) had concocted a mixture of vaseline and lamp-black and rubbed it on all the white markings on faces and legs.

Ken said: 'You must take us for proper b.f.'s. Go and rub it off.' This done, and all the hair plastered down flat on the horses' faces, they looked worse than ever. The man was practically in tears by this time, declaring that he had put a lot of money into these horses, though Ken's private opinion was that he had got them in on speculation.

'Well,' he conceded, 'We'll see the others.'

One black mare was not too bad, but they insisted on seeing her ridden and there was, of course, no one to ride her. Just when they were about to take their leave, however, a large car drove into the yard and the dealer sighed with relief.

'Here is Mr X!' he exclaimed. 'He will give you a show on her.'

It transpired that Mr X was a point-to-point rider of some renown, and he lost no time in assuring them that he had won an adjacent hunts race South of London only the previous day. Up he got, while the mare humped her back a little, and proceeded to ride her round with his knees touching his nose.

'A bit faster,' urged Ken, and X gave the old skin a couple up the ribs. She put in two bucks, deposited X on the floor, galloped out of the yard and on to the road, and was last seen tearing off along the tramlines in the main street of Northampton.

'What am I going to do?' wailed the dealer.

'I don't know, but we are going home,' was the firm reply — and that was the end of the search for black horses in England.

Ken held the firm opinion that no one really had the right to lay down the law. 'Who is to say that my views are more correct than those of anyone else? I do think there is a sad need for more professional showmen; and I think one must be very careful not to criticise anyone's horses at the ringside. The owners obviously think their horses are pretty good or they would not have them, but a lot of silly people think they are impressing their hearers by "crabbing".

'In my day we were very lucky — we spent far too much time in the stables as youngsters and learned an enormous amount from the old stud grooms. Then we went into cavalry regiments and learned much more, in addition to having the tremendous advantage of riding a lot of horses and knowing how they were "done", which we learned as boys. Today it is all snaffles and drop nosebands — simply a question of hauling or strangling. Then they used double bridles and they had hands.'

Jock Atkins

Another judge of the old school, though to Ken Wallis he was 'one of the young ones' is Colonel Jock Atkins, who started judging in 1930 when he was 25. He had always been passionately fond of horses of all types. He was lucky that in his youth his father was keen on breeding hunters, and besides keeping a few useful mares at his old home, Stretton House, Hinckley, he also kept some stallions which he used to show at Islington under the HIS scheme.

'It was during this time, after the First World War, when we had one of the nicest hunter stables in the country and a grand old stud groom of the old type, that I learned what knowledge I have about hunters. As far as the equitation side is concerned, soon after I joined the Leicestershire Yeomanry in October, 1923, I went on a course to Weedon where there were some of the best instructors ever, and I certainly gained immensely from this fortunate experience. I was extremely lucky to judge in my early days with Colonel Brian Robinson and Major Tiddly Lucas, which of course were experiences to remember.

'If I were asked whether I have enjoyed judging hunters, the answer would be yes, a thousand times! It is fun, in spite of the responsibility, to ride the best show horses in these islands. What could be more pleasant than riding good horses, meeting friends, perhaps staying in a pleasant house and being thoroughly well looked after? It is a responsibility and it can be an arduous job. It's a stupid man who thinks he can go to a leading show and do his job properly, probably having to ride 50 horses — some of which are far from easy — unless he is 100% fit. This is essential, and therefore though I find it all very pleasant, it is still a serious duty.

'Have I had many difficult situations confronting me? Awfully few. Occasionally a disgruntled owner, but oh! — so seldom. I find the owners of hunters extremely sportsmanlike and ready to take whatever decision I have made. I think that if they realise that you are working hard, and satisfy yourself that you mean to find the horses in the order of your preference, then they accept your decision with grace.

'Only once, fairly recently, have I had anyone "sulk" out of the ring, and as he passed he mumbled something about "Time we got some judges who knew what they were doing! This horse hasn't been out of the first three for the last four shows."

' "Then this will be a change for him!" my lady co-judge promptly replied; which I thought very apt!

'My experience of the professional showman is that they are a grand lot — about six or eight of them shine out — and thank goodness we've got them to set a standard in producing and showing a horse to its full advantage. If we had not got these men and women, we should not see our show horses in half the beauty, presence and rhythm that we do today. I love riding horses that have been produced by the professional showmen, and I have always found these men to be good losers, good pals and interesting characters. Good luck, therefore, to the amateur owner who can produce a good horse as well and beat them all. They are always the first to admire it.

'May I wind up with a few thoughts for the would-be judge? First of all you must be a good horseman—this is obvious. Secondly, when asked to judge always make sure that nothing can interfere if you accept, for one must never let a show executive down; I did it once and I can't forget it. It follows that you must be precise about times of classes and so on, so study your schedule carefully. Above all, get you to the show on time and well on time! If you remember these few simple rules and do your utmost to satisfy yourself that you have picked the best on the day you won't go far wrong, always assuming that you have been brought up among and "know" hunters.

'I was musing through a list of some of the wonderful hunters that I have been privileged to ride and judge, and I must say that, in my opinion, Mighty Fine stands out supreme, followed by probably His Grand Excellency and Work of Art. Of the middleweights there have been such great horses as Blarney Stone, Unique, Grand Parade and Spey Cast. I greatly enjoyed riding Prince's Grace, Casino, Palladium and Monbra, and of course those two wonderful small hunters, Burrough Hills and Some Gardener.

'How lucky can one be, to have had the opportunity of riding such great horses, and on looking back one can remember the feel of the ride, and the pleasure that each individual horse gave. I can remember a few which also gave me a good deal of concern—sometimes one wondered: "Will he stop?" But I always found that the longer and lighter the rein, the kinder a strange horse goes. One has to be ready, though—after all, a good show horse is pretty fit and well!

'I love the ridden hunter classes and hope they will go on forever. I do think, however, that if working hunter classes are given good fences to jump and are judged correctly they will increase greatly in numbers and popularity.'

G. T. 'Handy' Hurrell

Colonel G. T. ('Handy') Hurrell, Lord-Lieutenant of Cambridgeshire, is the great-grandson of the man of the same name who with his brother founded the Cambridgeshire Hunt in 1827. He himself started hunting a Welsh pony when he was 6 and spent the First World War at Rugby, where other sporting activities occupied his leisure hours.

'Being keen on shooting, I became friendly at school with C. P. J. Ionides (later to become The Snake Man.) Together we saved up for a single-barreled shot gun. It took many nights to saw down the barrel so that it fitted inside a coat, and then Saturday afternoons passed pleasantly enough on poaching expeditions. Great was the day when a brace of pheasants was bagged in the dark up a tree, and smuggled back to the House.

The problem then was what to do with the corpses, but Ionides had a brainwave and presented them to the chapel for the Harvest Festival. At morning service the then mangled birds were to be seen hanging near the pulpit, where the preacher made a point of thanking the donor for his generous gift.

Handy left Sandhurst in December, 1918, when a railway strike made it difficult to get his horse home. He solved the problem by cutting the leg off an old pair of canvas trousers, tying up the ends after putting pyjamas and toothbrush inside, tying the makeshift pack to the 'd's in front of the saddle and riding home. He started after lunch, put up for the night at Watford, some 40 miles on, and was home in time for tea, having covered about 90 miles in a little over 24 hours. Sixty-six years later it is hard to believe that he met only a handful of cars on the entire journey.

The next day he was lent a horse to go hunting, rode out to the Meet 12 miles away, found a fox almost immediately and, after a 10 mile point and 16 as hounds ran, finished at the back of the village church. By that time he could not get his horse out of a walk and there were few survivors. At that age one is very fit.

The next year he joined his regiment (then the 17th Lancers, amalgamated with the 21st in 1922) in Germany, in time for the triumphal march up to Cologne. He actually joined the Regiment near Liège in Belgium, by which time most of it had been demobilised; but the horses remained, to be taken up to the Deutsch barracks in Cologne.

In his squadron there were eight officers, a sergeant-major, SQMS, four sergeants, two corporals and one man! The officers' main job was to muck out, exercise and feed the horses. Then they were joined by a number of recruits from the Rifle Brigade and they started playing polo and racing on the Troop horses.

After six months the Regiment was sent back to Catterick, where there were no horses but a vast number of recruits. Posted to Longmoor, south of Aldershot, they were provided with new horses and then sent to Ireland in 1920 to cope with The Troubles — first at Ballincolig in Co. Cork and then up to Buttevant and finally to Galway for a little over a year. Three officers and a Sergeant were killed by the Sinn Feiners, but the Regiment still hunted regularly with the Galway Blazers, with pistols in their pockets — 'Most uncomfortable over the stone walls!' he recalls wryly. The Master in those days was a man called Pickersgill, whose father was the famous bookmaker. He was a wonderful huntsman and being a very light weight rode little Thoroughbred horses. 'He was difficult to follow over that stonewall country.'

After a short period at Tidworth he went to the Army Equitation School at Weedon on a 1-year course and then stayed on for a further year as an assistant instructor. 'It was a marvellous experience — we hunted with all the adjoining packs who were most kind, and let us in very cheaply.

'I shall always be grateful to Douglas Crossman, that well-known Master of the Cambridgeshire Hounds, who mounted me on so many occasions when I was on leave and also gave me a lot of shooting. One day stands out in my memory, when round the home coverts we shot just on a thousand head and saw seven foxes, which shows what good keepering can do. He was a great sportsman and I was fortunate enough to marry his niece.'

Until 1930, when the regiment went to Egypt, he got a lot of hunting in various parts of the country and also did quite a bit of show jumping. He rode a horse called Skipjack at Olympia — a horse which never did its best unless the band was playing, when it was never out of the money. So Handy would run round the back and bribe the bandmaster to keep on playing while he was competing, knowing that without a musical accompaniment Skipjack would not give of his best.

While he was at Weedon he took part in the International Ride, fore-runner to the Three-Day Event. It was held at Aldershot and he rode a horse called Job, who was actually bought for Colonel Malise Graham, later killed so tragically over the double bank at Dublin Horse Show. Graham never really liked Job, so Handy was lucky enough to get hold of him.

It was quite a stiff test — a fairly severe dressage test in the school, further complicated by the fact that each completed movement had to be repeated on a loose rein. Next morning on the steeplechase course they did 2 miles by themselves at an average speed of 20 miles an hour. In the afternoon they had 2 hours to cover 20 miles of roads and tracks before returning to the school, where they were judged on the condition of their horses before going round a show jumping course. Job was beaten by a horse ridden by Colonel Joe Hume Dudgeon of the Royal Scots Greys.

While he was in Egypt, Handy was adjutant to the Regiment, but instead of accompanying them to India he came back in the same capacity to the Yorkshire Hussars. Here he had a wonderful time, hunting 5 days a week, and most days going over to the renowned dealer, Bert Cleminson, at York, who taught him more about horses than anyone else, before or since.

In 1937 he was sent to Sandhurst as the last equitation instructor ever to be appointed. He was able to encourage the cadets to take up hunting by starting a hunt stable with some of the best horses. Cadets were charged 7/6d. a day for a horse which was taken to a meet of the Drag. They went out in a bus, rode the line, had their horses taken back and were in time for evening parade. It was a very popular innovation. Half-a-crown went to the groom and the same amount for extra feeding and their bus fare. Although 20 cadets were taken out at a time there was always a long waiting list, and it was excellent value. It was particularly encouraging to those who had not had the opportunity to do much hunting beforehand, and it gained a number of recruits for the Cavalry.

At the outbreak of war he went to Edinburgh as equitation officer and then to Colchester as second-in-command to another training regiment, having handed over his job and his horses to Joe Dudgeon. In 1940 he achieved his ambition by being given command of his regiment, but owing to duodenal trouble he was forced to give up after a few months. He finished the war as chief instructor of the Driving and Maintenance wing at Bovington Tank Training School in Dorset, but after more duodenal trouble he was invalided out eventually.

His chief criticism of modern showing concerns the bad stewarding at a great number of shows. 'Time can be saved and the judge's work lightened by good stewards. At Dublin and most of the good shows the stewarding is absolutely superb, but at some of the smaller shows you have to do the stewarding as well as the judging.

'In the top-class show horses one expects more quality than 25 years ago. Unfortunately, it now seems to be the fashion for everything to be overweight. A heavyweight does not stand much chance unless it is about 17 hands and up to 16 stone, likewise middleweights about 16.2 and up to 14.7, and lightweights about 16.1 and up to a good 13st. There seems not to be a place for the true 15.3 lightweight, which is a pity. But in 1979 judges started putting horses up to a higher weight.'

In common with everyone else who judges regularly, he has had some amusing experiences in the ring and out of it. Once he was judging a local class at a show in Yorkshire with a local lady. To him there were only 3 horses in it, and the task seemed very easy, for it was pretty obvious how they should be put. He said: 'I think it's obviously that that and that.' But his co-judge disagreed. 'I'm afraid you have put them all the wrong way about. I know them out hunting and you put the worst up top.'

He suggested calling a referee, but she said: 'Do you see that gentleman standing by the rails? He owns all 3, so let's go and ask him how he'd like them put!'

Another time he was judging ponies. He put a chesnut animal up top and on leaving the ring he met a lady whom he knew vaguely by sight coming out of the produce tent. She said: 'And what do you think Honey is worth now?' In blissful ignorance of the fact that she owned the winning pony or that its name was Honey, he replied: 'I've no idea — I should imagine about 3/4d a pound?' The lady never spoke to him again.

On another occasion he was allotted a learner judge. He summed up one horse by saying that it was long in the tooth, had worn joints and was probably 14 or 15 years old. When leaving the luncheon tent he was met by an irate lady owner who was apparently a great friend of the learner and who threatened to sue him on the grounds that she could produce a certificate from the previous owner to say that the animal was only eight. He had great difficulty in escaping.

Once at the Royal Highland Show I unwittingly aroused Handy's ire due to the vagaries of the telephone between Edinburgh and London. He judged all the ridden hunters including those of the Working variety, who as one made a hash of negotiating the water jump. Explaining why so few had survived for the final judging, I blamed their absence from the field on the 'qualifying' course: but in *The Times* the next morning the adjective used was 'horrifying! I explained what had happened, but I do not think that he ever believed me!

Peter Borwick

Major Peter Borwick was the son of Colonel Malcolm Borwick, known to his friends as 'Peach' on account of his pink and white complexion as a boy. Colonel Borwick joined the Royal Scots Greys during the Boer War and served until the 1914 War, playing in the regimental polo team and winning point-to-points. Then he became chief instructor to the Cavalry School at Cayeux before coming home to fulfil the same function at the Cavalry School at Netheravon from 1919–20.

When he left the Army he became joint-Master of the Middleton Hounds in Yorkshire with Lord Grimthorpe for 10 seasons. But he had a very bad fall hunting hounds in 1931, landing headfirst on a turnip and fracturing his skull, so he migrated to his mother's home in Northamptonshire.

Peter Borwick was born just outside York and started hunting at the age of 3 with the York and Ainsty, led on his first pony which he still recalled with feelings of revulsion as a middle-aged man. 'He was an absolute brute of a Shetland called Smut. I started hunting properly when Father took the Middleton. At Sandhurst I was Captain of Riding and rode against Woolwich; I won the odd 'chase and several point-to-points before I was sent to Palestine with the Royals in 1938 for the Arab-Jewish troubles. We were used operationally with horses, and kept the peace very successfully, then we were mechanised and sent to the desert in 1942. I was wounded twice — once in Normandy and once in Italy — seriously the second time at the end of August, 1944. I rejoined the Regiment for 18 months and then left the Army in 1947, and got married when I took over my 900-acre farm. I breed a few hunters, but there is no lime in the land.'

For 17 years, from 1949, Peter Borwick was joint-Master of the Pytchley, and after a 3-year-gap he took on again with Miss Grant-Lawson. Previously he was teamed with Colonel J. G. Lowther and his son, George. He rode in the British Olympic team for the Three-Day Event at Aldershot in 1948, in company with Colonel Duggie Stewart and Brigadier Lyndon Bolton, on his brother's horse, Liberty, but when one horse broke down the team unfortunately was eliminated.

'In a quarter of a century's judging I have had a few embarrassing moments. Once I was judging at Southport with one of the Youngs, the hacks had just done their final round-up, and suddenly a fat old lady ran out from the stands and hit us both on the head with her umbrella because we hadn't given her horse a prize. On another occasion I was judging the championship in Dublin and was cantering round on a very lovely 4-year-old. When we were just level with the water jump an old steward walked out from the stand side and the horse ducked into the water. I was sitting up in the region of his ears and he started to lower his head — then, mercifully, he recovered and I escaped the ignominy of a soaking!'

The people who taught him most about judging horses were Herbert Sutton and Harry Bonner, each an expert in his own sphere. In fact, every top judge pays tribute to the knowledge he has acquired from the dealers. Nat Galway-Greer had forgotten more about the horse than most will ever know, and half-an-hour spent in his company produced a wealth of knowledge, all gleaned from practical experience of a great many horses of all shapes and sizes and temperaments that passed through his hands.

Neil Foster

Colonel Neil Foster, for many years senior Joint-Master of the Grafton Hounds, has followed in the footsteps of his uncle, Major Gordon Foster, who judged continually before the war — he officiated at Dublin on no fewer than 20 occasions — and was a Master of Foxhounds for 38 seasons, first with the Badsworth and then with the Sinnington, hunting hounds himself. His brother John was the leading G.R. before the First World War.

Neil's father died when he was only 14 so he spent a great deal of his youth with his uncle, starting hunting very young and properly when he was 14, mounted for two or three seasons on an old charger from the Great War who had been wounded in the shoulder but still remained a tremendous performer.

After Eton he was Commissioned into the Life Guards from Sandhurst in

1933, where he did some point-to-pointing, undeterred by the fact that he broke his leg in the first race he ever rode in, at the HH meeting. He had strong connections with the HH when George Evans was Master from 1926–39 and got him interested in hounds. He did a year's course from Weedon in 1937, when Dick Sheppard was chief instructor, Jack Talbot-Ponsonby took the NCO's ride and Alec Scott the officers'.

He was abroad from 1939 until 1945, first in the Middle East, then in Italy and finally for a few months in North-Western Europe. When he came home he started up the mounted squadrons again at Knightsbridge Barracks and then retired from the Army in 1947. He went into his family brewing business until it was taken over, when he took up farming in Northamptonshire. In 1950 he took on the Grafton Hounds, continuing for 27 seasons.

He believes that so long as hunting and point-to-points continue there will always be hunter classes, and that the standard of the best is as good as it ever was. 'There was a lean period in the middle 1950s with very little breeding taking place, but the HIS has got things going now and there are a lot of good horses about. I always look for a quality horse with substance, a good mover in all his paces with a certain amount of courage, natural balance and a good set of legs. Indeed, when you've got all your horses in the stable and you've got to hunt two or three days a week and mount hunt servants, you sometimes begin to think that a set of good legs is more important than anything else, plus a good constitution.

'Arkle will always be my ideal of a quality Thoroughbred, but they are too expensive. You have to pay at least 3 times 4 figures today for a three-quarter bred horse. Gold Dust was one of the few heavyweights with action like a thoroughbred and all quality — I hunted him a time or two and he was a marvellous hunter, during his show career and before he went to America, of course. He rode like a blood horse. I think Mrs Ransom's Spey Cast was one of the best I've ridden in the middleweights — and then perhaps Nat Galway-Greer's Prudent Lover, who was supreme in Dublin.'

Colonel Foster also married into a foxhunting family. His father-in-law, Captain George Drummond, was 'the best man in England' up to the war and piloted the then Prince of Wales and his brother, the Duke of York, when they hunted from his family home, Pitsford, in the 1920s with the Pytchley, the Grafton, Quorn, Belvoir and all the Leicestershire packs. It was from Pitsford, too, that the Queen had her first hunt.

Bob Matson

Bob Matson, whose son Richard is a steward at the Society's shows at Newmarket and Shrewsbury, was Master of the Wynnstay Hounds, founded in 1843 by Sir Watkin Williams-Wynn, the sixth baronet, from 1953 to 1961. He was also renowned for the sales of hunters which he held annually at Leicester, where, being renowned as performers, they fetched very high prices. Richard once remarked, when his father was talking of giving up his sales: 'My father has had as many "last sales" as Mrs Topham had "last Grand Nationals"!' It goes without saying that he is a very fine judge.

The son of a bank manager in Chester, who was treasurer of the Cheshire

Hunt for 25 years, he was brought up on good rough ponies. During one of his last school holidays he staked his pony badly out hunting, whereupon G. B. Radcliffe of Poolbank, Tarvin, offered him two horses to hunt six days a week. They were as green as grass and quite a lot were runaways, but he had a lot of fun hunting them, and their successors, for three years. Mr Radcliffe whipped in to the Cheshire Forest, was still hunting four short days a week in his 80s, was a fine chapel preacher and dealt in horses, as well as being in on the first importation of Friesians from Holland.

Although he enjoyed his hunting tremendously, Bob Matson always made the farming come first. He started farming in Cheshire in 1928, with 40 acres and 6 cows. In 1940 he moved to The Twemlows, near Whitchurch in Shropshire, where his son Richard still lives. With the adjoining Ashacres, the property of Colonel A. Heywood-Lonsdale who owned the Cloverley Estate, it amounted to 518 acres. He also owns Twemlows Hall with a further 280 acres, a hill farm in Wales and one on Exmoor, where he now lives, giving him a total acreage of 1,100. Richard joined him on the farm in 1962, having pursued his agricultural education at Cirencester and then gone to Norfolk as a farm pupil.

When he gave up the Wynnstay his wife Rosemary took over from 1964–7. She started hunting as a child with the Earl of Harrington's hounds in Derby and Nottinghamshire, thinking nothing of hacking on 18 miles to a Meet. After her marriage she continued to hunt with the Wynnstay in Cheshire, Shropshire and the Welsh borders, which is chiefly dairy farming land and all grass.

As Master Mrs Matson, who was also a magistrate, continued to be a guiding influence in kennels, and with a foundation of tough-constitutioned hounds, notable for their drive and tongue, she introduced an increased quality and produced doghounds of her own breeding. In 1959 these hounds killed 59½ brace of foxes before 31 December. Captain G. Percival Williams, ex-Master of his family hounds, the Four Burrow in Cornwall, asked her during the 1960s to judge at Honiton Hound Show with Mrs Bob Hoare, whose husband was then Master of the Cottesmore. 'There was an uproar, and many people said they would not send their hounds to be judged by women, but we had a lot of entries in the end.'

When the Matsons went to The Twemlows they had 10 work horses and only one tractor. They bought Shires as colts and broke them to harness, little dreaming that barely a decade later they would build up a stud of hunters widely known for its excellence, which could turn out a dozen fit horses on a Saturday. They were bought as youngsters, broken and made at home, hunted on with the help of their family and a seasonal helper known as the 'galloping cook', and sold at auction each spring.

'Tell me they can't keep a horse in his field and I'll buy him,' is one of Bob Matson's maxims. He often buys young ones with curbs, gets them fired and has no further trouble. 'A heavy man in deep going soon makes curbs on a half-bred horse, anyway,' he reasons. 'Especially on those going back to Shire of Irish Draught.'

His horses were bought at 2 or 3, broken at 3 after 6 weeks long-reining and turned away when they rode quietly down the drive. They are hunted at 4, hunted hard at 5, 6 and 7 and then sold. If they prove difficult when cubhunted as 4-year-olds they are turned away again. Seven or eight horses thus went to Leicester every year really knowing their job. Even 25 years ago they were averaging £700 apiece, latterly it was well into four figures, for Bob Matson was one of the best across country, with a marvellous eye for young horses, a system of nagging and schooling second to none, and every facility in his stable yard, where the hunt horses were also kept.

From his youth onwards, he learned a great deal from the colt breakers. 'They did not ride but they walked about colt-breaking to a tremendous age. We still break eight a year. I used to buy them as 4 and 5-year-olds but for the last 15 years I have only bought yearlings up to 4-year-olds. I always like them between 16.1 and 16.2 hands, middleweight horses up to 14st, 7lbs to 15st.

'I have been sending horses to Leicester for over 20 years. The fortnight before the sale is a very social time, with people coming to see what we have to sell. Yet half of my horses are bought by people who never come and look, and the other half by people who have had one before. I have never given commission — one can afford to be independent with a good farm as well! I sell a good many 6-year-olds, and sometimes a few 5-year-olds.

'I started sending horses to Leicester as a result of buying a mare at auction for 260 gns who turned out to be unridable, though there was intense competition for her, with catalogues waving and so on. When we got her home my wife never let me ride her and she was put in foal. I realised then that there must be a good market for the proven and made hunter.

'The type of customer who is not a very good jockey always seems to want the best horses. They will bid for the lot and then, in desperation, buy the green one at the end. I get them to come here and ride, and start them off on something quiet.'

The Matsons' right-hand man was their colt-breaker, Harry Bowen, who was descended from a long line of colt-breakers on the Worcestershire side of Shropshire. His father always worked on the principle that after a lot of long-reigning, young horses would go straight on. He liked to drive them for a month or five weeks, and if they were difficult give them more work.

They spent a week in a mouthing bit, with a roller after two days. After a week he liked to start driving them, hoping that they would do everything wayward that might occur to them, like bucking, that they so often do when first backed. After the last week they were backed and eventually five or six young horses were ridden round the three farms every Sunday, jumping up to 30 fences.

Harry started breaking colts when he was 13. He is a great believer in getting a horse to play with its mouth and salivating. Side reins were used only when they were first driven, and they were driven off the bit from the start. He has worked with horses of all ages but enjoys breaking young ones best of all. 'Nearly all horses jump, a few better than others. Some never stop because they have never been overfaced. I never use tack, which I think makes for stiff necks and dead mouths. I like my horses to carry their own heads, and I hate tight girths or rollers. *All young horses are terribly kind if they are handled properly from the beginning.*'

Major J. N. Howie

John Howie was born in Ayrshire in 1911 and brought up at Stairaird, Mauchline, where his father, a businessman, farmed and went hunting a great deal, as did all the family. His father was for many years Hon. Secretary to the Eglinton.

Educated at Merchiston (Edinburgh), he hunted with the Eglinton and the Dumfriesshire until the war, when he served in the Ayrshire Yeomanry, and Pack Transport. After the war he and his wife went to live at Westhorpe Hall, Northallerton, where he hunted principally with the Zetland and the Bedale, as Master, Joint Master and huntsman for 9 seasons, in addition to training his own horses under permit.

Until moving to Yorkshire he did very little judging, but soon he was lucky enough to be asked to judge at a great many shows, both small and large, which he found very interesting as well as acquiring a lot of knowledge.

He finds it difficult to say which was his favourite show, as there were so many at which he enjoyed judging and he was always so well looked after. He found the HIS show at Shrewsbury most interesting and a great experience, to mention a few, perhaps Dublin, the Great Yorkshire and Peterborough, though he has very happy memories of many more.

He had no hesitation, however, in naming the horse who gave him the most outstanding ride — Mr Appleyard's wonderful bay Thoroughbred heavy-weight, State Visit, who was shown so well by Willie Hope and was bred by Mr and Mrs Christopher Marler, by the premium stallion Steel Point out of the Irish mare Narrow Margin by Steel Point.

His most distressing experience was when he and his wife arrived in Johannesberg to judge at the show and his back packed in completely, but he was lucky enough to get Jean Ballard, who was there at the time, to ride for him on the first day, and a splendid doctor gave him powerful injections so that he was all right for the rest of the show.

He recommends young judges to go to as many shows as possible and to try to be understudy to a good senior judge, and above all not to be slow in making one's decisions.

Major-General Sir Evelyn Fanshawe, who has a chapter to himself later, had this advice for judges: 'To the old I would say "Give up judging riding classes as soon as you get the feeling that you want to steady a 4-year-old instead of shoving it on; and when you feel that the ring is slippery. This is just old age and is very apparent from round the ring. You can still enjoy your hunting for years to come and nobody notices you. Of course, you can and should help the young by judging with them.

'A word to young judges; always have a jolly good look down the line before you make your final placings. It is awfully easy to miss something really good! And remember that the orthodox method of judging is the quickest and the best. Do not talk to the exhibitors and do not stay with friends who are likely to be exhibiting — it is remarkable how the showing fraternity notices these things!'

Hunter judges must be like Caesar's wife, above reproach, and most of them are. The very fact of being on the Society's panel of judges constitutes a virtual guarantee of integrity and ability. Very few dealers are accepted, for though it is unarguable that those who have paid through their pockets for experience must be the best judges, it is sometimes inevitable that dealers may be, or may have been, at some time financially involved with a certain exhibitor or animal. Human nature being what it is, there are always those who will believe the worst. At the top of the panel list, therefore, the following appears:

THE COUNCIL HOPES THAT, WHEN A JUDGE ON THIS PANEL FINDS BEFORE HIM/HER AN ANIMAL IN WHICH HE/SHE HAS OR HAS HAD A FINANCIAL INTEREST, HE/SHE WILL STAND DOWN FROM THE CLASS.

THE PRACTICE OF A JUDGE EXHIBITING HORSES FOR SOMEONE AND THEN, AT A LATER DATE, JUDGING THESE HORSES FOR THE SAME OWNER IS VERY MUCH DEPRECATED BY THIS SOCIETY.

Justice, to be done, must be seen to be done.

CHAPTER 11

The stallion owners — a special breed

DURING THE last 100 years there have been a handful of stallion owners who have been exceedingly successful in winning on numerous occasions the King George V Cup for the champion stallion; in having especially fertile stallions whose percentage of foals was in excess of all their rivals; and in having stallions whose progeny went on to do better things than their contemporaries.

This last is, of course, the acid test, and it cannot be judged by the simple expedient of finding the best conformed, best moving horse likely to sire hunter-type offspring at a show of stallions. Indeed, he was a wise man who said: 'Don't bother to go and see the stallion. Go and see what he has produced,' which of course is the very thing that the judge in the show ring cannot do.

Captain Tom Wickham-Boynton was the first of the exhibitors of premium stallions to establish a lien on the King's Cup, soon after it was first presented at the Royal Agricultural Hall in 1911, to be won by his partner, Mr H. A. Cholmondeley with Berrill, by Rouge Dragon. By 1913 he had bought the 1912 winner, King's Courtship, from his breeder, Donald Fraser, and had won the King's Cup himself. In reserve was a horse called Birk Gill, who was the winner in 1914 for his then owner. A year later he won again, now owned by Capt. Wickham-Boynton jointly with Mr Cholmondeley, and he won for the third year in 1916.

In 1917, Captain Wickham-Boynton had bought a new horse, Rathurde, with whom he won from 1917 to 1919 and was the outright winner of the King's Cup, which his son Marcus still has at the Burton Agnes Stud near Driffield, in Yorkshire. He was one of the leading figures in the affairs of the Society from the early years of the century. In 1920 he brought out Scarlet Rambler, a grand-looking horse by William Rufus, to stand reserve to the Compton Stud's quadruple champion Gay Lally until in 1924 he finally succeeded in turning the tables on him. Then he won it in 1925 and 1926 with Ardavon, a son of Ardoon, followed in 1927 by his stable companion, Hector by St Amant, with Ardavon in reserve.

It must have been stimulating but none the less discouraging to try to beat the Wickham-Boynton/Cholmondeley horses, but the man who finally managed to do it was Stephen Mumford from Warwickshire. With Brigand, a son of Lemburg, owned in partnership with Captain Douglas Blew-Jones of the Lifeguards, he won the King's Cup three times and outright from 1928 (beating the Burton Agnes Stud's Hector) to 1930, and in 1933 he brought off a double, winning the cup with Pal o'Mine and standing reserve with Double Bed. This was really a foretaste of things to come, for Stephen Mumford's son

Charlie, then a boy of 16, was helping his father with the horses at Islington, and after the Second World War he became the most successful exhibitor of premium stallions that has ever been known.

Captain Wickham-Boynton, who was Joint-Master and huntsman of the Middleton East and Hon. Secretary to the Holderness, was finding that changed conditions with mechanisation of the cavalry regiments had greatly reduced the horse requirements of the War Office, and thus the premium business interests of his stud gradually ceased in the early 1930s, when it switched over to breeding Thoroughbred yearlings for the sales at Tattersalls and at Doncaster, though its owner still continued to judge hunters and to be an active member of the Society. His last premium stallion, Jean's Dream, won the King's Cup in 1938, beating the celebrated Haine and bringing his owner's remarkable tally to nine King George V Cup victories and seven reserves.

W. J. (Bill) Manning, like Charlie Mumford, was raised in the premium stallion business and both he and his father were born in the comfortable farmhouse at Wing, near Leighton Buzzard, where he now lives. The family originated in Northamptonshire and owned a brewery of the same name in Northampton. Charlie Manning, his grandfather's brother, was one of the founders of Towcester racecourse and the leading amateur of his day, in the 1860s. Towcester was known, in fact, as 'The Mannings' Tea Party' after Charlie won five of the six races there one day, beating that legendary figure, Captain Bay Middleton.

Bill's grandfather went south to Wing from the family home at Roade and took West Park, which was then part of the Wantage estate. Then 400 acres, it now extends to some 600. Bill's father hunted all his life and Bill, an only child, showed his first pony, a short-tailed grey ride-and-drive called Joey, at the Bucks County show when he was seven, in 1914. All the horses on the showground were requisitioned that day.

His grandfather had kept Shires, but his father acquired a threequarter-bred stallion and a lot of useful mares. He was the first person ever to show a mare to be put above a riding horse as supreme champion. This was at the East Berkshire show at Maidenhead in 1921. Bill, who had just left school, helped his father to show May IV and four of her progeny—foal, yearling, 2-year-old and 3-year-old. It was a great hunter show with between 20 and 30 entries in the brood mare class, but May IV won and so did all her children.

The favourite for the supreme championship was a chesnut heavyweight called Red Fox, who had won all over the country for the Reading dealer, Oliver Dixon. But Alec Campbell, one of the judges, asked his co-judge: 'Which is the most valuable—a gelding, or a mare who can produce all that lot?' There was only one possible answer, and the mare stood supreme—a decision which caused a sensation at the time.

Bill started with Thoroughbred stallions in 1929, the first being Cashier, lent to him by another famous stallion-owning family, the Hillmans of Worcestershire. A year later he had his first premium stallion, a French-bred chesnut called Oudrey who was a useful racehorse. He cost less than 100 gns at Brig.-Gen. Winser's sale. He was very temperamental and his offspring too were very hot-tempered. In those days the stallions travelled to London by train for the Islington show, and the Hillmans, Mumfords and Mannings all arrived on the same train. The Manning horses were loaded at Leighton Buzzard, which was the last stop. It must have been quite a sight to see upwards of 50 Thoroughbred stallions unloaded at Maiden Lane on a March afternoon and then led through the streets to Islington with a police escort. The other owners let Bill go first with Oudrey because if there was a horse in front of him he would sweat up in no time: temperament is without doubt a hereditary trait.

When the Second World War broke out Bill had Exeter and Solan. He kept the latter right through the war and then showed him at Derby, where the stallion show was held until moving to Newmarket in 1959. Here the horse was bought by the Cornish stud owner, L. B. Bloomfield. Soon afterwards, Bill bought his first winner of the King George V Cup, Henry Tudor. Howard Dixon, son of the Reading dealer, told him that Jack Bamber, a member of a very old-established and reputable dealing family in the North of Ireland, had a good stallion in his yard at Ballymena, Co. Antrim; he was a good judge, so Bill bought the horse 'sight unseen'.

This was during the hard and snowy winter of 1947, and Henry Tudor was delayed on the boat coming over. Jack Bamber telephoned and said: 'Sure to God, you can show him tomorrow morning,' but when Bill picked the horse up he had a coat like a Teddy Bear. There was snow up to the hedgetops, and they had to dig a path to get him home. Then they picked out all his coat and took him to the show, where he was fourth. But for the next two years, 1948 and 1949, he won the Cup. Later he died of an aneurism due to redworm infestation.

In 1949 Bill won the Macdonald-Buchanan Cup for horses new to the premium stallion scheme with Erin's Pride, who 2 years later won the King George V Cup. In *Horse & Hound* Major Chase Meredith, a great judge, wrote: 'If you want to breed, or try to breed, a racehorse use Erin's Pride.' His words came true when this stallion sired the great Pas Seul out of Mrs Harry Frank's good mare Pas de Quatre, who was also the dam of another outstanding 'chaser, Gay Donald. In fact, Erin's Pride sired the champion ridden hunter and the champion children's pony in the same year, which has probably not been done before or since. The animals in question were Mrs Maurice Tollit's Silverin, a champion led filly before she started her ridden career with Harry Bonner, and was eventually sold to the United States; and Mrs E. C. Skelton's Tara, out of the Irish pony Chocolate Box, who became in her turn the dam of champions.

Erin's Pride was eventually sold to Portugal, in company with Whim II; Bill's last winner of the King's Cup was Border Legend, again a double winner in 1959 and 1960. But in between there were many other illustrious stallions who started their career as premium horses from West Park. Solon Morn won the Macdonald-Buchanan Cup in 1957 before he was sold to Mr Bloomfield, for whom he won the King's Cup in 1962. In fact, Bill sold him to the Duke of Northumberland, from whom he bought his champion Border Legend.

Parlehay, champion in 1961, Spiritus (brought out of training, trace-clipped), Bondage (winner of the Macdonald-Buchanan Cup in 1956), Pollards (sold to Fred Hillman, who wanted a horse for the young horse class before

Top Periglen (by The Ditton). 1986 Champion Lightweight Hunter. *Below* Top Notch.
Supreme Champion at the Horse of the Year Show, 1969 and 1970.

Top 1983 Champion Middleweight Elite, ridden by Vin Toulson. *Below* State Visit. Winning Heavyweight and Champion Hunter of the Great Yorkshire Show, 1968, with Billy Hope up.

Top 1984 Champion Show Hunter, Seabrook, with Vin Toulson up. *Below* The Small Hunter Burrough Hills, in the 1950s, ridden by Miss Ailsa Smith-Maxwell (now Mrs Pease).

Top Aldaniti (by Derek H). Winner of the Grand National, 1981, ridden by Bob Champion.
Below Beagle Bay (by Pannier) gave Lucinda Green her sixth Badminton win in 1984.

Top Oxford Blue (by Cagirama). Member of the winning British Event Team at the Los Angeles Olympics 1984. Pictured here at Badminton 1985 ridden by Ian Stark. *Below* Blazaway (by Weathercock). International Dressage horse, here shown with Pammy Sivewright, 1985.

International Show Jumper St James (by Crown Again), ridden by Nick Skelton, 1982–1986.

Major-General Sir Evelyn Fanshawe, with the original 'HIS caravan'.

.e Viscount Knutsford judging Youngstock
.lasses at the National Hunter Show, 1959.

Major Sir Reginald Macdonald-Buchanan.

Lt.-Col. G. A. Murray-Smith. President of the HIS 1957. Chairman of the Council 1978–

The Lord Margadale of Islay. President of HIS in 1953 and 1971.

HM Queen Elizabeth the Queen Mother presents the King George V Cup to W. J. Manning at the 1961 Stallion Show at Newmarket.

Mrs George Gibson (left) and Lady Violet V non judging the side-saddle classes at Dubli

he was shown, and won the cup in 1953), and Little Cloud were all found and sold by Bill Manning.

He came out of the premium scheme because it was so hard to get grooms and because, as both Border Legend and Doubtless II were getting winners, he was getting more mares than he could cope with. So with five of his own stallions standing privately, five mares of his own and anything from 150 to 180 visiting mares, some 50 to 60 being foaled down at West Park, time does not hang exactly heavily during spring and early summer.

The greatest lesson Bill has learned in all his years with stallions was taught him by that great judge of young stock in Ireland, the late John Codd from Co. Wexford, who told him many years ago: 'Never go and look at the stallion—look at his progeny. What a horse produces is what matters, not what he is himself.' Doubtless II, sire of Princess Anne's 3-day-event European champion, Doublet, Bill considers to be a glaring example of this truism.

'Part of the trouble with the Thoroughbred situation today is that conformation is neglected — particularly the shape of the hocks, which predisposes that horse to soundness or to unsoundness. I like quality mares and I don't care for big mares — 15.3 hands is ample as long as they stand over enough ground. The same applies to stallions.

'My father taught me that if you see a new-born foal while it is still wet, and before it has got up, its body conformation (not its legs) will come back to that at some time in its life, with maturity. I have proved this to be true. Foals alter to a certain degree immediately they are born, and they go on altering every week. I give hind legs 6 months to improve — sometimes even longer.

'With show hunters, the trend today is to get them over height. There is a tendency to go for tall horses, especially among the middleweights. It astounds me the number of people who judge horses and are expert enough to judge a horse's limbs without putting a hand on them. I think that it is totally impossible to assess the density of bone without feeling it. The width of the shin is all-important.

'There is also a tendency for judges to go for *too* straight a hind leg, not the hind leg that is going to stand work. A horse whose hind leg is ultra-straight often finishes right down on his pasterns. There must be a happy medium between the sickle hock and the dead-straight.

'Great strides have been made by the layman who has tried to breed a foal since the war, but a lot of knowledge is required to be a successful breeder. I had a man here who runs a stud and a big estate. He said to me: "One of my mares came back from a stud where she had foaled down last year, and on the certificate of service, with the last service date, there was a space for remarks. There they had written THIS MARE WAS STITCHED. I haven't a clue as to what that might mean!" A number of mares need veterinary attention after they have foaled, chiefly because they get torn while foaling. If this is neglected it is often difficult for them to conceive again.

'I think, too, that vitamins and other supplementary additives can also be overdone. Sometimes mares arrive here accompanied by what is virtually a chemist's shop. Nuts, too, are all right in their proper place but not as a substitute for corn and bran and linseed.

'I drive all my stallions in long reins every morning, for from half to three-quarters of an hour. My reins are longer than ploughlines, and I drive them off the tail in the late J. B. Walker's tack, which gets their hocks right under them. Sometimes they are disappearing round the corner as I come round the wall, which gives them a feeling of freedom, though actually I have more control than I would have with shorter reins. I started doing this with Solon Morn and I have done it ever since. In May, when the foals are older, I walk the stallions through the fields with the mares. Those who have turned come up to him, the others take no notice.

'I use a teaser for the maiden mares but the others are tried by the stallion who will serve them — it is more natural. The stallions are never tied up, except to be dressed. I treat them as *horses*, not as stallions, which some people seem to regard as a sort of wild animal. In over 40 years I've only had one really bad one. He picked up my son, Richard, in a lonely box when he was being fed, and he would have savaged him. As it was, he tore the zip out of his jacket. Luckily, Richard remembered that the horse was ticklish behind his knees — he had discovered this while he was dressing him — so he leaned down and tickled him there and was dropped. The horse was shot straight away.'

Bill Manning, so conscientious a stud owner — he sits up all night with visiting foaling mares rather than delegating responsibility — decided that he had reached the end of the road in 1971, when he sent Don't Look to David Barker at Winslow, while continuing as a most informed and informative commentator at the Stallion and Hunter shows, and much in demand as a judge at other major shows.

Charlie Mumford broke all the records and set up what must surely prove to be an unbeatable target when he won the King George V Cup on no fewer than 16 occasions since the war. From 1950–52 he brought off a hat trick with War Star, Court-Nez and Cul-de-Sac. In 1954 he won again with Inchydoney, and in 1955 it was Court-Nez again, whose celebrated son Halloween won many good 'chases including the King George VI at Kempton Park.

In 1956 another branch of the family, William Mumford and Sons from Warwickshire, won with Your Fancy, but in 1957 and 1958 Charlie was back again with Starlata and Parting Shot.

Bill Manning had two wins next with Border Legend and then Parlehay and Solon Morn, both horses he had sold, followed on. But in 1963–5 Charlie was back with a vengeance when Bleep, who was later sold to Germany, won three times off the reel.

The very next year, 1966, Charlie Mumford recorded his first of a record five victories with Quality Fair, who has been a legendary servant to him and is with him till as I write, in 1984, and still serving a few mares. He was unbeaten from 1969 to 1972, and we have to go back to the Compton Stud's Gay Lally (1920–24) to find another that triumphed four times on the trot, but Quality Fair's win in 1966 makes him the best ever though he never succeeded in breeding much of note. A bay-brown horse of 16.2 hands, by Hook Money, by Bernborough, out of Fairy Flower, by Fun Fair, grand-dam Forced Flower by Forerunner, he was in training from 1962–4, starting three times as a 2-year-old, four times at 3, winning the 5 furlong Boston Handicap at Lincoln, and out of eight starts at 4 won the 2 mile Brampton Hurdle at Huntingdon. The last of Charlie Mumford's stallions to stand supreme at Newmarket was Royal Clipper, in 1976.

One of the unluckiest exhibitors at the Stallion Show was George Maundrell, owner of the Blacklands Stud at Calne in Wiltshire. His great sire Game Rights, who really stamped his stock, was runner-up for the King George V Cup on three occasions but never succeeded in winning it. His successor, Armagnac Monarch, did win it in 1973 for his wife, Beryl, sister to Captain Brian Parry, but George was no longer there to see.

George's family bred carthorses before the war, and kept a Clydesdale stallion, but George started breeding Thoroughbreds while he was still at school, and four years later had the sixth generation of his own breeding. His first mare, acquired when he was 16 or 17 was Brown Cherry II, by Imperview, but the family that lasted was by General Gough (by General Simons, who got two or three Grand National winners) out of a mare by that good 'chasing sire, Hackler., Prudence V, the third generation, won five point-to-points in 1939 and won again after the war. A slow breeder, she had her first foal when she was 17 and bred five, all winners, up to the age of 25.

After the war George acquired his first Thoroughbred stallion, Gay Scot, who was followed by Game Rights, whose name will go down in history. Bred by Miss Philippa Vaughan, he was by Big Game out of Just Right, by Orthodox. He was brought out of training as a 5-year-old and became one of the most prepotent sires ever, who always stamped his stock, in addition to passing on to his progeny his delightful temperament. He also had a high fertility percentage as far as premium stallions go, a subject about which George Maundrell held strong views.

'Fertility is a big subject,' he told me once. 'It is not generally realised how unfair it is to compare fertility figures of the horse who stands at a high-class stud and is limited to 40 mares, with the premium stallion who has to take all sorts of mares, a large percentage of which are worn out before they start breeding. Opportunities in regard to trying mares, veterinary attention and general expert supervision during the breeding season are so slender as compared to mares at a high-class stud.

'Of course, when mares come to stay at your stud they stand a far better chance of being got in foal. In the old days when premium stallions travelled a route, spending a night here and then walking along the road to the next night's resting-place, the chances of a mare being presented at the proper time were very erratic indeed. Luckily, owing to the practical difficulties of travelling a horse on the road in modern traffic conditions, more and more premium stallions stand at home — or at most visit one or two places on the route during the week, with much wider use of transport as opposed to walking. Now they have a much better chance of getting their mares in foal.

'The mares, too, have the benefit of much better veterinary attention than was formerly the case — not only because mare owners are, on the whole, more enlightened, but there is much wider knowledge of these matters within the profession itself. One of the factors which precludes many mares from breeding is injury at previous foalings, which makes it impossible for them to breed again without veterinary attention — until, in fact, they are sewn up.

'Nutritional problems can have a big influence on fertility. With breeding stock, I am careful to give minerals and vitamins at seasons of the year when it is necessary to keep this in mind. Another thing I have discovered over the years is the necessity for worming horses every 3 months. I used to think that 12 horses on 1,500 acres would be worm free, but this is a fallacy. By keeping your stock free from worms by dosing them at regular intervals, you are able to keep far more horses than if you have fewer horses grazing a larger acreage. I don't think people realise how much they can save in feed bills by keeping worms under control, or the wastage of food that occurs when horses are subjected to uncontrolled worms.

'With all classes of stock, the medium-sized dam is the truest breeder. I have derived great benefit from studying these things over a number of years and trying to interpret them into something useful. A general knowledge of animals, I have found, is very useful in applying to the particular. All these principles are sound and complementary. People are rather apt to get bees in their bonnets about certain things. All animals have faults, some larger than others, and the real art of assessing merits lies, I think, in being able to differentiate between the important and the unimportant faults, and in keeping a balance.

'Most horses, particularly young ones, are shown too fat. An excess of weight on an animal's legs is bound, sooner or later, to be a handicap.'

The older stallion men learned their lessons the hard way, in the tough school of experience. Every owner of breeding stock has proved some homily for himself over the years — Bill Roberts, for example, who owned Solon Morn in his later years, found that so many mares turn after a service in the foaling heat — once universally believed to be the surest period to get a mare in foal — that he often did not bother to cover them at this time. The younger men not only have the benefit of their elders' experience but veterinary science and opinion is becoming increasingly proficient.

Max Abram, whose stud near York always carries off a full hand of premiums from Newmarket, started to keep premium stallions almost by accident. His grandfather's hobby was breeding hackneys, his father dabbled in Shires, Max had his own pony from the age of 4 and was keen on hunting from boyhood. But when he married and life became earnest with a growing family, he decided to put his hunter mare in foal.

He got in touch with a neighbouring farmer who kept a stallion, and when he discovered that the owner was more interested in selling his horse than in taking a mare to him, he decided to take the plunge.

'Once I had bought Quel Espoir, I began to see why his owner had wanted to part! He was quite a handful — the worst I've had since. But he was the first stallion I had anything to do with, I did not realise he was quite as wild as he was. I sold him after two seasons and was asked to take Prince Barle in 1961, the premium horse for East Yorkshire. At that time he travelled the district by Land Rover and trailer, covering about 50 mares, so I met many hunter breeders, many of who are still good customers and friends.

'The next year I bought Weathercock, who in 1963 was joined by Troilus, the number of visiting mares began to increase to around 300, so I bought Impelo, Nearest and Kadir Cup. Nearest ruptured a lung and died on the last day of the season, and his replacement, Royal Encore, broke his back a year to the day later. Others have come and gone, two who stayed being Arrigle Valley, who stood training for eight seasons, and Foxstar, bought in 1971 from Leslie Scott of Minehead.

Kadir Cup left the premium scheme at the age of 20, 'with his head held high', as his owner remarked. He was quite a horse — running over 100 times, winning 11 races under all three codes, retiring sound at 10, and winning his class at Newmarket four times. After a shaky first year when he was nearly sacked from the scheme, he won the Henry Tudor Cup for the best fertility percentage, as in 78/79 did Max Abram's American-bred Ascertain.

'In November the stallions receive an extra daily feed and after Christmas their preparation for Newmarket begins in earnest. It includes six to eight miles roadwork for an hour and a half daily, either led or driven. At one time they were ridden out, but they often lost as much condition as they put on, due to their anxiety to get back to their stables.

'You need six stallions to make a profit out of premium horses, and six visiting mares can make the difference between profit and loss. I don't like mares arriving too early before the grass has grown, they are harder to get in foal and they stay in season much longer early in the year. But if an owner wants an early foal you have to accommodate him, or he'll go elsewhere.

'Only about 25% of mares hold to a service until mid-April — particularly the barren ones. It is all a question of watching a mare when she is right. I have one, and I've known others, who appear to ovulate during their first day in season; the others we leave for a couple of days and try to catch them when they are going off, which seems to work with 95%.'

Max made a wise move when he bought Current Magic from Graham Lloyd Hay-on-Wye, one of the younger stallion men who had been to Ascot sales with Vivian Bishop, Master and huntsman of the Golden Valley in Herefordshire, and bought this son of Current Coin out of the Aureole mare Phosphorescence for a mere £600 in 1977. In training for six seasons, he had won seven races, three of them over hurdles, and his limbs were as clean as a horse that had done nothing. He won the Macdonald-Buchanan Cup on his first appearance at Newmarket in 1978; the following year he won the King George V Cup; and since being bought into Yorkshire he has won it on a further two occasions.

The stallion leaders, who in the old days used literally to lead their charges along the roads in the district to which they were allocated, take a great pride in 'their' horse, with whom they live in such close proximity for four months of the year. They are often so small, and seemingly frail, that one wonders at their ability to control a big, lashing Thoroughbred entire who is fighting fit. Yet in the collecting ring at Newmarket these little old men display the sort of effortless control exerted by a nanny with a high-spirited child, restraining an obstreperous stallion as he rears or tries to buck, with an admonition not to be so silly.

These men have a party on the night before the show, when friendships are renewed and stories swapped, for the fascination of the subject and the life seems inexhaustible. It is hard work, sometimes even dangerous work when difficult mares are involved, and sometimes during harvest a mare who has turned is brought in the dark, when the day's work is over, to be covered again in the light of a tractor's headlights. But it is infinitely rewarding, though all are agreed on one thing. It is essential to enjoy the life, for there is not much in the way of profit.

Keeping premium stallions is, indeed, more of a way of life than a living. The value of the basic premium is £750, and the super-premiums which go to the top 14 horses in the show vary from £660 to £360 for the horse in fourteenth place. The Horserace Betting Levy Board annually award £85,000 for the 61 premiums and 14 super-premiums, and the donation also covers the new mare register which was started in 1983. The stud fee, £2 in 1884, was still only 10 guineas to HIS members and £21 for non-members in 1967, but by 1983 inflation had driven it up to £60 for non-Thoroughbred mares owned by members and £100 for non-members. The stallions produce between them some 2,250 foals annually. Membership now stands at 10,000 and subscription, which stood at a guinea until well after the Second World War, has risen to £11.50 — still excellent value.

Most of the stallion owners are farmers, but some are enthusiasts like Jimmy Snell, who was a baker at Breage, near Helston in Cornwall. Riding was his hobby from boyhood, and after buying the stallion Little Cloud (by Derby winner Nimbus out of the Epigram mare, Little Britain) he became so successful with his horses that he sold the bakery and concentrated on stallions. In 1968 he won the King George V Cup with Brother — later killed when kicked by a mare — and in 1976 he won the Macdonald-Buchanan Cup with Saunter, by Charlottsville out of a mare by St Paddy, who went on to win the King's Cup in 1978 and 1981.

CHAPTER 12

———————◆◆◆———————

The breeders

THE LAST Wednesday in August sees the fruits of the premium stallion scheme on exhibition at Shrewsbury, on the lovely ground that is loaned each year by the Shropshire and West Midland Agricultural Society. It is a splendid setting, close by the Shropshire hills and the Border Country, reached after a beautiful drive along quiet roads flanked by fields from which the hay harvest has recently been lifted.

In over 30 years I can only recall one wet day, though there may have been two; my memory of the Hunter Show is of an endless succession of summer days illuminated with sunshine, which blazed down on young horses on the eastern side of the divided main ring which is devoted to yearlings, 2-year-olds and 3-year-olds, and on the western side where placid matrons with full udders and shrill-voiced foals made an idyllic scene, observed by serried ranks of male members in panama hats with striped school or regimental hat-bands and HIS or BFSS ties, accompanied by their ladies in summer frocks and silk hats, a nostalgic vestige of an older civilisation that is in such marked contrast to the modern world.

The principal trophy on offer is the Edward, Prince of Wales Cup for the best of some 200 young hunters, and of scarcely less interest is the award of the HIS Champion Challenge Cup for the best brood mare, who must dispose of some 150 rivals before being acclaimed as such. Of recent years there has been a final battle of the giants, under a new judge, for the award of the Lloyds Bank in-hand championship qualifier, which determines the Hunter Show's representative at Wembley.

One of the most indefatigable supporters of the breeding classes was Mr Geoffrey Palmer, who lived in Berkshire and was one of the Huntley and Palmer family. He bred hunters for more than 50 years and so did his father and grandfather before him. He maintained that the more he bred, the less he knew — a refreshing, if disheartening, opinion.

'I have reached absolutely no conclusions on the subject! I like deep, short-legged mares with a long forearm and a short cannon bone, preferably a first, second or third cross from an Irish Draught. But I have also explored the possibility of crossing out to Holsteins; in fact, I bought four mares and presented them to the Society. The first cross was very interesting, and the second cross even more so. The colts, which the HIS do not retain, sell at quite high prices as they were all natural jumpers. One went to Holland at £1,500 some years ago, when that was quite a lot of money, and another made £1,000.

'The best mare I have ever had was Formula, who won the HIS Cup in

1966. I bought her from Paddy Carty in Dublin and it took me some years to persuade him to part with her. She was then called Killowen Lace, and she was by Interlace out of a Draught mare. She had three foals before I had her and she had another four with me. I keep the youngsters to break and sell on as 4-year-olds.'

Another most enthusiastic older breeder was Mrs Molly Cail, whose stud was near Richmond in Yorkshire. She used to hunt 4 days a week and when *anno domini* put a stop to her first love she soon found ample recompense in breeding hunters. In 1973 she achieved the summit of her ambition by winning not only the Walker-Okeover Cup for the best filly in the show but also the Edward, Prince of Wales Cup with her splendid brown filly, Lucky Strike, by Lucky Leprechaun. She had already won the former trophy on two previous occasions with her Parlez-Vous, by Parlehay, in 1968 and 1969.

Mrs Cail also made friends with Ian Thomas, the Queen's dressmaker, and imbued him with her own enthusiasm for breeding hunters. She had bred a horse which came into the hands of Major James Hanbury, and when he died it was sent to Jack Gittins to be sold. Ian Thomas bought him, and when Beckford won the ladies' hunter class at Wembley, he rang Mrs Cail to tell her the good news. She was delighted to have made contact with one of her 'babies', and invited Ian Thomas to stay.

'It was she who introduced me to young horses and inspired my great love for them — looking after them in their formative years, watching them grow, realising that each has a different character from the other, despairing of their naughtiness, rejoicing when one of them does something right!'

Also at Elmfield Hall was her right-hand man, Dick Threlfall, and when in 1975 he telephoned Ian to say that Mrs Cail had passed away in her sleep, he also asked: 'Shall I send Lucky Strike to stud? They're going to collect her this morning.'

'Why ask me?'

'Well, you want her, don't you, sir?'

So Lucky Strike duly became his, was broken by David Barker and had a year in middleweight classes before going to Bill Manning's Don't Look and winning seven brood mare classes in nine outings in 1978. In 1977 he won the Prince of Wales' Cup with his 2-year-old Fair Sport, by Quality Fair, and in 1979 Lucky Strike was champion at Peterborough, a significant and prestigious place to win.

In 1981 Lucky Strike produced, to Mandamus, a son called Lucky Fool who was champion foal at the Hunter Show. On his near foreleg he had a white stocking almost to the knee, and his owner-breeder traced it right back on his sire's side, through Petition and Fair Trial, to Spearmint, who won the Derby in 1906 and had the self-same stocking and star.

The most successful hunter breeders have been those who operate in a small way with one or two mares of carefully selected type, conformation, quality and antecedents. When one considers that only a miniscule proportion of full brothers or sisters to champions in any sphere ever turn out to be top-class, the gamble with the genes becomes even more apparent. Some big mares produce 'rabbits' consistently, whereas the small mares, who would be unimpressive in the showring, often seem to produce the goods.

Sally and Norman Skinner, who met in the East Devon hunting field, started breeding hunters; Norman's father had bred and shown hunters all his life, so that they already had a foundation of knowledge on which to build. The cornerstone of their stud was the outstanding mare Rouge Croix, a brown Thoroughbred by Erin's Pride out of the Blazonry mare Blue Mantle. Foaled in 1952, she was bred by Mrs R. Lucas of Shillington Manor, Hitchin, who had tried without success to buy their first mare, Nightshade, from them as a yearling. Later she agreed to sell Rouge Croix as a 4-year-old and bought a daughter back again, retaining a fifth generation of this good family. Blue Mantle was out of Black Valley, by the Gainsborough horse Suddaby, and won at the HIS show in 1948 and at Peterborough and the Royal in 1947. Black Valley, whose dam was Mount Juliet by Great Sport, was a prolific winner and mother of six.

Rouge Croix won countless major championships during eight seasons, including the HIS Cup in 1963, and bred eight foals in as many years. After two barren years, her ninth was Rougette, by Langton Heath, the most successful of them all. Champion young horse at the Royal in 1970, when she was also champion filly at the Hunter Show, she was sold to Mrs H. F. Jeffs of Wolverhampton and became champion matron at the Hunter show in 1978 and 1979, and at the Royal and the Great Yorkshire as well in 1979 and 1980. In addition her Son of Rouge won the Prince of Wales cup in 1981.

Rouge Croix's first foal, Denbow, won races for the Brookshaws in Shropshire and then returned to his birthplace to be hunted. The third foal, Portcullis by Jena II, went hurdling. Then came Game Cross, by Game Rights, who was sold back to Mrs Lucas and re-christened Rouge et Noir. Farringdon Cross won point-to-points for the Brookshaws and Early Morn, by Solon Morn, won the Rover section of the Army Horse Trials at Tidworth with his Norfolk owner, Linda Garrard. Criss-Cross-Quiz, by Question, represented the hunters in the now-defunct Fredericks Led Championship at Wembley and only Parlehay's son, Parlez-Vous, came to an unhappy end after a promising beginning.

When Rouge Croix — whose daughter Moulin Rouge by Occaney produced the 1970 Prince of Wales Cup winner, The Likely Lad — retired from the ring, her place was taken in the shop window by Ocean Cheer, a brown mare by Three Cheers out of Eastern Ocean and a former winner over hurdles. Trained at Hatch Beauchamp, near Taunton, by Tim Handel, she was sold at Ascot to Leslie Scott, owner of Langton Heath and a great judge. He got her home and then telephoned the Skinners to say he had a mare he thought might suit them, only to be told that they were not looking for one.

'We didn't go to see her for ages, and then we really only went in order not to disappoint Leslie. She was in a field up on Exmoor with 15 or 16 others and no one could catch her. Anyway, we thought she was exceptional and could not leave her behind.'

The judges found her exceptional too. In 1970 she won the Queen's Cup for the best light horse at the Royal Cornwall show before going into battle with the giants, finishing first at the Hunter Show, as did her filly foal, Kon-Tiki, champion filly too in 1971 and at the Royal, where they were reserve as well. Another daughter, Three Wishes, by Langton Heath, distinguished herself in 1977 by winning the Lloyds Bank qualifier at the Royal Highland Show in 1977 and then taking the title at the Horse of the Year Show for Mr and Mrs Andrew McCowan as a 3-year-old.

The mares that have produced the best hunters, capable of carrying a 14-stone man to hounds three days a fortnight, have usually been hunter-bred themselves, out of a mare who is at the most three-quarter-bred and possibly even less. But many of these splendid mares were destroyed during the war, and with the craze for breeding horses to win point-to-points, which has been with us since the 1950s, the truly hunter-bred mare becomes increasingly rare. The modern hunter has more quality than some of his ancestors, but it has all too often been acquired at the expense of bone and depth, and there are far too many horses about who would hardly carry 12 stone to hounds.

The old-fashioned 'chaser-type, capable of carrying weight, at speed, through the heaviest going, is rarely seen today. When it is, it is more likely to command a big price as a novice 'chaser than to gravitate to the hunting field; while the big, upstanding Thoroughbred mares are usually retained for breeding by the bloodstock studs. The ideal brood mare must have quality, straight and true action, while in conformation she must be as nearly perfect as possible, for all too often she will pass on the worst of her faults and few of her virtues to her siblings. Her limbs in particular must be good, and free from unsoundnesses, for ringbone, sidebone and hocks that are predisposed to curbs or spavins have an insidious propensity for reproducing themselves — yea, even to the third and fourth generations! She must have good, flat flinty bone, not less than 8 ins. and preferably more, below the knee and above all she must be deep and rangy — narrow mares with close-set hips and flat, slab-sided ribs are never good matrons. Roominess is a virtue, though slack loins are not. Height is no criterion of strength, and the mare standing only a little over 15 hands often produces foals that dwarf her when fully grown, provided she is big within her own compass.

Mr Ian Scott's Travel Alone, by Jilted out of Lady Member, by Political, bred at Usk by Harry Lewis in 1935, was a classic example. She was bought as a foal for £15, Mr Scott having owned and shown her grand-dam, Flannelette, by Hunty Gowk. Travel Alone won at the West Midland, Three Counties and Peterborough as a 2-year-old and at the Royal at 3, when as her owner was overstocked she was sold with another contemporary filly. But she turned out to be a one-man horse, unusually, her new owners could do nothing with her and Mr Scott bought her back again.

The war interfered with her riding days and when next she appeared in the show ring it was as a matron calculated to breed hunters up to 14 stone and over. She won the championship at the Hunter Show in 1949, and at the Royal, though only 15.1½ hands. In fact, she was never beaten as a heavyweight matron and also won Peterborough too, making a hat-trick of the three leading hunter shows with her exceptional quality and movement. After slipping twins in 1953 she was never really well and was put down in the autumn of 1954, having had five foals.

Two matrons have had the distinction of winning the HIS Champion Challenge Cup on three occasions since the war — Mrs M. H. Tollit's Seaward II (1954, 1955 and 1956) and Mrs A. L. Wood's Prince's Grace (1964, 1965 and 1967). Seaward II, who was foaled in 1940, was a war baby. Bred by Mrs T. F. R. Bulkeley in Gloucestershire, she was by the premium stallion Merely-a-Minor out of the hunter mare Shagreen II by Grenoble. Having put the mare in foal, her owner then went off to serve for three years with the Free French.

Having won lightweight and working hunter classes in her youth and, ridden by Miss Kit Tatham-Warter, won and being placed in 17 point-to-points, Seaward was bought by Mrs Tollit in 1952 and the next year she made her bow as a brood mare. 1955 was her best season. In 1955 she was unbeaten, her victories including, besides the Hunter Show, the Royal (where she was also champion in 1956, though only a lightweight) and the Three Counties and Peterborough. Her children — Seaforth, Seamyth and a colt by Archive — all won in the showring.

Mrs Tollit, who was also very proficient on a ridden hunter and showed many lightweight champions in Dublin for Nat Galway-Greer, was the original finder of Prince's Grace, who was bred in Lincolnshire by Mr Rex Chappell at his Beechwood Stud, near Brigg, by Prince's Game out of Collence, by Columcille (a sister to Laurie Morgan, of Australian 3-day-event fame's, College Master).

Foaled in 1954, Prince's Grace was shown first by Mrs Tollit and then sold to Mr Hugh Sumner for his daughter, Mrs Alec Wood, for whom she won many lightweight classes and championships at all the major shows. A beautiful pattern of a quality bay mare of hunter type, after her ridden career was over she went to stud and reappeared in the breeding classes as a matron and was just as big a winner as she had been under saddle, though she never bred anything of much note. Under saddle she was shown at the same time as Mr Sumner's Dublin champion, Work of Art, and he was just about the only one capable of beating her in a title fight.

For 3 seasons as a matron she virtually 'farmed' the major championships at the Hunter Show, The Royal, the Three Counties and Peterborough, and if she failed to produce any progeny to follow her in the showring, one would just say that no one animal can be expected to do it all.

Although the Skinners produced their champions from Thoroughbred mares, Colonel and Mrs Tony Coote from Devonshire bred Budget, their dual winner of the Edward, Prince of Wales Cup by Bill Powell's premium stallion, Raoul, out of a half-bred mare. The grey My Love II was originally bought as a hunter in Ireland, without any papers, by Captain Andrew MacIlwaine. She had great quality and won the 15.2 hands brood mare class at the Hunter show in the same year that her son won the Prince of Wales Cup for the first time — a notable and unique family double.

Budget won from foalhood onwards. Under saddle he scored his greatest triumph when he won the hunter championship at the Royal International in 1971 and went on to win the Winston Churchill Cup, nonsensically judged on public applause, for the supreme riding horse. His owners set off for home late that night, with their horse in the trailer behind them, tired but happy, arriving at their home west of Exeter in time for breakfast. Budget was hunted with the Ledbury and the Meynell, but hopes that he would one day make an international 3-day event horse did not materialise.

His owners, who farmed at Ashton, owned a number of good show horses in their time but were emphatic that nothing can ever compare with the champion one breeds oneself and knows from his earliest days. Most fail to achieve it in a lifetime of trying, but it is surely the spur which overcomes disappointment, frustration, sometimes even tragedy in the great gamble to see whether this year, at last, one will succeed in pulling off this achievement.

One of the nicest hunter mares since the war was bred by the Hon. Mrs R. N. Crossley, who lives near Malton in North Yorkshire and whose husband farms and is Master and huntsman of the Middleton Hounds.

Cuillin Hills was the first animal Mrs Crossley bred when she started in 1967, out of her original hunter mare — a brilliant half-bred by that wonderful sire of jumpers, Water Serpent. The mare was called Loch Ness and she was put in foal to the local premium horse, Count Albany, when she was having her third and last child. The baby and the foal were born within 4 months of each other! The filly was named Cuillin Hills as Count Albany was Bonnie Prince Charlie's French title; after the Battle of Culloden he was on the run down the shores of Loch Ness and hid with Flora Macdonald in the Cuillin Hills on Skye before escaping back to France.

Loch Ness (known as The Monster, or Mon for short) was a brilliant hunter with absolutely no mouth and Mrs Crossley had four seasons of the greatest fun on her before exporting her to South Africa for what in those days was a lot of money. Cuillin Hills was shown in hand and under saddle as a 4-year-old, and then she went hunting, first with her breeder and then with Colonel Crossley, who hunted hounds off her as a 5-year-old. She was put in foal at 6 to Kadir Cup, their well-known local super premium horse, and produced Spy Hill, who was very successful in hand, winning a lot as a 2 and 3-year-old, and as a brood mare in 1974.

By this time Mrs Crossley was 'so bitten by the showing and breeding bug' that she bought another TB × ID mare from the local dealer. Her name was Becky and she bred no fewer than 11 consecutive foals, eight of which were high-class county show winners. Her three best foals were Aces High, by Ascertain (again the local premium horse), champion filly at the Hunter Show: Three Aces, an outstanding yearling filly and full sister to Aces High, and Fox Bay, by local premium horse Bunny Boy. He won at Newark, Stafford County and Peterborough as a yearling in 1983.

The mare had to be put down but she has left a charming grey filly by Riki Lash (another local premium horse) called Silver Wedding, as the Crossleys celebrated theirs in 1983.

Becky and Cuillin Hills have been Mrs Crossley's two foundation mares. Cuillin has been very difficult to breed from, her next foal being born in 1980. This was the filly Cluny Castle, a tremendously prolific winner in hand; reserve champion foal at the Royal, reserve champion to her dam at Newark as a 2-year-old, champion at Stafford County and reserve champion filly at the Hunter Show, reserve champion at the Lincolnshire show and champion filly and reserve overall at Peterborough. She is by Archie Thomlinson's good horse, Ancient Munro, who has sired a great many winners in the show ring. Her owners hope to breed from her and continue a fourth generation of the family.

In between having foals, Cuillin Hills has done her share of work and has just completed her eighth season hunting hounds! She is now 17 and still has completely clean limbs. Colonel Crossley wants to hunt her again next season (1984–5) before they try to put her in foal again. She adores the hounds, is a great performer and is, he says, the best ever to go cubhunting on. She has immaculate manners, is wonderfully careful and gentle with the young hounds and in moments of drama he can leap off her, leave her standing, and she will not move an inch.

'It was beginner's luck, I think, to breed something as lovely as she right at the start, and although I have been lucky enough to breed some other lovely young horses, I'd not produce another like that if I tried for the next 30 years. I am very lucky, too, that my husband is a farmer and has encouraged me with the breeding, and helped by putting all the farm resources at my disposal.'

Foals, who alter so tremendously and so often, can be forgiven certain weaknesses for 6 months or even more and are in consequence notoriously difficult to judge. In fact, the late Judge Wylie, chairman of the executive committee of the Royal Dublin Society from 1925 for 40-odd years, once put it to me in a nutshell when he remarked: 'To judge a foal is the hardest thing I know. All you can do, really, is to look for two good ends and hope that one day they will join up!'

CHAPTER 13

The owners

WHATEVER inspires anyone to become an owner of show horses — to spend a lot of money on a horse or horses that they will probably never ride, to enlist the services of a professional nagsman and to follow them round the circuit of Newark and Royal Windsor in May, the Bath and West, Three Counties and South of England in June, the Royal, Peterborough, Great Yorkshire and Royal International in July, and after the major county shows, finishing up with the Horse of the Year Show in October?

Major Cecil Drabble was typical of the old type of owner. Both he and his father hunted, but he was the only one of his family who actually went into the horse world. He hunted, from the age of 16, with as many packs of hounds as anyone, starting in Cheshire, where he was bred, hunting with the Cheshire Hounds when the Duke of Westminster had them, before the First World War. 'Champion was huntsman and the whole turn-out was quite wonderful. There were three whippers-in, four covert hacks and it was an amazing show at the Meet.

'Then I hunted with the Eton College Beagles, when the Master was the Duke of Beaufort (as Lord Worcester), and then I hunted in Lincolnshire where I went to learn farming. My biggest piece of luck was that Tommy Jessop, Master of the Southwold Hounds from 1920, was a great friend. He had an accident and was unable to ride, and sent me a telegram to ride his horse in a point-to-point, which I duly did. I was then 19 years old, and I further widened my experience by playing polo in York and in London before going to the Whaddon Chase country, where I have lived ever since.

'I had my first show horse in 1936. He came from Oliver Dixon, who had a huge dealing yard at Reading, and he was a top-class heavyweight. After he had won everything at Olympia I sold him to the United States to Mr Dick Mellon, who rang up and said he was the best horse he'd had for years. He paid me £950 for him and never showed him again. I won the novice class with him, he was not entered for the heavyweight class but I brought him back for the championship of the Saturday and he won that too, and also the Champion of All England gold cup at Peterborough.

'I lived in the Argentine from 1924–26, playing a lot of polo, and brought 23 ponies home to sell. When they landed at Liverpool they cost £83 a head (£50 purchase price in camp and the cost of the journey) and they sold at a top reserve of £450.

'From 1930 until 1939 my wife kept as good a stable of horses as any — 14 of them, for we hunted four days a week, and showed. Then war came. I went as a Second Lieutenant in an ack-ack regiment and came out a Lieutenant-Colonel. Then I went home and started showing again. I had very good horses and Harry Bonner to ride them for me, as I had become too heavy — not to mention too old! — to ride them myself; so I did the next best thing and got Harry to do it for me. I was Master of the Whaddon Chase for seven seasons, from 1947 to 1954, and I hunted hounds myself the first season as the huntsman was ill.

'The next really good horse I had was Gold Dust, who was bred in Co. Wexford by Roy Latta, who has bred so many outstanding heavyweights. He holds a record that has never been beaten, and I daresay never will be, of having never been beaten in 15 major championships. In 1960 Bert Cleminson bought him from me and sent him to America — he was one of the best I ever rode and a great hunter. Neil Foster rode him in a very good hunt with the Grafton and he carried him top-hole.

'I have been lucky enough to have judged at practically every show — Dublin, the Stallion Show, the Royal; the Hunter Show several times, and I had the great privilege of being the first person to put up Mighty Fine at Richmond. He had won the championship at Dublin for Nat Galway-Greer the previous year, 1947. I was judging with Bert Davies and he said: "He's a very lazy horse, but the more you ride him the better he goes. Don't judge him on the first twice, go round four or five times."

'But the best horse I ever rode in my life was John Peel, a dark brown horse belonging to Lady Helen McCalmont. He was hunted in the Cottesmore country by Mr Bob Strawbridge, an American, and was sold at Tattersalls for £450. Horace Smith, who taught most of the Royal Family, including the Queen and Princess Alexandra, to ride, came up to me and said: "Buy this horse, take him to Tunbridge Wells and he'll win."

'I was a young man and a fool so I didn't, and he was shown with great success by Binty Marshall, the mother of Bryan, who won two Grand Nationals in the 1950s on Early Mist and Royal Tan. But he still did not hold the record like Gold Dust.

'I started judging with Tiddly Lucas, who introduced me to showing, and we judged together every other year at Bath from 1935 onwards, and again after the war. He was a great judge who really knew what he was doing.

'I've had a few funny experiences in this business. Once I remember buying a horse in Yorkshire, and the Colonel of a very well known cavalry regiment came up to me and said: "I like your horse; will you find me one like that? — but I want the tail off." So I took him home, took the tail off, put resin on the stump, and two weeks later I sold him to the Colonel for £50 more than I had asked him before!

'One of the best deals I ever had was when I bought a horse which no one thought was any good at all for £150. I kept him four months, rode him very hard, everyone suddenly thought he was a marvellous horse and I was able to sell him for £1,000!'

The doyen of show horse owners for a great many years was Hugh Sumner, who was Master of the Worcestershire Hounds from 1933 until 1945. His father, who had hunted with the South Staffordshire, started the Typhoo tea company in 1902. He went to Ceylon, brought back a few chests of small tea which in those days was thought to be worth nothing, threw it into the roots and dug it in to grow Typhoo.

Born in Yardley, he remembers hunting through Coleshill woods as a boy, though now it is simply a vast area of housing estates stretching for miles through the suburbs of Birmingham. Before the First World War he was the first Hon. Secretary of the Worcestershire, and had his first point-to-point horse, Tidelock, which Jack H. Gittins rode for him, followed by Jack Fowler.

Then at the old Cheltenham Repository he bought a mare called Fancy That who nobody could stop for the first mile-and-a-half, after which she fell. He gave the ride on her — a dubious privilege, one might think — to Martin Gibbs, who was renowned as a good man on a bad horse. He then rode Tidelock, bred by his brothers-in-law out of a sister to Sunlock, the winner of the 1914 Grand National. Tidelock was difficult to keep sound until he won, but having crossed that hurdle he went on to win another 13 races with no trouble at all. He was trained from home by old John Collier, his stud groom, who was with Hugh for 30 years and used to think nothing of leaving Droitwich station at 6 in the morning when they were racing on the Shropshire/ Herefordshire side of the country and not getting back until 1 a.m. on the following morning.

'I started showing in a small way in the 1920s. I loved to buy a horse and try to make him into a show horse. Then I graduated to bigger shows and went to Ireland for my horses. I was made to begin showing by Dr Harrison of Harristown, fifty miles from Dublin. He ran a mental hospital and he said that if I didn't get out and do something else I'd be in there with him!

'We first met selling horses at Tattersalls in the 1930s, and Tiddley Lucas had sent some up at the same time. He came up and said: "Why don't you come over and look at my horses?". He was the first man except the dealer, Oliver Dixon, who had asked me to look at horses, and I'd had a lot of trouble with private people.

'I remember the time, before 1914, when you could go into a field with from 17 to 25 unbroken horses in it, 3 and 4-year-olds, grand sorts all of them. I bought the lot, hardly able to believe my eyes. Then the war came, the horses had to go out, they did badly and there was no corn for them. I lost three or four — or rather, I had them put down because I couldn't bear the sight of them. In fact, I put down what would have been the best I'd ever owned — a racehorse, he ran in the Dudley Cup: a big brown horse, a bit impetuous in his first season — I can see him now . . .

'Point-to-points were the only thing in my head, on the farm I was getting deeper and deeper into the mire, so in 1905 I went to Canada for four years with £10 in my pocket. I farmed for the first year at £1 a month plus my keep, then got onto a survey party on the railway line from the Dakotas up to Brandon; it was to go on to Hudson Bay but they found another route and shut down.

'I stayed the winter with friends I had got to know during the first year; everyone was trying to get on to survey parties. I said to my hosts, who were fine old Scots folk: "I'm going to try my luck", and I walked a mile out of town down a dirt track, all done with mules and donkeys and a two-handed digger, walked into the engineer's office, the old Mac was at work at his drawing board and I said: "Any chance of a job?"

'He didn't bother to look up, just said "No". The following week it was "No" again, the third time he looked up and said: "This is the third time you've been, get the hell out of here, I'll let you know if I ever want you".

'The fourth time he sent a boy out on a bicycle who said: "If you are ready in an hour he will give you the job", so I took my haversack down to the livery stable to wait for him. When he arrived he said: "Do you know why I sent for you? Because you're a damn nuisance!"

'I went to Wakapole and drove stakes in for the first season, working with carthorses and bronchos, and I got quite handy with the instruments. There were four of us — the Canadian surveyor, old Mac the engineer and an Englishman who died that summer in hospital with a temperature of 103 or 104, having caught typhoid as there was no proper water to drink.

'I alternated between driving stakes and shingling roofs, and the fourth winter old Mac put up for a job in British Columbia. He was given a ticket to Portland, Oregon, and after that he had to pay his way.

'Typhoo was just getting into its stride and doing well, but I told father I couldn't sit in an office, I wanted to be an agricultural engineer, so I went to Percy Toone at Nuneaton, served articles, finished the job at Melton and Woodhall Spa in Lincolnshire, then went home and took up a partnership; but the man went broke, and I got out just in time.

'I had been turned down for the Army three times on medical grounds and in 1916 my father said again: "Pity you don't come into Typhoo", and offered me a day's hunting a week as a concession. By then I was really interested in horses and that did the trick! I started showing seriously in the 1930s. My first champion was a strong middleweight called Loyalist; the biggest gentleman of a horse I ever owned. At the end of the war he won at a little show on the Birmingham side of Stratford. He'd been out all through the war, but I could still ride him round the outside of the ring with one hand, without his trying to cut in. Old Harry Gittins was there and brought Beau Geste too, but we beat them over the ridge and furrow.

'I had a lot of horses from Nat Galway-Greer, but never a really good one until Work of Art, who won his class in Dublin with Jack Gittins in 1957. I didn't tell a soul I was interested, but said to myself: "Wait till he gets in the big ring and then see if he gallops". Then, before I did, I saw Nat and asked him: "Do you want to sell your big horse?"

'Nat said: "I'll take so-and-so for him." I said: "I'll give you so-and-so."

'"He's yours!" said Nat, so I beat Selby (a clothing manufacturer from England) and an Italian buyer. Work of Art came to England and won a great many championships, having won the Dublin supreme championship, though here he was beaten now and again by Prince's Grace, a lovely bay mare who won a great many lightweight and ladies' classes for my daughter Jean (Mrs Alex Wood), and then became a champion brood mare, winning the National Hunter Show title in 1964, 1964 and 1967.'

Mrs Wood had another good horse in Urney Road, the Dublin champion in 1967, ridden by Michael Hickey, whom Lord Daresbury once described as 'The Irish Jack Gittins'. Hugh Summer's best horses included the middleweight

Blarney Stone, a rare galloper, Fine Art and Tartan Bird. Latterly he became disenchanted with showing, which he said was: 'Killing itself with corruption' and turned instead to 'chasing, where he said: 'The winner is first past the post, for all to see.'

In the 1950s he bought a farm in Co. Wexford, which Brigadier Plunket looked after for him. At one time Toss Taaffe had four horses in training for him, all bred on the farm out of a mare Jack Gittins had bought him as a foal at Newmarket to run with another. She won four races and then bred four foals, of which the first three were really good ones. Both his show horses and his 'chasers were fine-looking specimens, with size and scope, depth and great limbs. 'I do insist on a good hind leg, and I've bought racehorses in all shapes!' One of the happiest days of his life was when he was president of the Three Counties Show in the 1960s and the Queen Mother paid an official visit. They talked steeple-chasing for much of the day.

Owners who breed a racehorse that looks like a hunter sometimes show it while waiting for it to mature, as Colonel and Mrs Frank Dean did with Troodos, who did very well as a middleweight with Willie Donaldson before being put to a sterner trade. Mrs James Hanbury (now Lady Keith) took up showing young hunters with considerable success after her husband died — he was Master of the Belvoir from 1947. Most people who have shown horses for any length of time generally seem to revert to it whenever they breed or otherwise acquire anything good enough.

Mr and Mrs Frank Furness are true devotees who breed and show their young horses and cheerfully embark on long journeys in the horse-box to and from their home in North Yorkshire, of which he has been High Sheriff. They have had their share of success and misfortune, especially when their Royal Show champion, the homebred Seta Pike, ran a nail into his foot at the Horse of the Year show and left the ring on three legs and pouring blood, on his way to the Royal Veterinary College.

Frank Furness served on the Council for three periods from 1953 to 1965 — the late Lord Digby was Chairman of the Council and took a very active part in the conduct of its affairs, owning a premium stallion himself. 'My appointment came about through coming to know Major K. P. Wallis, for whom I had stewarded when he came to judge at the Yorkshire Show. Major Wallis was also a very active member and was on the Council for the whole time that I was — as a Remount Officer it had been his duty to purchase for the Household Cavalry. Sidney Parker also took a very active part at the show, and subsequently established the section for blacksmiths when the venue was moved to Shrewsbury.

'The late Major Meredith was Hon. Show Director and was most highly regarded by the stud grooms and the exhibitors, as he made a point of being on the showground the evening before, to welcome them upon their arrival. During this period Mr C. C. Wright was Secretary and Gerald Evans came to us to help in the office and also attended our meetings.

'There were some very eminent people in the horse world on the Council at that time. The late Duke of Gloucester was President in 1955 and after presiding at a meeting he stayed on to talk for such a long time that many of us were in danger of missing our train to return home.

'As far as the Show is concerned, so many changes have taken place in the post-war years — I have my father's 1910/11 *Stud Book* in which there is a photograph of his champion lightweight hunter, Monarch, and before the War the London Spring Show as it was known was the most important event in the Society's year — an altogether unique occasion with entries from every part of the country. It was held at the Royal Agricultural Hall at Islington and the horses all came by train and had to be led down to Islington by way of the back streets, frequently with a guide who waited at the railway stations in the hope of earning half-a-crown. Despite the difficulties and discomforts it was an event to which the Stud Grooms looked forward from year to year. Many of them had to sleep in empty boxes with a horse rug, but nevertheless they looked very smart and tidy when exhibiting in the main ring.

'The show was held in February and the 4-year-olds were shown in hand. None of the exhibits were allowed to be clipped, and it required great skill to have their coats looking right, involving grooming and rugging-up as early as November.

'The Premium Horses were judged on the first day and the Young Stock on the second day with the Group Classes, and the Saddle Horses on the third day in their three respective weights. Unfortunately I have no catalogue of these respective classes, but it was so very interesting to see the progeny of the respective stallions, and particularly the Group Classes, all at one show. Each day there was what would now be regarded as a very elementary jumping class, and some of the Yorkshire exhibitors would bring a jumping cob with them in the hope of earning something towards their expenses.

'The judging was of a very high order, and the line of entries was stopped by the water jump halfway down one side and each horse run up to see how it moved. If the judges were not satisfied the entry was told to stand below the water jump, and at the conclusion those exhibitors were told they would not be required for further judging and were given permission to leave the ring. Incidentally, Eddie Griffith was one of the junior stewards at that time.

'The Agricultural Hall had a passage right round the ring below the Stands, and one could walk round to examine any particular entry in close proximity, just over the rails.

Women are often quite avid exhibitors, sometimes because they are bored or lonely and a hectic showing life helps them to pretend that they are not; sometimes because they really love it. When she gave up hunting and racing the Hon. Mrs Stella Cardiff, daughter of Lord Newborough, became very keen after being initiated into the delights of the show ring by Jack Gittins, who bought her a lightweight son of the premium stallion Top Walk and showed him for her with great success for four seasons. Afterwards he carried Major Bob Hoare hunting the Cottesmore for several seasons. His name was Palladium, and other successful members of her string were High Hope, Young Apollo, Hunter's Moon and Kilkenny Beau. They gave their owner infinite pleasure and a full and happy life.

Mrs Molly Dowley, whose horses were shown by Roy Trigg, also enjoyed her showing tremendously. Reg Tweedie, owner-breeder of that great 'chaser of the 1960s, Freddie, was her cousin. Her best horse was probably the last of a sizeable succession, Aintree by Devonian, who went on to do well under National Hunt rules.

Norman Crow's was a name to conjure with a few years ago, both with led and ridden horses. He virtually established a lien on the Edward, Prince of Wales Cup at Shrewsbury, which he won nine times between 1952 and 1976, but though he had some brood mares, almost all his big winners were bought in. 'Breeding is so much of a gamble' he told me once, 'that I prefer to buy my foals!'

The National Hunter Show is his 'local show'; he farms not far away at Ercall Park, near Wellington, and was Master for many years of the North Shropshire Hounds. The grandson of the owner of a woollen mill at Hay, in Perthshire, between Dunblane and Crieff. In 1900, when he was 20, the younger son was sent South to join his brother, who was farming, equipped with a new suit of clothes, a Bible and his train fare. As soon as he had earned the price of his fare he sent it back again. Now his four sons own and farm 6,000 acres between them.

Norman was born at Trysull, near Wolverhampton, where Mrs Howard Mander (mother of the late Mrs V. D. S. Williams) had the manor house and Norman's father had the farm. When Norman was 16 months old his father moved to Forton Hall, near Newport, but he kept on Trysull and all four of his sons served their farming apprenticeship there.

His father kept Shires, but Norman started hunting with the Allbrighton as a child, in General Hickman's day, and was blooded in 1926. The youngest son, he started farming on his own account when he was 18, helping to farm Cherrington Manor, near Newport. (This was the original 'house that Jack built', which information is written on one of the old beams!)

Norman's first success on a horse was to win the riding horse class at Pony Club camp on the West Midlands showground in 1935. There were some 25 entries and the age limit was 13 to 17 years. Then he showed the odd saddle horse up to the outbreak of war, and after the war ended he started showing young stock and hunting seriously. In 1948 he took on his right-hand man, Harry Jarrett, and his son Gordon, a good nagsman. Harry, a great judge of a horse, remained with him until he died in 1974, and in his memory Norman presented a cup at the Hunter Show.

One of the first horses to win from Ercall Park, where Norman and his wife Lena had moved in 1943, was Legacy, bought as a yearling from the Yorkshire breeder, Harry Shrubbs. He was shown successfully as a 2-year-old but fractured his skull in his box at 4. Eventually he was drowned in his flooded box when the river overflowed its banks. By George Here, he came from a very good family and his dam, Lorna, bred several 3-day-event horses.

At the same time he bought the 7-year-old Royal Surprise at the Royal at York from Tom L. Parke, who was in the printing business in Lancashire, and he showed him successfully for a couple of seasons before buying the Dublin winner Goody Goody from Nat Galway-Greer. After a season in the ring he was sold to the United States.

Then from E. G. MacAndrew of Basingstoke he bought the good heavyweight mare May Marcus, with foal at foot and in foal again, and she was a good winner and the dam of winners at the major shows. But his first real champion was Prenotion, bought in Ireland as a yearling, under the hammer at Goffs' Sales and unbeaten for the next two seasons in England. He was followed by Devotion, also Irish-bred. These two won the Edward, Prince of Wales Cup in 1952 and 1954 respectively. Devotion won 53 first prizes in hand and went on to win five 4-year-old classes off the reel.

Gay Gordon, another led champion, was sold to Mrs Gold as a dressage horse and Greetings, who came from Archie Thomlinson, also went to Mrs Gold and gained fame as Roman Holiday.

Mic-Mac was bought from Mrs Harry Frank and was Norman's third winner of the Prince of Wales' Cup, in 1958, before being sold to Italy to be show-jumped by the d'Inzeo brothers. May Marcus's son, Ercall, also went to Italy and did well as an event horse. Another son, Matador, was sold to Ireland, went into training with Joe Osbourne and was bought by Sir John Pascoe to run in the name of Timken. A yearling, Ballyhal by Prince Hal, bought from Nat Galway-Greer, won his first two novice 'chases by a distance, but slipped at the water third time out and never ran again.

Right Spirit, bred by George Maundrell by his stallion Game Rights out of a mare by Gay Scot won a lot in hand before being sold to Japan to do dressage. Berkeley, sold by the Franks to win the Prince of Wales' Cup in 1965, won three 'chases in 1966 but developed a cough before the National, in which he stood a good chance. Charmaine, bought in Dublin as a yearling, in 1962 became the first filly to win the Prince of Wales' Cup and in 1968 and '69 won the HIS. Champion Cup for the best brood mare. Her daughter Pennace, by Pannier, was a good in-hand winner in her own right.

Then came Gamekeeper, now in Canada, where he was ridden by Ian Angus, one of the best 3-day event riders, and rated the second-best horse in the Dominion; Goldwyn and Goldsmith, who won the Prince of Wales' Cup twice, in 1963 and 1964. Goldsmith won the Royal four years running, was never beaten in hand and must have won at least 70 classes, averaging 25 shows a year. Bought off the Yorkshire moors as a weaned foal, and after a hazardous car journey with a foot of snow on the ground, he was found tied up in a carthorse stable with a sow and piglets next door. Norman had already bought his brother the previous year and later bought their full sister, Caravelle. All were by Top Walk out of Quick Pay by Paques, and though Quick Pay never ran, the grand-dam was a winner of 'chases.

The middleweight Top Notch was also bought unbroken in Yorkshire, as a 3-year-old at the Great Yorkshire show from Mr and Mrs Guy Rob of Thirsk. He went on to a distinguished career under saddle, and in the hunting field after winning two Wembley titles and two *Horse & Hound* Cups at the HIS ridden show at The Royal. His successor, Fair Gin by Quality Fair, bred by Maxie Jones of the Elton Estates, near Peterborough, out of a little bay mare called Gin-Can, was shown in hand from Ercall Park with his younger brother, Gin Fair, who nearly always got the better of him in led championships. But whereas Gin Fair was never shown under saddle, Fair Gin went on to great thing in the ridden classes, winning the *Horse & Hound* Cup in 1971 and 1972. In the latter year Norman Crow had both the top middleweight and the leading 3-year-old, for his Fresco, by Foxstar, won the Lloyds Bank in-hand championship at Wembley.

All Norman's horses take their turn with hounds and they can all be hunted in snaffles. Although some young horses graduate from a heavy public life in young stock classes with a one-sided mouth, or even with no mouth at all, these youngsters do not suffer from being shown. The bits are suspended from straps on the headcollar and the weight of the lead rein is on the headcollar, not on the bit.

None of them go elsewhere to be produced, but are produced from home, which was a hunting lodge for Lord Barnard, Duke of Cumberland, of Raby Castle in the Zetland country.

Lady Zinnia Pollock was among the leading exhibitors in the 1970s, and became so because she is a lover of beautiful things, and especially of beautiful horses; 'As near perfect as possible. It is a challenge to find the perfect horse, and though one knows one never will, I love to see just how close to perfection I can come. Each year I try to do better than the previous one, but horses are becoming most difficult to find.

'Jack Gittins started me off when I was 17 and my mother (the Countess of Londesborough) sent me to work for him. I rode a small hunter that was sold on to Jane McHugh at one or two shows. Then, many years later, Roy Trigg started showing Plenty of Time for me. I have been lucky enough to associate with the people who are very knowledgeable, like the Toulsons, "Tub" Ivens and David Barker. David and Roy are two of the best all-round horsemen, Vin Toulson is a fantastic showman while Robert Orssich taught me a lot about looking at horses. He really has an amazing eye. Now I have acquired a good memory for a horse' — the old-time dealers used to say that once you have seen a horse you should never forget it, which always seemed to me to be a very tall order! — 'and I learned from him to be very quick to sum a horse up. If I don't really like a horse and can't make up my mind about it I never go back — it is always a mistake.'

Some people look at the hind leg first, others start at the opposite end with the head. Lady Zinnia is adamant that the eye is also an important consideration for her, followed by the general pattern and movement. 'A correctly-made horse is usually a good ride. I have been made aware of good forelegs recently as there are so many bad ones about.' (Which may, to judge by what one sees in Dublin, be put down to the type of draught mare which the *Old* Irish Horse Board tended to encourage.)

Lady Zinnia has sold a few horses abroad and always had a couple of trading horses at home to pay for the liveries. Ideally Thoroughbreds, to have several outlets, they always see hounds in their youth. They have gone as dressage and event horses to Germany, Holland, Italy, and one to the United States. She always buys in England, often out of *Horse & Hound*, direct from the breeders. This involves endless wasted trips and adds up to a tremendous mileage, but it has its rewards on occasion.

'I never keep a horse whose character I don't like. Mostly I buy broken horses but if I see a young one I like I sometimes have it — one can buy them better.

'The biggest thrill is to win with a horse that has never won before. I was also extremely lucky to win the Champion of England Gold Cup and the reserve at Peterborough's East of England show for two years running.'

Despite sponsorship, she feels that prize money is still very poor indeed, even at the big shows, and still gauged to the days between the wars when people did not have to cover their outgoings or attempt to make it pay. The professionals are still very necessary — they are so much better at the job and it is, after all, a professional sport; one wants to be completely involved, for it is not possible to play at showing and succeed. Few of those who showed until the early 1970s can now afford to do so. Some of the newcomers lack the sporting spirit that once prevailed, in which case they either learn to accept defeat gracefully or drop out.

As a concession to financial necessity, Lady Zinnia finally kept her horses at home, drove her horses to the shows herself and David Barker just got up at the show; this promises to be the general pattern now, except for commercially-owned horses, of which both Robert Oliver and Vin Toulson have amassed a considerable collection.

CHAPTER 14

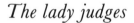

The lady judges

WATCHING the average side-saddle class, one is often inclined to think that the art of riding 'sideways' is a dying one, and that the ability to turn out correctly is also moribund — until, that is, the judge gets up. Mercifully, there are still people who look both elegant and effective on a side-saddle and for whom horses go extremely well — it has of course always been a fact of life that horses which do not go particularly well for men often become saints when they are shown in ladies' classes; though I do recall one Dublin reserve champion who ran away with a lady judge at the Great Yorkshire Show and went round that huge arena three times, faster than light, before he could be pulled up. The poor lady had missed the presidential luncheon in order to judge the class — but at least she was spared the embarrassment of being observed by too many friends in her headlong flight.

Perhaps the greatest expert of the side-saddle in recent memory was Mrs Doreen Archer-Houblon of Thomastown, Co. Kilkenny, whose book on the subject was published by *Country Life* between the wars. She it was who not only taught The Queen to ride side-saddle, but used to give Her Majesty an annual refresher course before the Trooping the Colour ceremony.

The Hon. Mrs James Baird, whose husband was Master of the Cottesmore in 1921 and again from 1928–31, was one of the best lady judges. The daughter of the Viscount Harcourt, she was tall and statuesque and every horse went well for her, as they did too for the Hon. Lady Hardy, daughter of Lord Hindlip, whose husband, Colonel Rupert Hardy, was in the Lifeguards. Another lady judge who looked marvellous on a side-saddle was Mrs Arthur Smith-Bingham (Iso), who also had wonderful hands, Lady Stanier (sister of Colonel Sir John Miller, the Crown Equerry), Mrs Maurice Tollit (Nat) and Lady Violet Vernon, wife of Major Mervyn Vernon and daughter of the second Earl of Cromer, who married the daughter of the fourth Earl of Minto, Governor-General of Canada and Viceroy of India.

Letty Vernon was bred to ride, for Lord Minto was a celebrated amateur steeplechase jockey, riding in the name of Mr Rolley (pronounced Roley), his nickname at Eton. At Trinity College Cambridge his contemporaries included the Hon. W. H. and Charles Fitzwilliam, Lord Aberdour, the Rev. Cecil Legard (of *Foxhound Kennel Stud Book* renown), Mr J. Maunsell Richardson, who won two Grand Nationals, and Mr Leopold de Rothschild.

He took his degree with his gown concealing racing gear, after which he galloped most of the 7 miles to Cottenham and just arrived in time to win the

University Steeplechase. He rode in the Grand National five times, finishing fourth once and breaking his neck on another occasion, but he fared better in France, winning the Grand Steeplechase de Paris at Auteuil on Miss Hungerford in 1874, the only amateur in a field of 17 professionals. Like his niece, who hunted with the Duke of Beaufort's Hounds, he was a keen foxhunter with the Brocklesby (of which his friend Maunsell Richardson was a joint-Master) and a fine judge of a horse.

Mrs George Gibson, widow of the celebrated Oakham veterinary surgeon, is also equally proficient on either type of saddle, and has an infallible eye for any horse or pony. In 1975 she became the first woman to be invited by the HIS Council to judge their Stallion Show. Her co-judge, Jack Waugh the Newmarket trainer, said afterwards: 'She is a wonderful judge of a horse and her attention to detail is unending. Until one has the honour of judging with her, one does not realise the full extent of her knowledge'.

The eldest of a family of six, her father, Percy Bradley, was a farmer and horse dealer in the Cottesmore country, of which hounds she has been a joint-Master since 1976. He bred some high-class show horses which were shown all summer, carefully broken at 3, continued on to hunting and sold at 7 — anything younger was not considered to have had enough experience for Leicestershire.

When she was 6 she rode in her first show and everyone was most kind and said how well she'd done except Papa, who told her in no uncertain terms how half-baked her performance had been. But hunting was always the proper business. Her ponies were clipped out and rather fresh and she was often frightened. On quiet, less fashionable Mondays and Thursdays she was allowed to hunt all day and stay with Papa, who would be on a young horse. There were no horse boxes and they left at 9 a.m. for the furthest Meets, getting home around 4.30. On Tuesdays and Saturdays she was allowed ¾ of a day in charge of a kind old lady. When she got home she was always asked if her pony had refused, and why (it was always one's own fault) and if she had got in the way or been a nuisance. Otherwise, it was wonderful coming home to tea of eggs and toast and to talk over the way the horses had gone.

Her best pony came from Mr Horace Smith, the Royal riding master, and was a chesnut mare called Columbine who started by being fussy and hot but was an incredibly good hunter. When her father called back to her 'Let her have her head and come on', the ditches were really big. Columbine settled well and together they won at many shows. 'Unfortunately, I have always been short and square. In my teens I was far too heavy — Mother was too good a cook! At that time we saw quite a lot of Reg Hobbs, whose son Bruce (who won the 1939 Grand National on Battleship) used to show a white mare called Lady Marvel. I recall him saying to father at the Royal, where I'd been lucky enough to win: "Yes, the pony is grand — but Percy, old boy, you'll have to 'fine down' the girl quite a bit!"'

School was secondary. At first she shared a governess with a doctor's daughter before progressing to a local day school. The moment school was over she was in the field being schooled by Father. At first she was scared stiff, being nearly jumped off every night. Then one night she seemed to get the hang of it and suddenly all was well.

They lived in an attractive old farmhouse with lovely stables that had been occupied by the Hon. Lancelot Lowther. There were masses of out-houses and they had great fun keeping ferrets. A dear, large old lady used to do the family washing there, and one day when she was bending over the washtub, Joan and her brother let loose a couple of ferrets under her long petticoats. They got into terrible trouble.

The children had to keep their riding clothes clean themselves, but their boots were polished for them. Joan had curly hair to her shoulders, which was tightly plaited by her mother on hunting days and sewn up with black thread, like the horses' manes. A bowler crowned the edifice, right on the centre of the head. All the children had jobs to do and were kept very busy, but every evening in summer they and their parents played tennis, cricket or hide-and-seek games.

When Joan was 16 they moved to Chapel Farm, just outside Oakham, which had a yard to hold more than 16 horses, off the road, with light grass, small coverts and fences of every type. Some of the fields were used by friends to gallop their point-to-point horses. By now she was hunting four days a week on their own horses, while on a Belvoir Wednesday and a Quorn Friday she would go over to Scalford Lodge, near Melton, to hunt Mr Jimmy and Lady Eileen Clarke's horses with them.

'All the horses were high-class, top performers. It was practically all grass and one just kept jumping, and never had to look to see if any obstacle was safe. Once when someone broke her collarbone over a piece of wire in a fence on her father's estate the farm manager got a dreadful wigging. New horses were coming in several times a week. If they came from Ireland via a certain place in Yorkshire they were ready for sale after a couple of good hunts. If they came from another place in the South they had never seen a ditch towards and would give their riders many a fright, and took longer to get the hang of standing right off the top of a ditch.

'It was always exciting when they came straight from Leicester Repository with a full warranty and had to be tried hunting — and even more exciting when Father hoped he'd bought a bargain with no warranty!

'One was always taught to take care of horses and never to ride "out" an unfit or tired horse. Similarly, always to check carefully every bit of tackle before riding or hunting: to make most careful adjustments to bridles, and to observe most carefully the temperament and type of horse, as well as assessing very quickly indeed that this horse would suit Mr So-and-So, and that one Miss So-and-So.'

As a girl, Joan had always hunted all winter and shown all summer, chiefly home-bred youngsters. The horses were always turned out to perfection and behaved immaculately, and Percy Bradley showed them himself. One day he went into the stables with a side-saddle and told his daughter: 'You had better learn to ride this way as well. It must be very easy, because many of the women who ride side-saddle very well cannot ride astride at all!'

Always ready to have a go at anything, Joan was put up, sideways, on a strong middleweight horse that was very good-looking but had not yet been sold as he was such a coward out hunting. In vain did she complain that it was most uncomfortable. In a very short time the horse was shown at the

Royal Norfolk, and she had to ride him there. A very kind hunting lady, Mrs Joan Kimball, gave her one of her very well-cut Roberts and Carroll habits, and they managed a very bumpy second in the class.

'Since then I have had the most wonderful advice and help from the Hon. Mrs D. Campbell, Mrs Oliver Gilbey, Mrs Dinah Kent, and I kept reading that Bible of side-saddle riding, written by Colonel Jack Hance. I always watched his daughter Jackie's every graceful movement on a side-saddle. I had no one to teach me, and was so grateful for their expert advice.

'I was first asked to judge when I was 19 or 20, my "sponsor" being a very well-known side-saddle judge, the show a fairly large county one where her husband was a steward. The side-saddle class was not too difficult but the hack-hunter class, as they were often called, was a very different job — quite a large class of rather indifferent animals.

'The obvious winner, a right type, stood top, followed by the lesser quality animals. However, the top horse made a very sticky show, to be followed by even worse. The only animal that behaved was very plain and poor but a good mover. All this was a bit galling, and when I went to ride them they went even worse, except for the plain one. When they were trotting out I suppose it was obvious that I was going to do something drastic so my "sponsor" sent in her husband, the steward, to whisper that the plain one was, he was sure, going lame.

'That really made me flaming mad and bang to the top went the local plain hack. I was taken severely to task by the lady afterwards, when she admitted trying to "save the day" for me. I apologised, I hope politely, but said that if I was to judge I should put exactly what I liked at the top, no manner what public opinion might be, and I have certainly never changed my tactics — nor, I hope, ever will.'

Mrs David Bourne, daughter of the celebrated veterinary surgeon J.B. Walker, is an excellent side-saddle judge as are Mrs Nigel Pease, the former Ailsa Smith-Maxwell, and Nikki Gretton, daughter of Mrs Tollit, and Sally McCanlis, daughter of the late Mrs Christopher Mackintosh, one of the most elegant riders in the ring in the 1950s and 1960s and, as the former Irene Mann-Thompson, bred to ride properly. The three Bullen sisters — Jennie Loriston-Clarke, Jane Holderness-Rodden and Sarah Bullen — are also first-class, as is Mrs Sherwin from Yorkshire. But good judges were thin on the ground until Royal Windsor Horse Show Committee decided to put on children's side-saddle classes, which has brought on a new generation of enthusiastic exponents of this considerable art.

Lady Violet Vernon compiled a list of truths about this form of riding after many years of doing it very well indeed. Though slim and light, she was equally successful astride and often judged hunters under both saddles.

The broad principles of riding side-saddle she considered to be the same as those for riding astride. Balance and suppleness are essential to each. Poise comes from firmness of seat and, consequently, independence of hand. As you cannot fall off, at times it is all too easy.

Saddles should have a general fitting tree, for too wide a horse can crack a tree. A horse unaccustomed to a side-saddle will at first turn in a small circle, due to the balance strap. The skirt or apron is similar to a rug. The saddle weighs from 16 to 20 lbs. — compared with a cross saddle at only 11–12 lbs — and is far more costly.

Pretend there is a tin-tack under left bottom. Balance from right thigh and leg. The leaping head is for jumping and in an emergency.

(1) The base of one's spine should at all times be directly over the horse's spine.
(2) Hips square to the front.
(3) Shoulders level.
(4) If left hip gets further back from right one loses strength of seat.
(5) Don't lean to the right — if the horse bucks or shies to the right one will fly off.
(6) Hands should almost meet.

There is a vast difference between a woman sitting correctly on top of a horse and a woman who sits *into* it.
Common faults are:
Bending from shoulders.
Poking chin.
Putting toe down.
When rising, the impetus comes straight from the right thigh, *not* from one's weight in the iron.
When jumping, go with the horse.
When showing, have a straight horse, soft at the trot.

CHAPTER 15

The dealers

THE TWO categories of horseman who can be depended upon to know more about the horse than almost anyone else are the dealers, who have paid for their knowledge, and the cavalry officers, now an extinct breed. Before they passed into limbo the latter spent a considerable part of their lives buying remounts, and though they were not spending their own money, as the dealers were, they would still not have been allowed to make the same mistake too often.

Captain Andrew MacIlwaine, who lived for many years at Guilsborough, in the heart of the Pytchley country, combined both rôles. Born in 1894 in the East Riding, his earliest recollection was of the fireworks and bonfires which accompanied Queen Victoria's Diamond Jubilee when he was 3 years old.

His father was a businessman who brought oil into Hull, but he took an interest in horses as soon as he could walk and throughout his life thought of nothing but horses and farming. He went to school at Marston Moor and when he was 10 he asked the headmaster, who happened to be his cousin, whether he could take his pony home for the Christmas holidays. The answer was in the affirmative, provided he rode him. Nothing daunted — by now he was hunting one day a week with the York and Ainsty — he set off at 7.30 a.m. after an early breakfast and cantered up his own front drive in time for 4.30 tea.

The pony was a strong, cobby 14-hand roan, and in York they stopped to ask the way to Hull. Andrew stopped for lunch in a pub at Market Weighton, where the ostler fed the pony. There was an overpoweringly delicious smell of roast beef coming from the pub, but he was too shy to go in by himself and went instead to the corner shop, which is still standing, where he bought himself a bunch of grapes covered in cork shavings and a 3d. bar of chocolate.

Those holidays he hunted with the Holderness, as he continued to do all his life until a few years after the Second World War; Baily's states the best-bred horse available to be a necessity here, and the boy had so much fun with his pony that he was allowed to take it back to school by train.

He hated his public school days at Rugby, and persuaded his father to let him leave on the day before his sixteenth birthday, when he went to a local farm as a pupil. He had two horses, one given him by the farmer; he paid £35 for the other, and he hunted three or four days a week and rode round the farm on the other days.

'The gardener looked after them, and though one was a strong whistler and the other had sidebones, they were both good hunters. The £35 one, who had a short tail, I bought from a sporting builder in Hull, and before he let me have him I would ride him 40 miles to the Meet and back at night.'

When the First World War looked imminent he became a Government horse buyer at 20 years of age, when the man in charge of the requisitioning of horses asked him to take on a district. 'They were all commandeered, and I bought literally hundreds of horses all over the East Riding. They were nothing but draught horses for Artillery and Transport and I did the job with two assistants and rather a nice girl secretary, plus a vet. As soon as we finished buying, a month after war broke out in 1914, I enlisted in the cavalry as a trooper and was sent to Dublin, having applied for a commission. Less than a month later I was commissioned into the 6th Reserve Cavalry Regiment at Marlborough Barracks, Dublin, and I was there until the Spring of 1915, often hunting six days a week, in addition to riding at Punchestown and Fairyhouse.

'Then I was sent out to the 18th Hussars in France just after they had had a very bad time with the first gas attack and were very short of officers. I remained with them for the rest of the war and they were the grandest lot of people — Col. James Harman, the C.O., was later to become Commandant of the Army Equitation School at Weedon.

'I was lucky enough to come through the war unhurt and afterwards I got demobilised as quickly as possible and tried to get on with my life in the way I knew best. On getting home in the Spring of 1919 I was lucky enough to become the tenant of a 1,000 acre farm, Kellythorpe, near Driffield. There was more sport of various sorts to be had there on that farm than most. The shooting was good — partridges, pheasants, duck, snipe, hares and literally thousands of rabbits. And last but far from least, the Driffield Beck ran through the farm. It is reputed to be the best chalk stream in the north of England, or it was in those days, and probably still is. Within 100 yards of the house there was a charming small fox covert.

'More than once I filled in a September day as follows, without going off the farm: The Holderness hounds, having met at the farm, would kill a brace of cubs. After a late breakfast I would get on another horse and with my two lurchers would kill 2 or more hares. Nice little cock fences divided the fields, so it was not too difficult to keep in touch, even on a green horse.

'After lunch my delightful keeper, Snaith by name, and I would get up to 10 brace of partridges and numerous rabbits. After tea it was down to the stream for the evening rise — home at dusk with at least a brace, often 2-pounders. Then came a late supper and after that a walk round the farm buildings with the terriers and a torch. I remember one evening when they killed 40 rats. The stackyard usually had 40 beautifully built and thatched stacks in it — each one was a day's threshing.

'A good day's shooting I remember was when four of us killed 50 brace of partridges and 80 hares. Meat was scarce in 1919 and the local butcher gave me £40 for the hares — those were the days! But this idyllic life soon came to an end when Ramsay MacDonald and Lloyd George repealed the Corn Production Act and all the big farmers on the Yorkshire wolds found themselves virtually bankrupt. They opened cafés, took in paying guests, ran riding schools, and one after another collapsed, because by 1923 they were heading for the bankruptcy court. It was absolutely impossible to make farming pay.

'I was trying to keep going by selling a few horses when my great friend Colonel "Peach" Borwick, then Master of the Middleton Hounds, said: 'Pack up before you go broke, move into my country, set up as a horse dealer and I'll help you all I can'; which he did. Otherwise I should have been a certainty for bankruptcy. My total capital when I sold up was £2000. My daughter is married to "Pop" Arkright, former Joint Master and huntsman of the North Warwickshire, where my grandchildren are carrying on. But the horse dealing prospered. The financial crisis of 1930 was very trying, but I got through it and in 1931 "Peach" Borwick moved here to Hazelbeach, bringing with him that fine huntsman, Stanley Barker. The next year I moved down here too, built this house (at Guilsborough) in 1934, and I've been here ever since. There were a lot of good horses coming into the Midlands, for it was all grass up to the war: now there's a lot of plough, but that's inevitable. People thought me stupid to set up within a few miles of the Drages at Chapel Brampton and John Hardy at Rugby, but we were all friends and business prospered. When the Second World War broke out I was selling 350 a year.

'From the early days I was always so lucky to have topping fellows like Charles Reynard in Yorkshire, Geoffrey Bevan in the Cottesmore, and when I came here I asked Frank Hill near Cirencester to join me and act as my buyer. I couldn't be here selling and away buying. He agreed to come in with me and remained a long time. I bought a certain number in Ireland and went there once a month, but I also got a lot of good horses out of Norfolk, Lincolnshire and up in the North.

'In 1935 I was joined by Leslie Weaver. He had inherited a good business from his father in Cheshire, and he supplied the Duke of Westminster. He brought with him an exceptional horseman called Sydney Taylor, who is now on his own in Leicestershire. He had bought 90% of his horses in Ireland and became buyer for Ireland, buying all the Irish horses and showing a lot. Oliver Dixon and John Henry Stokes of Market Harborough all showed their best trade horses, and they were 2 of the biggest dealers between the wars.

'Then war came again, and the whole business was dispersed; 72 horses on the day war was declared, and no customers but the Army. On Sunday morning the Army buyers turned up just before 11 a.m. "What about your horses?" they asked. "You know we are now at war with Germany?"

'They bought 45, and we sold them at £55 apiece — many of them came from Dublin and had cost £200 the previous month. Anyway, it reduced our liabilities from 72 to whatever, and Jackie Upton got 12 point-to-point horses to the United States, to Mrs Hope Scott in Pennsylvania, for which we were eternally grateful: it was a very kind act.

'We kept the six best from the 72 — the sort of horses that are not to be found today, 14-stone blood Irish horses — until January, hoping against hope that it might be a short war. They were turned out on 1,000 acres. Then I sold them for £15 apiece. The Army had stopped buying. One was a mare that the late Captain Lionel Cecil of the British Bloodstock Agency had bought for me at Newmarket sales for £45. I gave her to my wife, and we sent her to the local premium stallion, Woodcote, who stood at a fee of £25.

'I wanted a mare to breed a good hunter or 'chaser, and asked Tattersalls to find me one at £100 or less. Lionel Cecil bid £45 for Conceal who was by

Big Game out of Nivea by Nearco. When I first inspected her I thought she was exactly the sort of mare I *didn't* want — weedy, light of bone, wouldn't make a decent hack and she had bad, bent hocks into the bargain. I was almost thinking of sending her to the kennels, until Tattersalls said that as she was a half-sister to French Beige and Rowston Manor, she would have cost nearly 50 times as much had her hocks been perfect.

'In 1957 she had Hidden Meaning, by Woodcut, who won three races out of five, and in 1962 she won the One Thousand Guineas Trial Stakes at Kempton, ridden by Eph Smith, from all the classic hopes. Then she was bought by the Duchess of Norfolk, was joint-favourite for the Cambridgeshire, and became the easiest winner for years when she beat 45 rivals, the first favourite to win for 34 years ... The Duchess of Norfolk mated her to Alcide and paid £12,000 for her. Her dam, Conceal, had a filly by Articulate in 1960, followed by a yearling colt by Jock Scot who was sold as a foal at the December Sales for 2,100 gns.'

Andrew MacIlwaine was a first-class judge of a hunter, and one of his pet abominations was common horses: 'Most of all, I think I hate their lack of energy after comparatively little work. They tend to stumble and they are less pleasure to ride than the quality horse because they have fewer brains.

'I don't like oversized horses — 16.0 hands to 16.1 is plenty big, and I abominate tall, narrow horses. I always find they are the first to go in the wind. I like plenty of depth throughout, well-sprung ribs, and not too much length in the back. And I like shoulders that are freely used. On the other hand, I tend to forgive a young horse a little thickness in the shoulders, for they so often "fine" with age.

'Strong, flat hocks with plenty of bone and width below are essential, and I do like to see a horse pick up his hind toes — a horse that drags his toes is definitely one to avoid.

'One often hears people say: "Give me a hind leg that is as straight as my walking stick". I say, let them have them. Experience has taught me that the really straight, *over*-straight, hind leg soon produces curbs or thorough-pins.

'Finally, my advice to would-be buyers of horses is, never take more than one friend when you go to look at horses. By the time that several people have picked holes in him there will be no horse left. Remember that you are not going to see the perfect animal — no horse is perfect, nor ever will be.'

In the old days, when wages were low, the big dealers used to maintain huge yards full of horses, all done the best, and they could pull out any number for their customers to try. Today, few keep more than half-a-dozen, though they know where others can be found.

Andrew MacIlwaine had a most remarkable dealing experience in 1939. Reggie Wright took on the Fernie Hounds and he rang him in mid-summer and said: 'I want 12 horses, Andrew — what have you got?'.

'To tell the truth, I had very little — two myself, four hunt horses for Nimrod Capel and six whippers-in horses — but you never want to say that you haven't much, so I said: "I've got forty at grass, give me a week, I'll catch up a dozen and have them shod, trimmed and ridden, come a week today and see what you think of them". He did, and bought the 12 without rejecting one.

'I sold the Queen her first pony and I sold Prince Henry, the Duke of Gloucester, the only horse on which he ever won a race.

'When Lord Linlithgow was Viceroy of India he asked me to send him a horse that he could ride on parade with elephants. That was a bit of a poser, but I got a great big, good-looking horse from the Metropolitan Mounted Police Depot in London and I had him ridden out for about 6 months with zoo elephants before he was sent out. Lord Linlithgow weighed about 18 stone ...

'Before the war I used to sell to the late Lord Halifax, and he sent one of my ex-horses out to our ambassador in the United States for a day's hunting with Mr Plunket Stewart's Hounds (Mr Plunket Stewart, as president of the Masters of Foxhounds Association of America, was the Duke of Beaufort of the U.S.A.). When he went to get on the horse he asked its name, and when told "Andrew" he asked: "Could you possibly have bought it from Andrew MacIlwaine?" Mr Plunket Stewart replied that he always bought his horses from me!'

Horse-dealing and judging often give rise to a fair bit of repartee. Captain Guy Lucas told of a stout lady riding side-saddle who told him: 'You should be judging cows, not horses', to which he countered: 'If you were in the class, madam, you'd trot it!' Similarly, another lady, put twelfth in a class of 13, demanded why, to which he replied: 'The last horse was lame!'

When war broke out Andrew was buying horses for £95 and sending them to the ex-huntsman of the Meynell, who had a pub in the Meynell country. A lot of troops were stationed there, and he kept the horses at grass and let them out to young soldiers to hunt.

The Army took over his stables and yard throughout the war, Andrew joined the Remounts with Leslie Weaver, and when the war was over they set up in business together again. This lasted for several years, but eventually he went farming again and Leslie went to Ireland, where he remains in Co. Waterford. Andrew carried on in a much reduced way, farming only 400 acres instead of 600, keeping a couple of hunters for himself and trying to fit up old friends and customers when he could. One such was Colonel Lowther. In the 1930s and after he had supplied all six or eight hunts with whom he had been associated, from the Eridge to the Warwickshire, and he had sold horses to Colonel Lowther, Master of the Pytchley, for 35 years. 'We still dine together once a week and drink a bottle of port, and we have never had a wrong word in 35 years.

'Harry Gale, who was buyer for the Drages for 40 years, made fewer mistakes concerning horses than anyone I have ever known. He looked for good legs first, and horses that were thick between the legs, and on a short leg, needless to say. Like me, he loathed tall, thin horses, and very largely avoided Thoroughbreds. With one in 50 there is nothing in the world like it, but in the rough and tumble over a biggish country you want something other than Thoroughbred.

'Sometimes, with the best will in the world, you come unstuck. I once had a Thoroughbred horse who appeared to have the most perfect manners. I had been riding him round the farm for 2 weeks and he had never offered to do a thing wrong, until one day he bucked me off harder than I'd ever been bucked

off in my life. In 2 days' time I was going to send him off as a super patent
safety hunter for an old gentleman. I ended up instead sending him off to
Leicester Repository without a warranty, and without putting my name to
him, as "The Property of a Gentleman" — and everyone knows what that
means.'

Really good, made hunters have never been thick on the ground and are
now in short supply, for the international trade in show jumpers and 3-day
event horses, which is booming, has increased the demand for the type of horse
once destined for the hunting field. Dealers like Bert Cleminson, who lived at
Rowcliffe Manor, near York, and supplied a good many Masters of Foxhounds
with their horses, are now a dying breed. The overheads are too high, labour
too expensive and the young are less dedicated to hard work. Major George
Rich, the son of a dealer in the Pytchley country, was one of the last Leicestershire dealers and Captain Brian Parry, son of Victor Parry of Cheltenham,
has one of the few remaining yards, at Oakham, but they are indeed thin on
the ground. Roy Trigg, near Billingshurst in Sussex, breaks Thoroughbred
yearlings for leading trainers such as Ryan Price and Guy Harwood. 'The
modern owners are unbelievable', he told me recently. 'They know nothing
about horses and care less.'

Archie Thomlinson is one of the very few surviving dealers, though he too
has diversified into owning a thoroughbred stallion, the well thought-of Ancient
Munro, and keeps a number of brood mares and home-bred youngsters, and
in 1984 was delighted to sell a horse to the former show jumping ace, Colonel
Piero d'Inzeo, in Italy. A fine judge of a horse, he always buys on conformation
and has proved it to be the only reliable way, always provided one knows what
one is looking for.

His father, Willie Thomlinson, was in hunt service. He hunted the Eglinton
for 17 seasons and was also with the Portman, the York and Ainsty and the
Middleton until he retired to farm and deal at Harewood, in Yorkshire, on
the Princess Royal's estate. He dealt exclusively in hunters and the young
Archie, who was born in Ayrshire in 1920 and came to England when he was
10, remembers him shooting 22 when war broke out.

From show ponies he graduated to riding bad horses in point-to-point races,
but All Honour became the dam of John Moore, who won the Chester Cup.
After the war he set up on his own at Grewelthorpe, near Ripon, dealing in
quality horses, never more than 15 or 16 at a time. Of the seven maidens he
sold, the best were Most Notable, Kari Sou (who won the National Hunt
Chase) and Paul Pry; the last-named cleared out the bookmakers when he
won the Dudley Cup in 1953. Arthur Stevenson had so much money in the
boot of his car that he was afraid to go and have any food!

Another outstanding horse he found was the champion hack, Blithe Spirit,
which he sold to triple Badminton winner Sheila Willcox and later to Mrs
Christopher Mackintosh, who kept him at the top for several seasons. Archie
bought him for £50 at York sales. He also sold numerous hunters of champion
class, among them Col. Tony Coote's Counter Attack, Bardolin to Ronnie
Margolin and Mighty Fine, which he sold to Mrs Olive Jackson. But the best
was his own Piperton, first and foremost a 'chaser; bought as a yearling from
Ernie Johnson of Hexham, whose daughter rode Archie's point-to-point horses,

he was bred by Denis Brown, who farms on the Astor estate, by Border Legend out of a polo pony by The Carpenter.

Although not in the *Book,* Piperton won the Champion Chase at Cheltenham, the same race at Manchester in May, and four other good races that season. Then Archie accepted a bet that he would win the hunter championship at the Great Yorkshire show that same year, 1963, which he duly did with no difficulty at all, proving that conformation and performance generally go hand in hand. When Piperton retired from the race-course, he sold his good horse into the hunting field, where for several seasons he carried the Master of the South Notts, Dick Peake.

He no longer buys horses in Ireland. 'They have got so expensive there that one can only afford one's third or fourth choice. They are as good over here if you can find them, which is the difficult part. I always buy privately — only one in 300 or 400 comes out of a sale. I also buy store fillies out of training for Irish stud owners, which has been quite successful.' He has owned top international show jumpers such as Archie, which Harvey Smith used to ride, and New Yorker, who was ridden by Caroline Bradley.

Ireland still boasts a few of the old type of horse dealer, but not in the legendary Nat Galway-Greer category. Many more private people have started dealing, or dabbling in horses, and I have one friend who, when her husband died, not only went on producing champion young horses in Dublin but turned them over so well that she managed to educate her children on the proceeds, to her eternal credit.

Bone and depth carry weight, and for a horse that will work hard and last, strong, flat hocks are essential, with plenty of bone, short cannon bones and big, flat, convex knees. A straight hind leg from the hock to the ground is generally regarded as essential, though some judges consider it possible to have too straight a hind leg, which is predisposed to thoroughpin and other symptoms of strain. But a 'hooky' hind leg is prone to curbs and hideous to behold; both sickle hocks and cow hocks are signs of weakness.

I have heard racing people say that the French have been breeding good horses with sickle hocks for years, and winning races with them, and that as long as the horse *uses* his hocks that is all that matters. But if a horse is to stand up to a career in the hunting field, jumping out of the deep, holding going of the average English winter, a good, correctly-shaped hind leg is probably more important than any other single attribute.

CHAPTER 16

——————◆❊◆——————

The officials of the Society

COLONEL G. A. (Tony) Murray Smith, one of the most famous figures in Leicestershire, has an impeccable foxhunting pedigree and does a wonderful job as chairman of the HIS. His father, who was killed in 1914, was a keen hunting man and Master of Trinity Foot while at Cambridge. His uncle, Sir Thomas Ainsworth, did Field-Master with the Cottesmore before going to live in Ireland, where he was Master of the Meath, Galway Blazers, Tipperary and Kildare. His cousin, George Murray Smith, a former 7th Hussar, runs the Mount Juliet Stud for Major Victor McCalmont in Co. Kilkenny; whose son, after six years with Dick Hern, is now with Vincent O'Brien and his daughter is married to William Edgdale, second Clerk of the Course at Ascot.

After the Great War his mother married John Pollock of Mountainstown and went to live in Co. Meath, which became his home while he was at prep school and at Eton. Until he was 14 he was invariably sea-sick crossing from Holyhead to Kingstown (now Dun Laoghaire).

After school came Sandhurst and The Blues. 'The war was a long session of boredom, interspersed with moments of acute fear and peril, but there weren't so many and one remembers the good bits. We had some lovely people in our regiment. We started off in Palestine, then we had a war against the Iraqis, then against the French in Syria, then another against the Persians in Iran and then I went to the Western Desert to command a battalion of canvas tanks. That was rather fun because we pretended to be real ones. I think the other side knew we weren't, but we could go like hell and get out of the way if we had to.

'Next we all got into the Western Desert with our armoured cars, did Alamein and that sort of thing, went back to Palestine, then up the middle of Italy, and when we were hauled out of that we came back here for the first time in four years — but only for a month! Then off we went to Holland and over the Rhine, finishing up somewhere this side of Hamburg in 1945, and that was the war effort. As I say, it went on too long.'

He was demobilised early in 1946 and as his home was let to a manufacturer of 'those china things one has to use when bedridden — the whole house was packed with them' — he lived at Whissenthorpe, in the Cottesmore country, for a year. In 1954 Sir Harold Nutting asked him to help out with the Quorn, and he took them on for six seasons, first with George Barker and then with Jack Littleworth. In 1960 he took on the Fernie, first with Walter Gupwell and then with Bruce Durno hunting hounds. He hunted them himself for four seasons, 'realised I wasn't half good enough' and Bruce took them over from being kennel huntsman.

'Hunting has changed out of all knowledge from before the war, when there was only one ploughed field between Market Harborough and Melton (some 22 miles) and everybody in the Quorn country complained about it and said that Sir Harold ought to buy it! (It was only a very small field, too!) Every bit of wire was taken down and one could go where one liked, and as it was all old turf it was virtually impossible to do much harm to the land. Fences got broken — but they still do, and the horses were far better schooled; there was more expertise about. Many of the charming young people who go out hunting from the towns and suburbs of Leicester enjoy themselves madly without quite knowing, anyway to begin with, what it is all about; and the difference between a field of wheat and a tarmac road, and things like that — though they learn very quickly.

'Numbers are our chief problem in these days of intensive farming. With all the subscribers and all the farmers and all the children we have 220–230 people out. The ideal would be 10 people, each subscribing, which is impossible! A hundred is reasonable for the Field Master to control. One has to be polite, but firm; it's no good losing one's temper at that game, otherwise one loses control.'

Having been connected with the Society for 30 years, he removed himself from the judges' panel when he attained 15 stone, too heavy to ride small hunters on hard going. As president, he suggested that there should be a chairman for the sake of continuity. 'There are now so many contacts, not only in this country but in Europe, that it is impossible for the president, in his one year, to get to know these people and talk to them. I had three nominations but I was out-voted and they nominated me. We have a superb chief executive in Gerald Evans, but it's a bit much to ask him to deal with that side as well, which is not really his job. He looks after the office and administrative side and does it supremely well.

'The pathetic thing is the amount of money we get. The Irishmen get £950,000, the French get £1.5 million, the Germans £1 million. And we get £85,000 from the Levy Board. It's very generous of them, but to do that job we want to get our brood mare registry going, we want to increase subsidies for the stallions, and do all sorts of things — but we just have not got the cash. No Government over the last hundred years has considered the horse to be an agricultural animal, which it is. They regard it as a rich man's plaything — so out of date. Look at these tens of thousands of Riding Club people, people who come out hunting, people who go show jumping or do dressage — all relying on us to breed the horses for them to do it on.

'If we ever get the cash we need — I don't know if we will but we might, if water keeps dripping on to the stone — we could do so much more. This is not a very good time to ask for anything. We all miss Evelyn Fanshawe a lot — he was a great supporter and a wonderful man at putting things over, sadly missed by us all. We've got a lot of pretty good people on our Council, though, and we've got a lot of things moving, in particular the Grade One Premium Mare Scheme, the Grade Two Mare Scheme (a basic grade, replacing the existing *Stud Book*), and the Identity Record with Identity Papers available on application. We have also implemented the National Stallion Approval Scheme to fill the gap left by the abolition of stallion licensing by the Ministry of Agriculture. All these schemes came into effect in January 1983.

'We need £600,000 a year at least, then we can really get to work. What we really are top of is the Three-Day-Event, and that is why I believe that our Thoroughbred stallions are the best breed in the world, still. Queen Wilhelmina of Holland gave George VI 50 black horses after the war. They were mostly Hanoverian bred and I had quite a few of them to ride hunting. They were very amenable, placid horses, but they'd last for about a mile and then collapse — soft, you know. But they can do their show jumping or their dressage beautifully — just the job for it. Of course, they breed something like 40,000 Hanoverians a year — they eat three-quarters of them and ride the rest! It's very big business. All the mares and stallions have to be approved and then they produce these thousands and thousands of foals.

'On the Continent, too, they are very keen on what they call performance testing, and the Irish have started going through the motions with their tongue, I suspect, firmly in their cheek, with their Draught horses. But just because one horse can jump six feet, there is no guarantee that his brother can.

'It has no meaning whatsoever — look at racehorses. You pay vast sums to buy the full brother or sister of a Derby Winner and it often is quite useless. Of course, ID is just a little bit of Irish make-believe, really — it's a type, and a very good type, not a breed. Before the war they really did work in the plough and draw a trap and on Sundays the owner got up and went hunting. There are very few of them left but they're trying to reintroduce them.

'Thady Ryan, who's an old friend of mine, is chairman of the Irish Horse Board and I heard him talking to the Germans in Essen a few years ago. He told a lovely story and it went down frightfully well! Now, there is a case in point. They had this big hall, endless drink and asked everyone in sight to come. There were about 200 people there — we couldn't begin to do it. If it hadn't been for Evelyn we shouldn't have got to Equitaner Essen at all — it's mostly done at the private expense of our own people, who go to promote our horses.'

Major-General Sir Evelyn Fanshawe, CBE, CB, DL was 'Evelyn' to his contemporaries, 'Sir' to their juniors and 'The General' to the premium stallion owners, who held him in a loving, almost feudal respect. He regarded himself as a 'prehistoric relic'; certainly in the present age-of-the-common-man he was almost an anachronism, though by no means unique, which is perhaps the highest compliment that could be paid him, for his old-world attributes of courtesy, charm and integrity are increasingly rarely found.

For many years he presided with an individual distinction over the yellow caravan which the Society bought as a publicity medium in the 1950s. One could say that he was the Society's Public Relations Officer. Most certainly he contributed in no small measure to the respect and affection in which the Society is held all over the country.

His maternal grandfather, Field Marshal Sir Evelyn Wood, lived in Essex. One of his pronouncements was to the effect that he saw no reason why an efficient staff officer should not hunt 100 days in a season. Among his literary output was a book called *From Midshipman to Field Marshal*, having bought his commission in the 17th Lancers to fight in the Crimea, and winning a VC in the 'Mutiny'.

He made it a practice to hunt seven days a week, going out after church on Sundays with beagles or terriers. When the HIS was formed in 1884 he was the original War Office member.

Sir Evelyn's father hunted throughout his life as one of three brothers who did the same, all reaching the rank of General. Apart from soldiering, indeed, hunting *was* their life. His father hunted the Norwich Staghounds for three seasons in the early 1890s, when stationed at Norwich. They had some incredibly long hunts, and his diaries record one of 30 miles. He commanded the British Cavalry Corps in the Great War and The Bays before his son.

Sir Evelyn's eldest uncle, General Sir Edward Fanshawe, was Field Master to the Kildare for 25 seasons and his younger uncle, General Sir Robert Fanshawe, was honorary secretary to the South Oxfordshire from the time he retired from the Army after the First World War until he died, some quarter of a century later.

In pre-war years the Military Tournament was, in fact, a tournament, the competitions taking place in the morning. The Bays at this time held a supreme position in the Army, both for mounted and dismounted events, in addition to being the Army fencing champions. Sir Evelyn himself was 'Champion All Arms' of the British Army.

In 1917, when serving as a Flight commander in 72 Squadron, RFC in Mesopotamia, he was attached to Dunster Force and rode a 14.2 hand Arab up the old caravan route over the Paitak Pass from Baghdad to the Caspian Sea. The object of the exercise was to reconnoitre landing grounds that he could use when he got back to Baghdad to fly a team of 'Jumbo Martinsides' (an old type of single-seater aircraft) up to Kasrine, where Dunster Force HQ was situated. In fact all the time he was serving with the RFC in the East, he managed to keep an Arab horse, one of which won him several races in Cairo.

In 1918 he rejoined his regiment from the RAF at Aleppo, where The Bays were the British regiment in the Jodhpur Cavalry Brigade, the two Indian regiments being the Patiala and Jodhpur Lancers. 'We soon had a racecourse and polo grounds laid out, playing polo every day and racing once a week.

'When we handed Syria over to the French we trekked down through Damascus, Homs, Hama, Balbeck, over the Lebanon Mountains, Beirut, Tyre, Sydon, Acre, and Tel Aviv, where we camped for a year. 'Boy' Selby-Lowndes and I got some hounds out from England and hunted the orange groves and surrounding country, and this was the origin of the Vale of Acre Hunt.' In 1920 he went to Ootacammel and hunted the Ooty Hounds for two seasons, in a joint-Mastership with Lady Curry.

Between the wars, from 1919 until 1928, he was abroad in India and played polo endlessly — the day before leaving India he played 24 chukkas with Major Bill Enderby, the well-known hunter judge. Then he went to Colchester and hunted the garrison beagles for two seasons, and also kept horses in the Pytchley country at Nortoft House, at Guilsborough, the other end of the village to where he later lived, at Guilsborough House. Lord Rosebery and Colonel Peter Farquhar, who were Joint-Masters of the Whaddon Chase, very kindly took 'a regimental subscription' and there were two regimental stables, each holding 30 horses, in the Whaddon country, where before hunting one day they put on a sort of cross-country race for young officers which has now become popular with civilians.

Next Sir Evelyn went to Weedon, gaining a 'special certificate' which qualified him to be an instructor at the Equitation School. 'It was a wonderful life. We worked very hard on our horses — one trained, one half-trained, and a remount — and were ordered to hunt at least two days a week with all the Midland packs. One season the Regiment took Cottesbrooke Rectory, and many of the officers hunted there with the Pytchley. In those days, leave was granted for at least two months, and then I hunted six days a week. When I was not on leave, I only managed four! At this time I had one of the best hunters in England, Ich Dien, who won for me the Army Heavyweight 'Chase (Lord Beatty Cup) and 16 other races.

'I was commanding The Bays when they were mechanised, in 1936, and had the sad task of finding homes for, and arranging the sale of, 700 horses. The War Office allowed cos to find suitable homes for older horses. Incidentally in those days, as a means of keeping up a reserve supply of horses for the cavalry, approved people could hire troop horses to hunt by paying a 15 shilling insurance premium. Forage was supplied by the Government, for this was a way of keeping the horses fit. We were desperately short of men but had a full establishment of horses, in case of mobilisation. They were sold in various markets but the cos had the authority to have certain old horses put down, and I stretched that authority a bit and had a lot put down. I had all too vivid memories of Cairo, after the First World War, when a great many horses were sold into terrible conditions.'

Sir Evelyn formed the 20th Armoured Brigade and then went on to become Director of Armoured Training in the War Office. After the War was over he was made Director of UNRRA (United Nations Relief and Rehabilitation Association) and spent seven years looking after refugees in Germany, where General Sir Brian Robertson, the High Commissioner, asked him to start polo in the British zone of Germany. The year after leaving Weedon he had been invited to go to Saumur to teach the French cavalry to play polo, and he was appointed by the HPA to be captain and manager of the English polo team at the Olympic Games in Berlin in 1936, where they won the silver medal. In 1938 he played for his regimental team, captained by his brother, when it won the Inter-Regimental Cup.

Now he had two quite passable grounds laid out at Büdefeld, organised a stable of 30 ponies, run by Captain C. Cooke (KDG) and got polo going three days a week. It was a wonderful opportunity for young officers to start playing polo for nothing, as all the expenses were paid by reparations. Sir Evelyn ended his career with a 7 handicap.

'This period of my life was one of the most tragically interesting things it is possible to experience. It is quite astonishing that these half-starved people in the internment camps, devoid of hope until the war ended, still managed to breed. Altogether, 25,000 babies and children passed through our hands. We had seven babies' homes, run by a marvellous Australian lady, Dorothy Marshall. Most of the children were lost, and many came out of Belsen. The World Jewish Congress gave me a standing invitation to go to Israel as a guest of the Government. We had to close down in 1952, through lack of funds, but at least we had cleared up all the babies.

'Then I was seconded as Major-General to the United Nations for two years, and after being asked if I wanted to go back into the Army, I transferred permanently to the United Nations for the next five years, as a civil servant. I also found time to make two very nice Trakehner polo ponies.

'When I finally came home I started breeding from a very good hunter mare called Tallulah. She bred two foals without much success — the first one was killed, the second died of pneumonia: but the third was Last Word, by Parting Shot. She won as a foal, a yearling, a 2- and a 3-year-old. Then she went hunting, was served as a 5-year-old, and a year later was supreme champion brood mare at Peterborough. Her foal won the Summer Knight Cup for the best foal by a premium stallion at the National Hunter Show, and three double firsts at the Three Counties, Peterborough and the Cambridgeshire show. One of her foals won 14 firsts in as many shows and was champion at the National Hunter and East of England shows.

In 1956, Sir Evelyn took over the chairmanship of the HIS Stallion Committee from the late Lord Digby. Five years later he became one of the three trustees of the HIS, of which he was President in 1965 and again in 1975, with Major Sir Reginald Macdonald-Buchanan, KCVO, MBE, MC, and The Lord Margadale of Islay, who as Colonel John Morrison, MP, was Master of the South and West Wilts.

At that time, Sir Evelyn was still hunting four days a week. He always kept very fit, as he proved at the British Timken show at Duston, Northampton, in 1976, at the age of 81, when he forestalled with a rugby tackle two youths who were caught in the act of stealing the silver from the guests' reception tent. The next day, in the HIS yellow caravan (of which more anon) he was seraphically forebearing in the face of an astonishing attack on the policies of the Society by a singularly ill-informed visitor to the show who had partaken unwisely and far too well of the hospitality so generously offered. He contented himself, after the departure of this uninvited guest, with observing mildly that he was 'as tight as a tick'.

A great de-bunker, he seldom put pen to paper in this capacity, but on the few occasions when he did, it was done to some purpose. But he did great service by championing the cause of fitness in the 3-day-event horse, and self-discipline in the rider. In the higher echelons of the sport, at least, unfit horses and untrammelled ladies are a thing of the past, and his influence on this happy state of affairs is by no means coincidental.

Moreover, as at many shows the yellow caravan is and was so conveniently situated for the observation of disgruntled show jumpers leaving the arena and venting their spleen for their own inadequacies on their unfortunate mounts, he has on many occasions been responsible for offering a few well-chosen words of advice to the riders.

It was his great sorrow that lack of funds prevented him from taking on the Mastership of a shire pack. But his loss rebounded to the gain of the HIS. During his years of voluntary service, his very example did much to point the way and the means of service to all who strive to follow in his footsteps. He was one of those rare beings whose shining character and personality give the lie to the old saw that no one was or is indispensible. When he died on the boat, on his way back from Essen in 1979, he left a gap that will never be filled.

His secretary, Mrs Harry Townsend, accompanied him in the Range Rover which towed the yellow caravan to shows all over England, Wales and up over the Border to the Royal Highland, with a small but lethal mixed pack of a terrier, a spaniel, a white pekinese and a pair of lurchers. Bettie Townsend, a delightful person, is as much a part of the HIS as was he himself. The caravan was always bursting at the seams with exhibitors, judges, stewards and friends, who were legion, embracing all the afore-mentioned categories. My children were never happier than when 'helping' 'Sir' or Mrs Townsend, selling raffle tickets or whatever.

Sometimes the caravan is full of seekers after knowledge, those who wish to discover their local premium stallion, or to purchase an excellent booklet on breeding a foal. On one occasion, 'Sir' had an enquiry for the address of the stallion standing nearest to central London. When he discovered that the applicant was proposing to rear his prospective foal in a mews stable, feeding its mother on nuts, he tactfully provided the address of the stud nearest to London where the mare and her offspring could enjoy a summer's keep at grass.

The increased membership (over 10,000), influence and success of the Society must be very largely attributable to this admirable and kindly man, always so immaculately turned out, who devoted so much of his life to this enterprise, even sleeping in the Range Rover (and in the Land Rover which preceded it) when on tour.

Since the original yellow caravan set out on its travels in 1967, its outer walls bedecked with topical photographs of equine heroes and heroines at places like Aintree, Cheltenham, Badminton and Burghley, got by premium stallions — and some of the most illustrious stallions themselves — it has recruited thousands of members for the Society, because it has always been manned by amateurs who believe in the Society, rather than by glib public relations men and women who proliferate in the horse world nowadays and cut very little ice with country people.

Sir Evelyn's influence is perpetuated to this day by Bettie Townsend, often accompanied by her husband Harry or her brother Paul, who are equally avid custodians of the Society's work — converts to the faith in which so many are nurtured, owing their loyalty to the Almighty, their Monarch and their Society.

Major Sir Reginald Macdonald-Buchanan, KCVO, MBE, MC, DL was three times president of the Society — in 1950, 1951 and 1966. He had so many claims to fame — as Senior Steward of the Jockey Club, in which office he is followed by his son, John, the current HIS President: as Master from 1933 of the Pytchley Foxhounds for nearly 20 seasons, joined in the early stages by Colonel Jack Lowther and afterwards by Brigadier 'Bogey' Bowden-Smith, who managed his family studs — Lavington, Lordship and Egerton.

Chairman of the Hunt for 25 years, he initiated the rebuilding of the kennels. As a regular officer in the Scots Guards he served through both wars. In his youth he rode many points-to-point, and married the daughter of Lord Woolavington, the celebrated owner-breeder who won two Derbies with Captain Cuttle and Coronach. They had two sons and two daughters, and Lady Macdonald-Buchanan bred and owned the 1941 Derby winner Owen Tudor, who sired her husband's best horse, Abernant, second only to the The Tetrarch as the fastest sprinter of the century in the hands of Sir Noel Murless and Sir Gordon Richards.

Elected to the Jockey Club in 1937, as Senior Steward he was responsible in 1952 for introducing racecourse commentaries. He was also a member of the Racecourse Betting Control Board from 1949 to 1959. Very keen on stalking and sailing, apart from racing and hunting the other great love of his life was the Hunters' Improvement Society, on whose Council he served for more than half a century. The young horse championship for novice stallions at Newmarket is the Macdonald-Buchanan Challenge Cup. Just before the last World War he won the King George V Cup with an ex-Classic horse of his father's, Dick Swiveller, who unfortunately died of pneumonia the following week. Director of the Distillers company and chairman of James Buchanan and company, Sir Reginald was also chairman of the House Committee of the King Edward VII Hospital for Officers (Sister Agnes). An immaculately turned-out and dedicated sportsman, he died at the age of 85 at his North-amptonshire home, Cottesbrooke Hall, in 1981. One of the last services he rendered to hunting was to sponsor the book on the career of Stanley Barker, the famous huntsman to the Pytchley. Sadly, he did not live to see the finished work.

The Hon. Alexander Parker was also thrice President of the Society — in 1911, when he was Master of the North Warwickshire; in 1925, when he had changed the suffix MFH for OBE; and in 1949. He was the eleventh son of the sixth Earl of Macclesfield, a title created in 1721 during the reign of George I. In 1881 he was the subject of a full-page cartoon in *Vanity Fair* as Managing Director of the Royal Agricultural Hall at Islington, first home of the Hunter Show. An extended caption to the cartoon declares that the first Earl 'Made himself a lawyer and by George I was made Lord Chancellor and a peer under the title Earl of Macclesfield.

'The present and sixth Earl was born over 70 years ago, educated at Eton and Oxford, succeeded to the title before he was forty and a fair Earl's property of some £20,000 a year. He married twice and sired 15 children. An excellent gentleman of the old school, he is courteous, right-minded and honourable, a thorough sportsman, a kindly landlord, a lover of the country and its pursuits. In politics, as becomes his order, he is a Tory, but takes no prominent part in public affairs. He is father of Lord Parker ...'

Lord Parker was the father of the Hon. Alexander Parker. The latter, and his son Sydney Parker, were both Masters of the Eton College Beagles. Each was also prominent in the affairs of the HIS. Sydney Parker had three children, two daughters and a son — Anne, David and Rosemary, now Mrs Taylor, who has a farm and a wild life park at Cricket St. Thomas in Somerset, and likewise has three children. She hunts with the Taunton Vale and the Seavington. Her mother, born Adelaide Everett of Knowle Hall, Warwick-shire, rode horses at Dublin Horse Show between the wars for Nat Galway-Greer. She was killed on an Irish hunting trip riding a young horse while staying in Co. Limerick with Lord and Lady Daresbury.

Rosemary was two when her mother — who had told the stud groom before leaving for Ireland to see that the children rode regularly — was killed. When she was 11, in 1956, her father had a bad fall on the road, landing on his head. After spending months in hospital he continued to hunt, but never again wore a red coat. He was a great breeder of horses, such as Erin's Legend, by Erin's Pride, reserve champion at the HIS Show. Rosemary's step-brother, Antony, won 16 point-to-points on him, but he never beat Baulking Green, a legendary horse that Andy Frank used to ride.

'My step-mother used to ask me to accompany her when she went to look at horses. When I asked why, she said: "As you have been brought up by your father, who was so exceptionally good, and bred lovely horses, if they did not look like his you would notice it!" I was very like my mother, though, and when I was 36, the age at which she had died, they say the likeness was extraordinary.

'My father was the son of the youngest son — the youngest of 11. He quarrelled with most of his 52 cousins. He was always telling us to "turn that bloody noise off!" In fact, when he had his last, fatal fall, and they put him in the ambulance, whose siren was going, those were his very last words!'

John Cory, Chairman of the HIS Show Committee, a past president of the Society, chief steward at all its shows and horse steward at the Bath and West, would have been a considerable asset to the Diplomatic Service. Never ruffled, never abrupt or peremptory, always with a friendly word for everyone, he is every judge and exhibitors' beau ideal.

He stewarded first at the Vale of Glamorgan show in 1947, and at the Royal Welsh in 1950, the Bath & West in 1952 and the HIS in 1956. From his family home, North of Cardiff, he has hunted all his life, as his father did before him.

'My only claim to fame is that I bred Snowdra Queen, who won the Dudley Cup and the United Hunts Cup at Cheltenham, among many other races. She was by an American-bred stallion, Maxim, out of a mare called Irish Jig II that I was given in Ireland by Mrs Michael Beaumont. But I didn't realise how good the filly was — I sold her to a farmer as an unbroken 3-year-old for £100!'

John enjoyed judging ridden hunters and now judges breeding classes. 'If more people could be persuaded to steward at shows, they would learn a lot about judging.'

John Sumner, Ted Davies and Richard Matson, all judges and the sons of judges, have followed on as stewards. As the officials of a society *are* the society, the future is certainly in safe hands.

At the beginning, the same secretary ran both the HIS and the Hackney Horse Society, then A. B. Charlton carried on for many years, to be followed in the 1930s by F. H. (Freddie) Badge. In 1929 George Wright joined the staff as a junior clerk, the chief clerk was R. A. (Reg) Brown (later secretary of the British Horse Society), and the office was in Hanover Square. In 1947 George Wright succeeded Mr Badge as Secretary and remained until his retirement, due to ill health, in 1970. Apart from service in the Armed Forces from 1940–45, his whole working life was spent with the Society. It was a tragedy that illness, borne with patience and courage, should have cut short his life. He was courteous, kindly and helpful.

Fortunately for the Society, Gerald Evans was there to step into the breach. An engineer's son, he was an enthusiast from his boyhood, riding ponies, and he planned to become a jockey, being apprenticed to Walter Nightingall at Epsom. But when he was 17 he was injured and becoming jockey was no longer feasible.

'This seemed to be the next best thing', so he became assistant secretary, then secretary when George Wright went and, in 1983, Chief Executive, a post created especially for him.

CHAPTER 17

The professionals

THE PROFESSIONAL nagsmen are the experts of the ridden hunter world and the best of them ensure that the standards are maintained even in these days of slipshod short-cuts. They are good losers, magnanimous in victory, hardworking; they know every nuance of getting the best out of a horse and ensuring that he is looking and going at his best every second of the time that he is in the ring — for the judge may be looking at him at any moment, and he must always be 'on parade'.

Harry Bonner, who was born in 1900, was a brilliant hunter showman, a foxhunter who crossed the country like a bird, and an outstandingly successful dealer in high-class hunters and steeplechasers. His father spent most of his life in Hunt service. He hunted the Meath hounds in Ireland for several seasons before moving to the Tynedale from 1891–8. Finally he went to the Meynell. In retirement he took over the King's Arms at Bicester, with a 200-acre farm and a yard full of liveries and trade horses. Without previous experience of farming or inn-keeping he did well and became a dealer of high repute, selling Ocean to Prince Henry and horses to the Duke of Beaufort.

Harry, the second son, took to riding early. His sister took him to Olympia for the first International Horse Show in 1907 to show a pony. When he was not riding for his father he rode for Lady Hunloke, mother of Mrs Philip Fleming, who is still showing hacks and driving ponies. In 1911 he took a 3-year-old pony to London by train in the first horse box to travel along the newly-constructed Bicester to Paddington line. He was met in London by a hansom cab, and he rode the pony behind it through the streets to show it to Lord Rothschild, who bought it through the window. This was the first deal in which he was involved.

In later years he was to buy such renowned 'chasers as Prince Regent and the Grand National winner Early Mist for Mr J. V. Rank, and many more for Lord Bicester. The next year he had his first Olympia win on his father's pony, Princess, and at 14 he won the boys' and girls' hunter class on Beau Sabreur. His brothers Jack and Cecil rode against him.

At 19, he went to Herefordshire to manage Capt. Jeffcock's horses — some 20, mostly home-bred, some unbroken as 6-year-olds, owing to the war. When the stud was sold, Harry went to the Kenneth Stevensons at Malvern, winning the hack championship at Olympia on Mignonette and the hunter championship on Lady Hunloke's Puzzle. He hunted with the Ledbury, and won point-to-points and hunter trials as well as hunter 'chases. The two best he rode were Ambition and Blue Train.

Once he took Blue Train down to Lord Tredegar's hunter trials. It was suggested that he should go out in the early morning to school over the local reens, which were enormously wide ditches filled with water. He rose early in the bitter cold and fog, Blue Train failed to rise at the first ditch and they went straight to the bottom, emerging covered with icy black slime. But after returning to Cardiff to borrow dry clothes, he won the trial, so the school was not in vain. This was one of the first hunter trials, over a very big course.

In 1921 he went home and took horses to make and break, his first big winner being Lord Hillingdon's Handley Cross, on whom he won the heavy-weight class and championship at Richmond Royal in 1930. A year later he rode Rue Barree to win the lightweight class there and at Olympia, while Mrs Oliver Gilbey won the ladies' class. That same year his daughter Beryl, aged 10, won all three pony classes at Olympia. She is now married to Basil Ancil, who like his brother Derek made his name as a jockey before managing his father-in-law's farm.

In 1931 Harry started showing for Mrs Vaughan, Master of the Albrighton for so many years, and that year and again in 1932 and 1933 he won the championship at the Royal on her Hecland, the best heavyweight he ever showed. By Captain Wickham-Boynton's Hector, he was a great galloper and so full of quality that he also won countless ladies' classes with his owner up, and when he finished showing he went on to win several hunter trials and two point-to-points. At Bath Show one year he won his class and his rider was informed that the winner of the three weight classes had to jump a fence to qualify for the championship. They stuck up a fence in the middle of the ring with 18 inches of daylight under it and no groundline at all, and Hecland was the only one to jump it.

The next good horse he rode was Mr J. V. Rank's Knepp. In 1936 he won two point-to-points, the following year he was champion at Richmond Royal and the Great Yorkshire, and at Olympia he was reserve to his stable companion, the middleweight Guilsborough, who came from Captain Andrew MacIlwaine. In 1938 he produced a good heavyweight, The Curate, for Mr Rank, and this son of Steel Point won at Olympia, the Royal and the Great Yorkshire.

When war came he got rid of all the horses, went farming seriously, and never expected to go showing again until, at Oxford in 1953, Mrs M. H. Tollit asked him to take Fancy Free, which she had bought as a 3-year-old from Nat Galway-Greer. She really wanted to have the horse produced to ride herself, but Harry wanted to ride him too so she acquiesced — and as he went champion first time out she did not really feel that she could take the winning jockey off him!

At Richmond, as a 6-year-old, he won the middleweight class from the Duchess of Norfolk's Penny Royal, ridden by John Moss, and Mr Hugh Haldin's Earmark, ridden by Count Orssich, finishing as reserve champion to Mighty Atom.

In 1956 Harry produced Mrs Tollit's homebred brown filly Silverin, by Erin's Pride out of Silvereen by Silver Fox, foaled in 1952 and a multiple champion in hand, at shows of the calibre of Peterborough, the Great Yorkshire and the Three Counties. She won her class at the Royal as a yearling and was champion filly at 3. After three brilliant seasons under saddle she was sold to America with Major Drabble's Gold Dust, who came from Bert Cleminson, having won the Hunter title at the Horse of the Year Show from Work of Art.

In 1960 Harry rode another of Mrs Tollit's breeding, Demas II, to win the young horse championship at Peterborough. His last top-class horse was Mrs Peter Beckwith-Smith's Robin Hood, bought from Nat Galway-Greer after winning the Royal Ulster Championship as a backward 4-year-old in 1962. In England he was virtually unbeaten for two seasons.

Harry thought that, between the wars, the back row was more impressive than the front row was in the middle 1960s, and 20 years on the same is probably true. He considered that the production of horses had suffered even more. 'It is impossible to spend too long in riding and making before the nagging starts. Most people do far too much nagging and rely too much on tack and artificial contrivances. A decline in the standard also shows itself in young horses being forced beyond their natural paces. They learn to cut the corners and get ring-crafty quickly enough without showing them the way.'

Jack Gittins was one of the best known and most popular showmen of the century in England and a brilliant man across Leicestershire, especially on young horses, but it was in Dublin above all, where Nat Galway-Greer reckoned him to be the supreme artist, that he really showed his calibre.

He was, in fact, two distinct personalities. The show-going public knew him in the summer as a highly successful showman, riding champion after champion in the ring. But hunting people knew him in the field, where everyone wanted to be his friend and, because he was excellent company and a very nice person, he enjoyed a unique social status, in constant demand at hunt balls and dinner parties.

He was born in 1908 on the Shropshire/Herefordshire borders, of a long line of yeoman farmers. His father joined the Yeomanry when he was 16, but when he returned from the Great War the agricultural depression had set in and the land that his great-grandfather had farmed as a tenant had to be sold in 1931. Brought up to hunt, to show ponies and to ride in point-to-points, he wrote to General Lucas, who had bought many of his father's horses in the past, and asked for a job in Remounts. Soon he was one of eight civilian nagsmen in the remount depot, with 2–3,000 horses.

He left after two years to join Leslie Weaver, who had inherited from his father a yard at Carden, in Cheshire which supplied the Duke of Westminster. In 1935 he went to the Drage brothers, Bert and John, at Northampton, and just before the war to Captain Cyril Darby, the son of John Darby, a famous dealer from Hillmorton in the Warwickshire country. This was the start of his showing career.

When war came he joined the Warwickshire Yeomanry and served in Palestine, first with horses and then with tanks. When the 1st Cavalry Division was mechanised Colonel 'Mouse' Townsend, head of the RAVC hospital and remount depot at Ramla, put on a 2-day commemoration gala. The Warwickshires were then stationed on the border at Roshpinna, some 120 miles away, but Jack brought a couple of horses down by rail in a cattle wagon to compete.

The Greys and the Third Hussars still had their horses. The first day was devoted to their farewell meeting. Colonel Duggie Stewart won the main race, a 2½-mile handicap, from a field of 32. Next day Col. Harry Llewellyn, who at Helsinki in 1952 was in the winning Olympic show jumping team with Duggie Stewart, won the officers' show jumping from Major Geoffrey Gibbon, another post-war show jumper, while Jack won the NCOs' and other ranks from 52 starters.

After the war he returned to the Darbys for a while and then went up to Leicestershire and asked his old friends, George and Joan Gibson, where he could find some stables. George invited him to manage his stud at Waltham-on-the-Wolds, where Seasick was standing. Two or three years later George closed down the stud and moved to Barleythorpe, but Jack stayed on to manage the farm and had the house and stables, where he started up on his own. Then he moved five miles to Eastwell, and kept all Colonel James Hanbury's young horses in what had been the Prince of Wales's yard. Hugh Sumner sent him youngsters to break each summer and Lord Ashcombe started him selling horses on commission.

After Jack had his first horse for the Hon. Mrs Stella Cardiff, he found a horse on which her son David Jackson won the Cambridge 'Grind'. Then he bought him his first three racehorses. When Sir Denis Le Marchant offered him a 90-acre farm, 15 boxes and a farmhouse which was also the village pub at Colston Bassett, he leapt at it. Always a frustrated farmer, he longed for some land to keep a few cows and sheep on, and turn horses out.

In 1956 he was asked by Harry Bonner and Mrs Tollit if he would like to prepare and ride Nat Galway-Greer's horses in Dublin. A year later he won his first supreme championship on Work of Art, in 1958 again on Tenirife, in 1959 on Munnings' Model and in 1960 on Superb. In 1963 Prudent Lover was a runaway winner, in 1964 it was Treasure Hill and finally, in 1966, Never Forget. It was a record without equal, unlikely ever to be challenged. Jack gave the credit to Nat for finding the horses and getting them so fit, but they were a unique team. 'He's the best judge in the world', he told me. 'He will buy a foal on its dam, pay the farmer for its keep, collect it as a 3- or 4-year-old, and a few weeks later it will win a cup at Dublin!'

At Colston Bassett Jack bought Palladium for Mrs Cardiff and twice won the Gold Cup at Peterborough with this outstanding lightweight by the premium stallion Top Walk. In 1961 she asked him to move down to The Old Manor in Armscote, Warwickshire, and kept her horses at home nearby while he was able to keep horses for other clients like Major Dermot Daly, Lady Reiss and Douglas Bunn, for whom he won the Peterborough Gold Cup with the former Dublin winner, Selsey Bill.

In 1977 he died of a heart attack while riding a 4-year-old for Miss Betty Galway-Greer, Blue Print by Blue Cliff, the last foal that her father had ever bought. His old friend, Dr Tom Connors of Waterford and Leicestershire, was beside him in the veterinary paddock when he fell. He would have wanted to die in harness, riding a horse at the scene of so many previous triumphs. At his memorial service the Rev. Ronald Shaw, who is married to one of Jack's cousins, said: 'How desperate is our need at this time for more like him, with his courage, his kindliness, his readiness to help others; a true Christian, which is not measured in church attendances. He influenced so many people and I thought, as I prepared this address, how great were his achievements compared with mine!'

Roy Trigg is another master showman whose rapport with horses and children is easy to understand, for his quiet character inspires confidence and reassurance in both, while he has the innate dignity which is the hallmark of the natural horseman. I shall never forget the hero worship with which he was treated by his step-children, nor how he ran to catch a dropped ripcord from one of the Red Devil's parachutes at Gillingham show, to present it to my delighted 9-year-old son.

His father, Robert Trigg of Fareham, was a horse-dealer, saddler, farmer, greengrocer at one and the same time. When Roy, his only son, left school he was sent down to Dick Hunt in the Portman country in Dorset for four years, and spent his time making young horses with the Portman, Miss Guest's and the South and West Wilts. He had already, at the age of 13, ridden his first point-to-point, finishing second by half-a-length.

Then his father sent him to Gerry Langford, the well-known veterinary surgeon, at Lingfield. It was a hard year's work but Roy enjoyed every minute of it, learning a great deal and riding some top-class point-to-point horses. Afterwards he took on a 250-acre farm at Cowfold, and has remained in Sussex ever since. He had a great deal to do with the late Harold Field, who had a big dealing establishment at Chichester, schooling his young horses (many of which came out of Wales, for Carmarthenshire and Pembrokeshire were his favourite hunting grounds for horses) and then standing-in when they were sold. He also had a lot of show jumpers from the late Len Carter — 'the stoppers, mostly, and the ones that messed about! We didn't keep track of our winners in those days, but I must have won well over 100 point-to-points from the time I was 13 until I gave up at 42, minus the war years. I did quite a bit of show jumping and then more or less drifted into hunters. I found you couldn't very well do both so I carried on with the showing side, having ridden ponies at Olympia and Richmond as a child for Percy Ricks of Weybridge.'

His first big owner was Ronnie Cardwell, manager of the Star Brewery at Eastbourne, who had a string of 20 which ranged from point-to-point horses to jumpers and show horses. Then he had a succession of top-class show horses in the 1960s for the late Mrs Molly Dowley — 'the best owner in the world', he called her, and there cannot have been many better. She even took the disappointment with equanimity when she arrived at Windsor one sunny day in May to find that Roy had forgotten to enter her best horse and he could not be shown!

The pick of her horses were Ship A'hoy, Come Dancing, Bright and Breezy and Aintree, and they were winners at all the big shows. She was there at the ringside bright and early, always immaculately turned out and with all the genuine charm in the world. She was greatly respected and loved, and sadly missed when, after a long and painful illness, she died. Like many others, she went on showing when she could no longer really afford it, for horses were in her blood and she loved the showing classes. Her cousin, Reg Tweedie, bred and owned the Grand National horse, Freddie, who finished second by $\frac{3}{4}$ of a length at Aintree both in 1965 and 1966. Bred in Ireland by Steel Point, out of a mare by Dado who was in Miss Prior's half-bred register, he is still alive and well at his owners' home, Middlethird, near Gordon in Berwickshire, with his contemporary, the mare Rosiewinks. She had 13 foals including four winners, one of which finished fourth in the Derby. He was by Telegram II, a horse they bought for the Kircudbright Society.

Roy, who breaks all Ryan Price's yearlings each winter, also used to school a number of horses that were bought in Ireland as 2-year-olds for the Queen Mother. After being turned out at Sandringham for a year to acclimatise they were sent to him to be broken and hunted before going into training with Major Peter Cazalet. Roy showed Brig-o'-Dee for the Queen Mother and also had a show horse for the Duchess of Norfolk, for whom he broke yearlings as well.

On his way across Bodmin Moor some years ago he was caught in a police speed trap and lost his licence. 'Never mind', said Lady Violet Vernon consolingly, 'I'm sure the lovely ladies will be queueing up to drive him about!'

Vincent Toulson first broke through to the top of the showing tree when, in 1973, he produced the failed 'chaser, Prince's Street, to win 10 major championships off the reel. He then sold the horse for £10,000, a record price in those days, to the South Essex Insurance Group.

He stems from a long line of Lincolnshire horsemen, his maternal great-grandfather, John Fox, having been a well known hackney man. His father, Charles Toulson, lived at Sudbrook Hall, near Grantham, where he was born, and farmed with two of his sons. Before the war he showed Herbert Jones's horses to win at Olympia and other leading shows, but Vin's interest was in racing. He lived at home till he was 28, and as there were always 30 horses about the place he gained wide experience of schooling, in addition to riding as an amateur under National Hunt rules and in countless point-to-points. In between 700 and 800 rides he sustained a broken leg, a broken collarbone 12 times, broken thumbs, and ended up with a plate in his head after a fall at Cottenham.

Always interested in showing, when he was young he thought it a bit cissy and wanted to be a steeplechase jockey. 'I always went to shows with my father but never got the rides. I hunted four and five times a week with the Belvoir and the Cottesmore and started showing when I gave up racing in 1969 at the age of 36. I suppose I was beginning to see the light! Most of the horses I have shown have been cast-offs from racing stables — I like to show horses that have been in training — they go forward and are well educated, I find.'

A few horses come out of training and never settle. Second Edition won the novice class at Royal Windsor in 1979 and could never be shown again. 'That one gallop in company hotted him up so much that he never forgot it. I took him to a lot of shows afterwards and just rode him about, but it was no use — he was quite scatty. He went back into training. I suppose he was just too highly-strung. He took two years to break and went through the side of a covered school in the process. His mother, Amba, who helped David Tatlow win his leading point-to-point jockey title, was scatty too. When she went racing the box had to be parked in a lay-by and she was walked on to the course.

Ruth McMullen, the one woman in the show ring who could compete with the men on equal terms, was born in Surrey. Her father preferred sailing to horses but his first cousin is Paul Mellon, among whose best horses was the 1971 Derby winner, Mill Reef. His mother, Norah Mellon, was renowned for riding her pony up and down the stairs of their country home, Guines Court in Essex. The family lived at the time at Hertford Castle, which is now a museum.

Ruth always wanted to ride, begging rides on anything from carthorses to friends' ponies from the time she was small. But the opportunity did not arise to have lessons until she was 9, and then she had to cycle 7 miles to a riding school and back. At this time they were living at the Cheshire Hunt kennels.

Then she, her younger brother and older sister each drew £10 out of their savings certificates and invested the princely sum of £27 in their very first pony. But, though it had been sold them as a 4-year-old they were taken for a very bad ride, for he was only two, had only been gelded a couple of weeks earlier, and when the children tried to put a saddle on him he nearly kicked them through the roof.

'That was my first lesson in the pitfalls of dealing and I am not even now a very good dealer, for I have kept all my favourites until they died!'

When their grandfather died he left them a boat, which they promptly sold to buy a jumping pony; a super-limbed, cobby Connemara called Crescendo that Joe Makin brought over from Ireland. When she retired she was equally successful at stud, all her progeny being by Charlie Mumford's premium stallions.

Ruth's reluctance to sell any of her animals led to complications when she left school, for they had to pay for themselves; so she started giving riding lessons to the local children. Then she went on a course to Captain Edy Goldman, who did her a lot of good, to the late Col. Jack Talbot-Ponsonby, to Seamus Hayes and finally to Dick Stillwell.

She started showing Court Calypso, a super cob by Court Nez, who won the Riding Club's dressage championship and horse trials championship and was struck by lightning in his field aged 18. 'I made the mistake of asking him to gallop flat out when we were both young and he got very excitable and never forgot that lesson, which he had learned for life.'

When the stables she rented in Hertfordshire were sold for building, Mr and Mrs Crawford invited her to move to their home in Norfolk, and converted the stableyard at Carbrooke where she has 17 boxes. Mr Pike sent her a very nice chesnut hack called Clearway and then Mrs Bill Ransom, whose husband was Master of the Blankney, gave her the brown Thoroughbred Brother Bill to show as a lightweight. Bred to win the Derby, he had cost £8,000 guineas as a yearling, but when Ruth got him he was an undistinguished 2-year-old. But he won at Royal Windsor, British Timken, as a working hunter at the Royal Norfolk and at Fenton Horse Trials.

Robert Oliver was 35 in 1977, when he shook the Horse of the Year Show by winning the Hack title on Mrs Goodall's Tenterk, the cob title on Kempley, the small hunter title (for the second year running) on Footpath and was runner-up for the Hunter title on Dual Gold. Nothing like it had been seen before, but, to prove it was no fluke, in 1978 he retained the Hack title on Tenterk and the Cob title on Kempley, while at the Royal International he won the Hunter championship on Swanbourne and the reserve on Dual Gold.

In 1979 he broke his own record by winning the championship at Royal Windsor, the Royal International and the Horse of the Year Show on Flashman, the hack title at Wembley and many other leading shows on Tenterk, all three weight classes and the 4-year-old class at the Royal International, and the hunter championship at the Bath and West and Three Counties (and many more besides) on Dual Gold.

Robert's main credo is turning the show horses out in the paddock and treating them as ordinary horses, no matter what they cost. Gill, his wife, did most of the basic schooling on the flat, and he rides them about. 'I can always get on and give the horse a good ride after she has schooled him for a fortnight.

'We have had so many horses sent to us that were super in the school, but when you tried to ride them in a straight line down the road, you couldn't! I ride them round the farm, opening and shutting gates, through the mud, into my neighbour Walter Biddlecombe's yard, among cattle and sheep — they have to go where I want to go, and pop over a fence or two as well if I feel like it.'

The son of the late Mr and Mrs Leonard Oliver of Hereford, his nearest horse-minded relation was his uncle, Billy Watts, FWCF, who died in 1977, and his son, another Billy. As a boy, Robert would accompany his uncle when he visited clients, including Mrs Michael Symonds, District Commissioner of the South Herefordshire Pony Club, one of whose ponies he rode when he was 5. Weekends, and much of his school holidays, he spent in the livery yard of the Hereford veterinary surgeon, John Ryan, some of whose ponies he also rode. He joined the Pony Club when he was 9, went hunting when he was 9, and rode in his first gymkhana at 11.

Soon he was asked to ride some of the Cusop Stud ponies for Mr and Mrs Vivian Eckley of Hay-on-Wye, and when he was 17 and too big for ponies the only thing he wanted to do was to go on and ride horses. So he went to work for Colonel J. R. Cleghorn on the farm and with the hunters; everything had to be done as it ought to be done, which was excellent training. In the summer he showed horses for local owners and qualified Foxhunter horses for Ernie Evans. Then he worked for Derek Crossman, who had taken on the South Herefordshire hounds. He whipped in and rode the young horses, gaining valuable insight into making and riding high-class young Thoroughbreds.

Next he took over Ernie Evans's Belmont stables, leasing 12 boxes and a flat, and with customers soon bringing him horses to break, to school and to show he realised that he would have to move and expand his business. He took on 25 acres and more boxes at Harewood End, and it was here that he had his first success with show horses, starting in 1970 with Lord Sorcerer, the small hunter which he bought from Mrs Rosemary Cooke and produced for Major Helme to be the top winner for two seasons. Next came the top middleweight, Game Moss.

'I was really lucky to have ridden all those good ponies as a child. It is not good for children to win too much, but it helps the morale to win sometimes, so that you know that you can. It also has a great bearing on the rides you are offered. Later I realised that if I was to make a name and build on a solid foundation for the future, I would have to specialise.

'By the time I moved to Harewood End I had decided to concentrate on producing and presenting show horses. I had already been started along this road and I was influenced too by the fact that, although there was a large number of young people trying to make their names as show jumpers, the same situation did not, and still does not, exist in showing.'

In 10 years, Robert had got to the very top of his profession and remained there. His success is thoroughly deserved, for he works hard, and is unfailingly courteous both in the ring and out of it, to judges, stewards and fellow exhibitors, and refreshingly relaxed as to the outcome of his endeavours. Robert feels that his horses sometimes win when they do not deserve to and are sometimes beaten when they should not be, but that all in all it levels itself out. He is also helpful to others, an attitude of mind which is unfortunately becoming increasingly rare.

CHAPTER 18

Champion hunters since 1945

WHAT MAKES a champion show hunter? Obviously he must be the prototype, serving as a model for breeders, and the overall picture must be of quality, strength and symmetry combined with presence, that indefinable combination of character and a commanding bearing, a pride and majesty which rivets the attention. He says 'Look at me!' to all beholders, and no one can take their eyes off him.

Those whose preoccupation is concerned with finding outstanding horses agree that they are increasingly difficult to find. Those who were active before the war are in no doubt that horses were better then, and it is easy to look back over the last 40 years, recalling the great horses, comparing them with the rank and file, and to think that the standard has declined. It is possible, too, that distance lends enchantment to some of them.

What is indisputable is that the quality heavyweight is in short supply, and the limbs of some of the present-day weight-carriers can leave a lot to be desired. Often their second thighs are weak, and a tendency to being back of its knees can be laid at the door of *some* Irish Draught horses, which puts unnecessary strain upon the tendons and causes a horse to break down. A foreleg that is over at the knee almost invariably indicates strength. Brown Jack, whose winning career on the flat lasted for years, was right over at the knee and remained as sound and his legs as clean and hard when he retired as when he ran his first race.

A sloping pastern of moderate length is also important — short, upright pasterns give a ride which may be compared to driving a car without springs, but too long a pastern, though giving a comfortable, springy ride, does not stand up to hard work and can lead to the fetlock almost touching the ground with age.

All movement of the forelegs should come from the shoulder and not from the knee. The shoulder is the crucial factor in determining a good ride, and galloping downhill on a horse with a straight, upright shoulder is purgatory, with an ever-open front door. For some reason, a straight shoulder is often the concomitant of a long back, so that the horse that is said to 'stand over a lot of ground' does not always do so for the right reasons. Similarly, a good front is sometimes simulated by a long neck coming out of a straight shoulder, and sometimes the outlook can be deceptive until one actually sits on the horse, when all becomes clear and the shoulder is shown in its true perspective.

Depth through the throat is very desirable to avoid wind troubles, and the head should taper finely down to the muzzle. A coarse head is an abomination, as in man, but a fine, intelligent head with an alert and kindly expression means that the horse has a generous temperament and innate courage, without which the best conformation in the world is worth nothing. Handsome is as handsome does, as Snaffles made so abundantly clear in his picture of that title, and the horse which the dealers describe as a 'christian' is a pearl beyond price.

To sum up, the champion horse must exemplify activity, energy and courage, combined with great strength in the quarters, which are the propelling force, and good limbs with short cannon bones. In movement he should cover the ground with long, low strides, and the well-made horse cannot help but be naturally balanced and a good ride. He will not necessarily be a top-class show jumper, event horse or racehorse, however. To shine in these spheres demands something extra on top of make and shape. One year in Dublin the buyers for the Italian Federation decided to go all out for conformation in their quest for likely show jumpers, and paid the then enormous price of £2,000 for the champion horse of the show, Nat Galway-Greer's Munnings' Model. He proved quite useless for this very specialised job, which presupposes the ability to jump 6 feet, and ended up pulling a water cart in a small village outside Rome.

One of the first really great horses to appear after the war was W. Horace Cooper's bay middleweight, Beau Geste. Bred in Shropshire in 1939, by that well-known breeder, Mr E. H. Croft of Brockton Hall, Worthen, Shropshire, he was by Tagman by Craig-an-Eran out of Diana XVIII by Alder, dam Diana by Red Prince II by Kendal. His breeder hunted him for three seasons before selling him and his first major victory was the championship at Royal Windsor in 1946, which eventually he won three times. He also won the Champion of England Gold Cup at Peterborough twice, the Richmond Royal championship twice and the City of Bath championship three times.

The next outstanding horse, and the first of the post-war heavyweights was the liver chesnut, Mighty Fine, who won the Dublin supreme championship as a 6-year-old in 1947. He was then bought by Reg Hindley, captain of the British Olympic Three-Day-Event team in 1952. Bred in Co. Cork by Mr Patrick Ball, by Al Quaim out of a mare by Duke of Sparta, he was foaled in 1941 and first shown at Cork, where Galway-Greer bought him, and when he won Dublin it was only his second outing. His first season in England followed two years later, in 1949, when he was unbeaten, winning nine major championships. The following year he won seven, including Peterborough and The Royal for the second year.

Mighty Atom, another world-beating heavyweight, was also champion at Dublin for Nat Galway-Greer, ridden by Jim Daly, in 1948, as a 4-year-old. By Rockminster by Rocksavage out of a mare of anonymous antecedents, he too was a liver chesnut, was first produced by Mr Ball at Clonmel and bought by Mr Galway-Greer. Shown in Dublin by Jim Daly, he was sold to Beau Geste's owner, Horace Cooper, and produced in England as a 5-year-old.

In competition with Mighty Fine, he never beat him, but Mighty Fine was already a mature horse while The Atom was an immature 5-year-old who had not begun to grow to his enormous, nearly 17-hand frame. At this stage Mighty Fine may have had more quality but Mighty Atom grew into quality and had better conformation. Mighty Fine did not stay sound beyond his second English season but the young horse, ridden by Harry Tatlow, Jim Daly and Ray Lester, continued showing and winning for six. He won the Royal Counties championship six times, the Bath and West and City of Bath championships five times, and the Hunter Show, Richmond Royal, The Royal International and City of Birmingham championships four times each, as well as the Winston Churchill Cup, the Royal Windsor championship, the Peterborough Gold Cup and the Harringay Horse of the Year title twice. For 5 years he was monarch of all he surveyed, and he well deserved to be, for no horse has approached his record.

He lived on in retirement in a field next to to his owner's home in Sutton Coldfield for many years, with a donkey for company. Shall we ever see his like again? I doubt it very much, for that sort of horse is becoming like the brontosaurus. There are still plenty of big horses about, but most are common and lumbering, badly balanced, round in their action, unable to gallop, with loaded shoulders that cause them to roll in their trot and flounder in their faster paces — the sort of horse who has trouble enough to carry himself through the deep going, without the added burden of a rider who with his accoutrements scales 16 stone.

The quality heavyweight, the embodiment of equine size and strength and virtue, possesses a magnificent majesty, has such control of his body and such balance that, where the underbred horse, if it gallops at all will shake the ground like an earthquake, causes hardly a tremour as he hurtles past the stand in top gear. The breeding of such paragons is a fluke, and one that seems to be confined to Ireland with its precious limestone belt in the midland counties of Limerick, Cork, Tipperary, Waterford and Wexford. Some are bred in South and West Wales, tracing back to the Welsh cob, but they have a tendency to bend their knee. In Ireland they are often by a 'chasing sire out of a half-bred mare stemming from Irish Draught. At one time there were a lot by Cottage, then Steel Point, Knight's Wax, Golden Years, Water Serpent, Blue Cliff, Nordlys, Ozimandias, Chou Chin Chow, now Carnival Night. As Thady Ryan told me once, Irish sires of half-bred horses are old before they make their names, and then they die. Only in recent years have a band of enthusiasts set about establishing a Society on the lines of the HIS and inspecting and registering mares. Then the Irish Horse Board took over and set the whole thing at nought by registering mares indescriminately without inspection, even ponies, and bred nondescript small animals to form queues at the abattoirs for the dog-meat factories. Now at last the scheme is being run by the original enthusiasts and is back on the right track.

When Mighty Atom retired in 1955 it was to be succeeded by His Grand Excellency, a brown heavyweight by Colare out of a mare by Ambassador. He won the championship at Cork as a 4-year-old when ridden by Tim Hyde, the brilliant steepleshase jockey who won the 1938 Grand National on Workman, partnered Prince Regent in all his races after the war and then tragically broke his back while riding a young show jumper at Clonakilty show.

His Grand Excellency was a great mover and galloper, and for two years was shown in England for Bernard Selby, ridden by Jim Powell. In 1955 he had to face stiff opposition from the 1954 Dublin champion, Major Michael Beaumont's grey What a Walk, by Long Walk. What a Walk was bought in Ireland as a yearling by Mr John Codd to win the Dublin title and so he did, for though John Codd died in 1953 he left the horse to his nephew, Matty Parle, who took him to Dublin as a 4-year-old and duly won the championship, after which he sold him for £2,000 to Major Beaumont, the bearded Master of the Kildare Hounds.

In England, What a Walk was shown first by Harry Bonner. He stood supreme at Oxford, Shrewsbury, The Royal and the Hunter Show, and took the Gold Cup at Peterborough. Then he beat his Grand Excellency at the Royal Counties and was beaten by him at Richmond and the Royal International before being retired to the hunting field.

The same happy fate befell His Grand Excellency, who was bought by Mr F. G. Starling, a farmer from East Anglia, and enjoyed many years of success in the show ring and fun in the hunting field with Mrs Hugh Gingell, Master huntsman of the Cambridgeshire Harriers, whose sitting room his portrait dominates to this day. A tremendous character, he was said to ride like a blood horse.

The next great heavyweight — an Irishman again — was Mr Hugh Sumner's Work of Art, yet another supreme championship winner at Dublin, for Nat Galway-Greer. A big brown horse by Soldado out of a mare by King Cob, he was 6 when he won his title at Ballsbridge in 1957 and bought by Mr Hugh Sumner to be ridden by his master-of-horse, R. Holloday. A great galloper, he won many championships but unfortunately attained notoriety when he swerved and knocked down a photographer at White City, and became the centre of attention, with his rider, of a rather unpleasant legal action in which the poor man claimed damages for the loss of an eye. The Royal International Horse Show disclaimed all responsibility for the accident.

For the next few years there was a decline in the standard of heavyweights, the best of which was probably Major Cecil Drabble's Gold Dust, who swept the board for a season with Harry Bonner in the saddle and was sold to America. Then came another very successful, also produced from Harry Bonner's yard, in Mrs John Beckwith-Smith's Robin Hood. Bred in Northern Ireland, which is not renowned for good horses, he was by Copernicus and held sway for two seasons. He did not really gallop, but his rider was far too good a showman ever to make the mistake of asking him to in the ring, and the big chestnut simply 'progressed' at a moderate speed, rather like a Rolls Royce.

Already the heavyweights were getting more quality, and the next good one, in the middle 1960s, was Fine Art, a chestnut bred in Co. Wexford by Roy Latta, who has bred so many good ones over the years. An impressive-looking horse and a powerful and convincing galloper, he was bought after winning in Dublin by Mr Hugh Sumner, who only showed him for a short time and then sold him to Mr Peregrine Murray-Smith, who was then Master of the Dartmoor Hounds. He did not believe in keeping horses only for the show ring, and Fine Art regularly took his turn with hounds across Dartmoor, hunter-trialed in Spring and autumn and went showing in the summer. He remained fresh and new in himself and never became jaded or ring-crafty.

His only drawback was a crooked foreleg, which judges tend to dislike. Several people pulled Hugh Sumner's leg about it, and asked 'was the grass so high in Dublin that he had failed to notice it?' More than one dealer remarked that he travelled thousands of miles looking for straight movers, only to be beaten in the show ring by a horse whose lower foreleg came out of his knee at an angle. The controversy raged thick and fast, yet Fine Art won at shows such as The Royal and the Royal International under judges whose knowledge and integrity were beyond reproach.

On one memorable occasion, after the horse had swept the board in the West Country for some three seasons, a well-known judge was invited to officiate at a show in North Devon. 'I hope Fine Art doesn't come', he remarked to his wife that morning. 'If he does, I shall put him down. I don't like horses with crooked legs.'

Fine Art did come, and won his class, and the championship, and the judge said later that as soon as he got on him the horse was such a super ride that he had to put him up. What is more, that same crooked leg carried him and his master, who is a big man, for many years over Dartmoor, which is some of the roughest country imaginable, and was never unsound for a single day.

Mrs Gingell, Master of the Cambridgeshire Harriers, always shows a good weight-carrying horse and perhaps the best of them, after she pensioned-off His Grand Excellency, was the Royal Ulster champion, Earl Bruce, who was also bred in the North of Ireland, by Keepatwoatwo out of a little mare who stood only 14.3 hands. He was fancied to win at Dublin but a pair of badly-capped hocks put him out of the running, though when he came to England his hocks were as clean as a whistle and he was champion at Royal Windsor in quite a good year.

The next champion heavyweight, State Visit, was in a class of his own, a Thoroughbred horse by a premium stallion, Quadrangle, out of an Irish mare by Steel Point called Narrow Margin. I saw him first at the Oxfordshire show as a 4-year-old, ridden by Jack Gittins for his breeders, Mr and Mrs Christopher Marler. When I saw him again a few years later at the Great Yorkshire Show I thought him one of the most glorious horses I had ever seen, a lashing great blood horse with tremendous presence and scope who fairly ate up the ground in his gallop. He had been in the wars, having got out of his field, galloped along the main Oxford road and crashed into a mini-car, which left a permanent blemish on one foreleg but mercifully did not make him unsound.

Sold to David Barker, the former Olympic show jumper and present stallion owner and amateur huntsman to the Whaddon Chase, he was sold on again to Mr Appleyard, a market gardener from near Leeds who loves a good horse and sent his new acquisition to Willie Hope of Garstang to produce for his daughter, Pauline. Their ambition was to win the Great Yorkshire championship with him, which they did with no difficulty at all on his first major outing of 1967.

Encouraged by this success, next year they ventured further afield. State Visit was champion at the Royal Highland Show at Edinburgh, where he caused a sensation, before winning the Great Yorkshire title for the second time, and Major John Howie declared him the best he had ever sat on. Three months later he ended the season by winning the Show Hunter of the Year title at Wembley, a worthy champion indeed.

He was not, however, a horse to thrive on a steady diet of showing. Willie Hope was able to produce him at his best by showing him just in and out. When he came South to David Tatlow's yard and his connections perhaps became a little too ambitious and over-showed him, he started to go downhill, both temperamentally and physically, and he was only half the horse when he had run up too light in condition. In 1969 he won the championship at Royal Windsor but then he deteriorated, and eventually he was sold to go eventing in Sussex, where he was put down with navicular disease in 1972.

He was only the second thoroughbred heavyweight, I think, to win championships since the war, the first being Mrs Gingell's Earl Bruce. The third and last — so far — was Prince's Street, the horse Vin Toulson bought out of training in March 1973, and produced 3 months later to win 10 major championships before Colonel 'Handy' Hurrell, then President of the HIS, introduced a rule prohibiting hobdayed horses from being exhibited at affiliated shows.

When his son William was passing out of Sandhurst and The Queen presented him with the Saddle of Honour, she asked him: 'Is your father my Lord Lieutenant for Cambridgeshire?'

William assented.

'I believe that he is having a little trouble with hobdaying', continued Her Majesty, aware that this dictum had caused a minor furore in certain quarters.

When I arrived at Dublin in August I was given a mild rebuke by Nat Galway-Greer. 'I was surprised', he said, 'To read that you were praising this broken-winded racehorse as a *hunter*!', he said reprovingly, almost waving a finger at me. '*Never* forget that it's the horse that can go the shortest way that will get you to the end of a hunt, *not* the flying machine! Before the war we could buy that sort of horse for £100 in any third-rate sale.'

Chatting with Captain Glen Browne at Dublin a few years ago, he suddenly asked: 'What's the best heavyweight horse you've ever seen here in all the years you've been coming to the show?'

I thought for a moment and then replied: 'Mighty Atom, I suppose.'

He shook his head and said: 'No. The best heavyweight that either of us ever saw here was Admiral.'

Admiral was a chesnut 5-year-old by Nordlys, owned by the brothers McEvoy from the North. He won the heavyweight cup in 1970 and was reserve champion, beaten by The Yank, owned by Tom Moore, Master of the County Down Staghounds and ridden by Willie Darling. Admiral was bought by Mr R. A. Bonnett, a contractor from Kent, and sent to Roy Trigg to be produced, but he was a nappy, headstrong horse and Roy did not risk taking him in the ring until the British Timken show in August where he won the championship, after which he won the Wembley title from Norman Crow's middleweight, Fair Gin.

The following year, 1972, he came out at the Bath and West to finish only fifth in his class, which was the considered opinion of his merit by ex-jockey and thriller-writer Dick Francis. The decision caused quite a fluttering in the dovecotes, but Admiral was supreme a week later at the South of England show at Ardingly. Kept away from The Royal by 'the cough', he was champion at the Royal International and retained the Wembley title at the Horse of the Year Show. His strong points were the fact that he was such a good pattern and his light and airy movement, which enabled him to cover the ground in his gallop like a much better-bred horse.

The next really good heavyweight, Irish again, was Douglas Bunn's Selsey Bill, named after his holiday camp on the Sussex coast but shown to win in Dublin in 1973 as Slaney Side. A chesnut son of Sunny Light, who got a lot of show horses and stood in Co. Limerick at Cappamore, he was sold by Jack Gittins, who won the Peterborough Gold Cup on his twice. An Irish heavyweight was also a consistent winner at the London shows in 1979, when Robert Oliver produced the chesnut Flashman, by Wilton House, a son of Epaulette who stands in Co. Kilkenny, for Mr Peter White, a London bookmaker.

A top-class heavyweight has a couple of stone in hand when fighting out a championship, but there have been many champion middleweights since Beau Geste. One whose career overlapped that of Horace Cooper's lovely horse was Hugh Sumner's Blarney Stone, who used to be shown by Jack Gittins's cousin, another Jack. A more robust type than Beau Geste he was bred, as his name implies, in Ireland, in 1942, by Praetor by Phalaris out of a mare by Denis d'Or by Tredennis, bought as a 3-year-old from Mr N. D. Mahoney of Blarney, Co. Cork. As a 5-year-old he was champion at the Hunter Show and a year later at The Royal. In 1949, his best year, he was reserve for the first-ever Hunter of the Year title at Harringay, after an epic battle with Mighty Fine.

He then pulled off a coup which has never been emulated, nor even attempted, when he emerged from retirement after two years on the sidelines, to take a tilt at the reigning champion, Mighty Atom, at the Great Yorkshire show. He beat the heavyweight out of sight, and went on to win the Gold Cup at Peterborough before sinking back into obscurity again to rest on his laurels. A very high-couraged horse, he was as keen as mustard and took a lot of riding, but he was a classical pattern of 14-stone blood horse, than which I doubt we shall ever see a better.

The next good middleweight was Unique, bred in Co. Wexford by Mr Peter Somers, by Match, by Hurry On, out of a mare by Ceylonese. Foaled in 1944, he was third at Dublin for Nat Galway-Greer as a 3-year-old and was then sold to an English dealer, E. P. Mills. At 4 he was champion at the Hunter Show, Oxford and Peterborough, when he was bought by the late Mr Robert Hanson, the transport magnate. Unique was given to his younger son, the late Bill Hanson.

Champion at Newark twice, to start the season, and the Royal Lancashire, reserve at Windsor, Richmond, Peterborough, the Hunter Show, The Royal and the Great Yorkshire, and a winner at the Royal International, he was retired to the hunting field and carried the huntsman of the Grove and Rufford for many seasons.

Ronnie Marmont's Rajah III was a British-bred horse. Bred in Hertfordshire by Brig. Sir Geoffrey Church, he was by Gough's Auction, by General Gough, out of Cottage Belle, a famous mare bred at Midleton, Co. Cork, by Mrs Glen Browne. First shown by Miss Mary Haggie (later Mrs Eddie Studd) who bought him as a yearling, he was the top novice at The Royal in 1949. The next year he divided Blarney Stone and Beau Geste at the Bath and West and then won the ladies' classes at the Three Counties, the Hunter Show and the Great Yorkshire.

He was then bought by Ronnie Marmont, who rode him in middleweight classes and put up Mrs Bea Haggas, a most elegant exponent of the art of side-saddle riding, in ladies' classes. He was never beaten side-saddle in 1951 and wound up as Working Hunter of the Year at Harringay. In 1952 he won the Show Hunter of the Year title and in 1953 the Working Hunter title again. He too retired to the hunting field in Leicestershire. A most genuine horse, he was never quite good enough to beat a really top heavyweight in a championship, but he was a great character, greatly beloved of the lady judges. One year at the Great Yorkshire, when the Hon. Mrs James Baird was judging him, the side-saddle slipped right around when he was at full gallop, to end up under his belly. He stopped, however, of his own accord, so that what could have been a very nasty accident was averted.

The next successful middleweight was Earmark, who was produced by Count Robert Orssich, the Austrian-born showman who was so successful with both hacks and hunters, for Mr Hugh Haldin. A bay Thoroughbred horse, by Cariff out of Okehampton, he was bred in Ireland by Baron de Robeck and bought for Lord Bicester by Harry Bonner as a potential 'chaser. Not fast enough to race, he was sold on and produced in the show ring in 1953, winning the Champion of England Gold Cup at Peterborough. In 1954 he was supreme at Royal Windsor and in his finest hour he defeated Mighty Atom in the Royal International Championship and went on to win the Winston Churchill Cup.

His successor, The Wise Man, was successful at the London shows but seldom went to battle at the shows such as Peterborough, The Royal, the Hunter Show and the Great Yorkshire, which really take a bit of winning. Here the victor was Boothby, a grand galloping brown horse owned by Mr 'Gino' Henson, Master of the Blankney Hounds in Lincolnshire. After winning the championship at The Royal, Boothby was sold to Mr Hugh Sumner to go 'chasing, but he never quite made the grade in this capacity.

The next top middleweight was Mrs P. Morris's grey, Romeo VI, who was by Monsieur Isy out of a grand little mare, Yvonne III by Tramail, owned by Beau Geste's breeder, Mr E. H. Croft, from Shropshire. She was the dam of several champions, among them Brockton and Dawn Chorus, who won championships for Mrs Nancy Sugden of Corton Denham both as a filly and a matron, yet Yvonne was only just over 15 hands.

Romeo was unusually versatile, for he hunted in Herefordshire, won hunter trials and point-to-points, and twice, in 1963 and 1964, won the Show Hunter of the Year title at Wembley, ridden by Bill Bryan. He was a short-backed, strongly-made, deep, grand sort of horse, a real workman and a show horse to boot.

Then came Mrs Bill Ransom's Spey Cast, from Lincolnshire, a brown horse by Nack, by Black Devil, out of an unregistered mare called Silk. Bred by the Hon. Mrs G. Pretyman in 1960, he was led champion at Lincoln, Rutland and the Royal Norfolk as a 3-year-old and, ridden by Jack Gittins as a 4-year-old, was champion at Newark, Leicester, Northampton, Peterborough, the Royal Lancs. and Rutland, and reserve at The Royal, the Hunter Show and for the Wembley title.

In 1965, when he took the Wembley title, he was ridden side-saddle by his owner in several classic engagements, usually contriving to beat his contemporary, the chestnut Herb of Grace, by Solon Morn, who had been as big an in-hand winner in the South as had Spey Cast in the North, if not indeed bigger. But they were worlds apart, Herb of Grace being a big, soft, flash type of horse, better suited to Rotten Row than to the hunting field.

There was a memorable occasion at one of the last Richmond Royal shows when Lord Allenby, the show director, dreamed up a brilliant and novel way to bring more interest to the hunter championship. He could not have succeeded better, for though he had only chosen the judges, not the horses and riders concerned in it, he had all the ingredients of high drama and the scenario was absolutely rivetting. The classes were judged by John Shedden, and the championship by a completely independent judge in Colonel Neil Foster, Joint-Master of the Grafton.

John Shedden, being an admirer of Herb of Grace, put him over Spey Cast in the middleweight class while Neil Foster made the most of the possibilities inherent in this divertingly explosive situation by reversing the class decision and awarding this valuable championship to Spey Cast, ridden by Jack Gittins, as we all knew he would. The only people who were not highly delighted by this splendid entertainment were John Shedden, who was indignant at having his judgement reversed.

This judging experiment was never repeated, alas, after the sparks flew and in the light of the subsequent controversy, but it certainly kept the experts well primed and exceeded Jaff Allenby's wildest anticipations. Spey Cast was that year's champion of champions, too, winning at Cambridge, Huntingdon, Newark, Lincoln, Richmond, The Royal, Royal International, Royal Norfolk, Suffolk County and the Horse of the Year show.

The following year Mrs Colin McHugh, whose parents, Bill and Dinah Kent, were two of the most successful riders in the showring between the wars, brought out a horse called Tudor Line. She bought him in Devonshire and swept the board with him before selling him across the Atlantic. Bred by Mr Jury at Torrington, North Devon, he was by Tudor Bell, by Henry Tudor, out of a grey Irish mare called Linda who came out of Exeter Repository.

Tudor Line's great rival was Mrs Waring's Sporting Rights, by Game Rights, shown by Donald Owen. These two disputed the championship at all the major shows that season, with the title at Wembley ultimately going to Tudor Line.

A year later, Sporting Rights came into his own with Tudor Line out of the way, though he was formidably opposed by Colonel and Mrs Frank Dean's Troodos, whom they bred, ridden by Willie Donaldson, and by one of the most memorable horses I have ever been privileged to see, Norman Crow's Top Notch.

A superlative bay-brown horse by Top Walk, by Concerto, out of May Queen, by the Gainsborough horse Gay Morning out of June IX by Hustle Bustle by Pommern, Top Notch was foaled in 1962 and bred by Mr and Mrs

G. N. Rob of Catton, near Thirsk, in Yorkshire. As a young horse he was very lightly shown, though he stood second at the Great Yorkshire, but as a 4-year-old he won the young horse championship at Peterborough and was reserve at the Yorkshire.

Shown consistently at the top shows for the next four seasons, he won many championships three times on the trot and, having won the *Horse and Hound* Cup at The Royal, he made it a double in 1970 and successfully defended his Wembley title to finish the season. He was a truly sensational horse with tremendous presence and personality, the tips of his ears turned inwards and almost meeting, and he matured into a rare, old-fashioned sort of hunter. When Thady Ryan, Master of the Black and Tans, rode him at Wembley it seemed as though he was reluctant to get off him.

The top-class middleweight horse remains the *beau ideal* of a Leicestershire hunter. Over the years, the best have not varied in type all that much. Great quality, bone and depth, with a raking great stride and inherent courage, and with an abiding look of eagles, are the characteristics of the 14-stone hunter, and the best example of an Olympic three-day event horse, like Mary Gordon-Watson's Cornishman III, is cast in the same mould.

Mrs Frank Furness's Seta Pike, a homebred son of Max Abram's Kadir Cup, won the *Horse & Hound* Cup at The Royal twice, as well as many other championships. Another top middleweight was Dual Gold, who was first produced by Vin Toulson for Mr Derek Cant, then for Lady Zinnia Pollock, and finally by Robert Oliver for two further seasons in the ownership of Mr Peter White.

Dual Gold, who came out in 1976, was bought by the Toulsons at the Doncaster show and sale in 1975. Bred by National Hunt steward Mr John Rose of Aslockton, Lincolnshire, he was a brown son of Le Dieu d'Or and Ann Dual, who bred three winners. The Toulsons bid 4,500 gns. for him as a 4-year-old but his reserve was 5,000, and when they got home, were unable to get him out of their minds and rang up to say that they would pay the reserve price, he had been sold into training. They asked for first refusal if he turned out to be useless, only to find that Lady Inchcape had forestalled them. Luckily, they had a show jumper which she wanted and eventually they arranged a swap.

They found the horse sour and uninterested in his work when he arrived, and during the course of a very successful season, when his colours were only lowered at the Essex show, he got increasingly jaded. The next season he was not so consistent, though he was runner-up for the Wembley title to David Tatlow and the lightweight Bunowen. Then Robert Oliver bought him and after a season's hunting with the Ledbury had cheered him up and got rid of a lot of his inhibitions, he had two further successful seasons; having finally made up his mind, Daphne Toulson decided, that he enjoyed his showing. 'He is the most beautiful ride, the only horse I was able to ride when I broke my back.' Now he is one of Robert and Gilly Oliver's best hunters and did a season with the Duke of Beaufort's in 1983/4.

The lightweights have changed more in recent years than has any other category of show horse, very largely because conditions laid down by the various shows with regard to weight-carrying capacity have undergone a subtle and insidious change. Instead of the top limit being set, as heretofore, at 12 st. 7 lbs., to cater for the true lightweight, 15.3 hands high and with 8 inches of bone, the upper limit was set at 13 st.

Human nature being what it is, exhibitors like to improve their chances by showing a horse that is well up to the specified weight, or even a little over it. Thus the borderline middleweight, up to 13 st. 7 lbs. came creeping in. At the same time there was a regrettable tendency for some judges to put up 'tall' horses of close on 17 hands, who at this weight were almost invariably 'on the leg'.

The first of the great postwar lightweights was Horace Cooper's spectacular lightweight, Wavering Bee, who was one of the most sensational movers and gallopers ever seen. He was really a pre-war horse as well to some extent, for he was bred in Co. Meath by Mr James Daly in 1935, by Wavetop, by Spearmint, out of Flying Bee by Honey Bee. Owned and ridden by Mr H. Davis Kenny, he swept all before him at Dublin in 1939. He won the 4-year-old class, the open lightweight class, the lightweight cup and finally the supreme championship.

Cooper kept him all through the war at his home at Hagley and in 1946 brought him out at Windsor. Despite his age, he was hardly ever beaten for the next two years, winning among many other championships the International Horse Show title and the Peterborough Gold Cup.

Perhaps the nearest to approach him in later years was Ronnie Marmont's Cufflink, a charming chesnut who doubled as a ladies' horse. By Bachelor's Convert out of a mare by Ben Alder, he was bred by Mr Bartholomew Cuff and shown in Dublin in 1951 by Eamonn Rohan, the farmer-dealer from Middleton, Co. Cork, whose son Jerry is now carrying on the good work. He was the winning lightweight 4-year-old and reserve for the cup to Nat Galway-Greer's grey Mighty Grand, by Steadlis, who did exceptionally well in England for Patricia Cope for many seasons, and lived until 1970.

Cufflink won several championships and virtually farmed the ladies' classes until he retired in 1956. His one defect was a pronounced dip to his back, which some of the best men judges disliked exceedingly, though under a side-saddle he was said to resemble 'an armchair in motion'.

But the most successful lightweight, particularly because she went on to become a champion brood mare, was Mrs Alec Wood's Prince's Grace. A glorious bay mare with a star, foaled in 1958, she was bred near Brigg in Lincolnshire by Mr Rex Chappell, by Prince's Game out of Collence by Columcille, a half-sister to the 'chaser, College Master on whom the Australian Olympic gold medallist, Laurie Morgan, won many good races.

Bought as a young mare by Mrs Tollit, who won with her, she was sold on to Mrs Wood, daughter of Hugh Sumner. She had a phenomenal career for a lightweight, and a mare at that, for in 1961 and 1962 she was champion at shows such as the Bath and West, Royal Windsor, Richmond Royal, Newark, Oxford, the Three Counties and the Hunter show, and if she ever failed to stand supreme it was usually because she had been beaten by Mr Sumner's heavyweight, Work of Art. She was almost as successful as a brood mare, though her owner very wisely forebore from carting a foal about all over the country and confined her to the Hunter Show, The Royal, the Three Counties and the Peterborough show. She was also twice winner of the Fredericks In-Hand championship at the Horse of the Year Show.

The Hon. Mrs Stella Cardiff's Palladium, foaled in 1956 by Top Walk, was bred in Yorkshire by Mr G. Widdall, and found by Trevor Banks. He was a big winner, taking the Peterborough Gold Cup twice, and under side-saddle with Mrs Tollit. Having learned his job in the hunting field before ever seeing a show ring, he retired to the hunting field, carrying Major Bob Hoare hunting the Cottesmore Hounds.

Next came Monbra, a bay by Hop Bridge out of Mona XI by Forerunner. Bred at Bracknell by Mrs Michael Smallwood, he was sold as a young horse to Miss Judy Frank in the Beaufort country and then to Mrs John Moss, better known as Rosemary Cooke. In 1964 and '65 he was not unduly successful, only to come into his own in 1966. Champion at the Bath & West, Richmond, The Royal and Royal International, he also took the Wembley title. By now, Miss Betsy Profumo had joined Mrs Cooke as joint owner.

The last of the champion lightweights for a while was Mrs Alec Wood's Urney Road, who won the Dublin championship as a 4-year-old in 1967, ridden by Co. Wexford stud owner, Michael Hickey, and by his horse Arctic Slave. He was not produced in England until he was 6, when he was brought out by David Barker, and he was only lightly shown until 1970. He won at Oxford and Newark, where he beat a somewhat recalcitrant Top Notch, and Royal Windsor, but at The Royal Top Notch gained his revenge and Urney Road went into training shortly afterwards.

In 1972 the honours were fairly evenly divided between Admiral, with Roy Trigg up, and Norman Crow's Fair Gin, by Quality Fair, who came on from the young stock classes and was supreme at Peterborough and the Great Yorkshire. Admiral kept on winning but was overshadowed when they met by Vin Toulson's Princes Street, who beat him consistently. 1974 was Fair Gin's year, but in 1975 there was an *embarrass de richesse* with Trigg's former Dublin champion Kit-Chin, Allister Hood with Paul Rackham's Langton Orchid, Mr and Mrs Frank Furness's home-bred Seta Pike (by Kadir Cup out of their Legendbelle, also bred at home) Mrs Peter Warren's Middleton Lad and Lady Zinnia Pollock's Picture Play, ridden by Ruth McMullen, all winning in their turn. Seta Pike took the plums, the *Horse & Hound* Cup at the Royal and the Great Yorkshire.

In 1976 it was Dual Gold all the way until the Horse of the Year show, when 'Tub' Ivens turned the tables on him with the heavyweight Ballymanor, by John Rawding's premium stallion Ghyll Manor out of Mrs Morton's Ballymore.

In 1977, Vin Toulson brought out for Lady Zinnia Pollock Balmoral, a heavyweight horse that he had found in the Border country, where he was hunted. An 8-year-old son of Game Rights, he won at Newark and Windsor and could do no wrong until The Royal. Here he picked up a clinker on the perimeter cinder track and retired from the fray. Thady Ryan, Master of the Black and Tans in Co. Limerick, gave the *Horse & Hound* Cup to David Tatlow on the Irish horse Bunowen, by Seven Bells, a strong lightweight.

Balmoral had already won at Peterborough under Mr Dorian Williams and Bunowen at the Royal International, but at the Horse of the Year Show he picked up a 4-inch nail and left the ring on three legs, so Bunowen won the Waterford Crystal trophy more or less as he pleased, as he did again in 1978, while in '79 he was reserve to Flashman.

Lady Zinnia Pollock, whose parents, the Earl and Countess of Londesborough, were joint Masters of the Blankney, had her last show horse, Beau Brumell in 1981. Found for her by David Barker, he was by the Duke of Northumberland's premium stallion, Hamood, out of a Cleveland Bay mare and was very impressive when winning the Royal Windsor Championship, but when sold lost a lot of his presence. George Chapman's Zatopec, champion at Dublin and winner of the middleweight cup there in 1979, was shown by David Tatlow to win the *Horse & Hound* Cup at The Royal.

Lady Zinnia also had an outstanding dark brown lightweight, Whaddon Way, who nearly won the Hunter of the Year title at Wembley in 1981, but one of the judges preferred the Healy-Fentons' heavyweight working hunter-type, the Brigadier.

For the next three years, only one heavyweight, the chesnut Assurance was to get a look-in. He reigned more or less supreme from 1980–82 with Vin Toulson, who bought him as a 4-year-old at the Horse of the Year Show. John Rawding had judged him at the Royal Cornwall and told Vin about him. By Crawter, a premium horse, he traced back on his dam's side to the full sister to a horse called Grudon, who won the Snowstorm Grand National in 1902 with his feet packed with butter. Grudon's sister proved difficult to get in foal so they turned her out with a Shire colt who founded a dynasty of TB-Shire heavyweight brood mares for Maxie Jones of the Elton Estates, near Peterborough.

In 1983 Vin Toulson swept the board again, this time with the South Essex Insurance Group's grey middleweight, Elite, who is by the premium stallion Manor Star out of Bally Valley by Acra, bred by Mrs Unity Greenwood of Pontardawe, Swansea. Elite won 12 major championships. Robert and Gillian Oliver seem to keep their horses sweet longer than anyone else, and Glenstawl, the former Cork champion, and the English-bred Brewster, who has been winning since he was a foal, both carried their colours throughout 1983, under both saddles.

Ladies' horses are often less good rides under a side-saddle than astride. Smooth cadence and a long stride are essential, and a slightly longer back is permissible for a side-saddle. The lady judges often prefer a middleweight to a lightweight, while Mrs Bill Ransom regularly showed the heavyweight Aces High under a side-saddle. The horse needs to be temperate, however, for a 14 st. blood horse pulling a double handful can be too strong for the average woman and, as Jack Hance used to say, there is nothing more dangerous than 'a loose horse with a woman on top'! A runaway in a side-saddle is a frightening thing, and a showring is not the place to adopt the classic advice to 'throw the reins to him and tell him to help himself'.

The small hunter classes came into being soon after the Second World War and were originally intended to be ridden by young people, under 21 years. But as more people rode smaller horses as an economy measure, the classes were opened to all comers, while the professionals acquired one as another string to their bow.

Yet strangely enough, although more small horses than big ones are bred, the really memorable small hunters have been few and far between. I can only recall half-a-dozen whose names will live on. In the old days, the small hunter was a misfit for showing purposes, too small for the lightweight class and too much of hunter type to pass off as a hack. But though the small hunter class has created a lucrative market for the smaller animal, by no means everyone approved of the efforts to promote them. Judge Wylie, for quarter of a century the benevolent dictator of Dublin Horse Show, declined to sanction them at Ballsbridge for several years after they had become standard in England. 'Too many little horses are already bred by accident without encouraging people to breed any more', he observed.

It was after seeing what must have been the greatest small hunter of all time, Burrough Hills, on a visit to the Royal International Horse Show at White City, that he changed his mind. Foaled in 1947, Burrough Hills was a bay gelding by the polo pony Grey Metal out of Norah's Star and was bred at Towcester by Major R. Bourne. Mrs George Gibson sold him to Ronnie Marmont in 1954. The next year he was unbeaten in 25 outings and was Riding Horse of the Year at Harringay. In 1956 he was beaten only once. When he was over 20 he appeared in the parade of personalities at Wembley, his legs as clean as ever. He won the Wembley title 3 times, as later did Mrs Rosemary Cooke's Tomboy, another bay with pony blood in his veins. Tomboy was a full brother to Miss Minnette, dam of the riding pony stallion, Miss Elspeth Ferguson's Bwlch Zephyr and his brothers, Bwlch Zingaree and Bwlch Zip. Mrs Cooke had the other top small hunters, Some Gardener and Lord Sorcerer.

In my view the third best was the liver chesnut Thoroughbred, Pelicamp, bred in Yorkshire in 1954, by the Pelican out of The Pensioner. He won three races on the flat for his breeder, Mr Hall, before being diverted to the showring. He first won the Wembley title in 1961 and 3 years later he won it again, owned by Mr Melville Lawrey from Cornwall and ridden by his daughter, Judith, winning also at Richmond, Windsor, and the White City. When he retired he was given to me — the best gift I have ever received, for he was the kindest and most generous horse thar ever looked through a bridle and once won the ladies' class at Windsor, giving away inches, for he was a marvellous ride and simply *flew* in his gallop.

In 1979 the HIS Council recommended to its judges that they should request the owner or rider of a horse which they considered to be in the wrong class to take it into the higher weight limit. This happened at Newark, where John Downes and Richard Matson decided (quite rightly) that Bunowen was a middleweight, although he had been top lightweight, ironically enough, for the past 2 seasons. It paved the way, moreover, for justice to be done, and at the end of the season the Council, in its wisdom, altered the lightweight limit to 12 st. 7 lbs., thus ensuring that the *genuine* lightweights got a fair crack of the whip. Human nature being what it is, it is understandable, though regrettable, that people should try to win by fair means or foul, but it is also to be recommended that they should be halted in their tracks by appropriate legislation wherever possible.

In 1984 and 1985 the scene was generally dominated by two chesnut heavyweights of very different type — both have had their best successes with Robert Oliver. He describes Standing Ovation (a son of Carnival Knight whom I first saw winning the supreme championship at Dublin in 1983 with Mrs Ned Cash) as 'a rich young man's horse, a real galloper and a county show champion'. He was champion at the Royal and Show Hunter of the Year at Wembley for his owners, Wendy and Nigel Trevithick, as well as underlining his supremacy at the Bath and West, South of England and Three Counties.

The other horse, who is HIS bred but looks Irish, being out of a draught-type mare, is Mrs Dewar's Seabrook. His sire, a premium horse of 'Dewi' Lewis's called Stretchworth Lad, stood in Pembrokeshire. Robert calls him an old gentleman's horse, sedate and steady, good in his slower paces and a London show horse. Among his victories was the Royal International at Birmingham, where he wound up reserve champion.

Elite, now ridden by Jane Holderness-Roddam, who is worth a stone in hand, was the Royal Windsor champion but Vin Toulson with Mr and Mrs Rose's Fireworks Night won the Waterford Aynsley Points Championship from all comers as well as standing reserve champion at the 1986 Royal to Mrs Croft's Periglen, by The Ditton. Roy Trigg's Devon County champion Fisherman won the Horse of the Year Show as he pleased, and was reserve to Periglen at the 1986 Royal. By Charlie Mumford's Royal Clipper, he was out of Heron, who won so much for the Burringtons until she died of colic in 1985.

Another colic victim was Celtic Gold, as a 7-year-old in early 1986. By Terence, a horse Vivian Bishop sent over to Ireland, he was unbeaten in Ireland at 2 and in England at 3, Robert Oliver bought him from Capt. Ronnie McMahon, the former 3-Day Event rider, and in 1985 he was champion at the Royal International.

The lightweight classes have been dominated by Mr and Mrs Andy Crofts's Periglen, who has the distinction of having won the Champion of All England gold cup at Peterborough, one of very few lightweights to have done so during the course of its long life, stretching back to the early years of the century. Another outstanding true lightweight is Dancin', by Pony Express from a mare by Doubtless II, sire of Princess Anne's Doublet. Six this time, Robert bought him from Mrs Richard Sumner, in the Heythrop country.

It is seldom indeed that a small hunter is even qualified to compete in a hunter championship, let alone winning it, but this was the happy fate of Mr and Mrs A. McCowan's Statesman, who beat all his larger cousins to take the Royal International title in 1985.

Robert Oliver's stable had an *embarras de richesse* in 1985, as it always does, but one at least will need to be replaced. In the autumn of 1986, Mr Creber's middleweight King's General, by the ID sire King of Diamonds — a great sort and a great galloper — will be joining Captain Mark Phillips as a potential event horse.

CHAPTER 19

The 'competition horse'

A FEW VOCAL members of the international equestrian hierarchy in this country are constantly bemoaning the fact that we do not, as a nation, set out deliberately to breed either show jumpers or dressage horses, as do the Germans, the Dutch and sundry others whom Kipling might have dubbed 'lesser breeds without the law', blinkered by the fact that their entire equestrian experience and/or ambition is bounded either by red and white poles or black and white alphabetical plastic markers.

The plain truth is that they conveniently ignore or overlook the fact that remarkably few people require a horse that will jump 6 ft. or win a dressage test. What they do want — and hopefully, always will — is a horse that will carry them well to hounds. I well remember the late Colonel Jack Talbot-Ponsonby telling me that if anyone asked him what sort of horse made the best show jumper, his reply was invariably: 'The sort I should hate to have to hunt!'.

A few years ago it was the vogue for some people to decry the hunter-bred horse (of the type of Foxhunter, Merely-a-Monarch, Sunsalve, Laurieston, Starlight, and Cornishman V, to name but a few jumpers and eventers of Olympic class) by premium stallions and agitate for 'warm-blood' stallions to be made available: warm-bloods being German or sometimes French cold-bloods (cart or draught horses) with infusions (though never enough) of Thoroughbred blood.

I have always found the really knowledgeable people to be cavalry officers and dealers; the latter because they thrive or starve in direct ratio to their knowledge of the horse. First I asked Archie Thomlinson, who in all the 35 years I have known him has never told me an untruth of which I have been aware, if he ever got asked for a warm-blooded horse. 'Quite honestly', he replied from his home near Ripon in North Yorkshire, 'I have never owned one. When my father was dealing he put me right off German horses when he told me that by the time they had gone 50 yards into a ploughed field they wanted to stop and walk — no guts! So I've never bothered with them.'

Next I asked Captain Brian Parry at Oakham. In the 1930s he was in business with his father, the late Victor Parry of Cheltenham. At one time they imported a lot of German horses, which certainly looked the part. 'But it didn't work out — in our opinion they were no good. They aren't bred the same as they are here or in Ireland. They have got to have a certain amount of instinct, inborn, to be good hunters. England and Germany are two very different countries, and the horses are as different as the people. They have a lot of courage — look at their show jumpers going down to a massive big wall — in many ways they are very brave horses: they go like the clappers till something goes wrong. Then they just die on you.

'English horses have very much the same temperament as Englishmen; unlike the Germans, they won't take a lot of regimenting. Klaus Wagner, one of their top 3-day-event riders, has bought a lot of horses from me. He says the German horses are soft, and therefore no good for the 3-day event. Oddly enough, he can't ride English horses — he is somewhat dictatorial and they resent him. But his son, who has been to Bertie Hill on Exmoor, gets on with our horses very well.

'You never see people buying German horses to win 'chases — it's the same thing. If I wanted a top show jumper I might well buy a German horse, but I'd never buy one to take hunting. Why don't you ask the Duke of Beaufort if he would have enjoyed hunting his hounds off a German horse 25 years ago? I'd love to hear his answer! I daresay they're all right if you don't want to gallop.'

Captain George Rich was never asked for German horses in Leicestershire, either. 'But I did have a good one once. A friend sent him over from Germany and I sold him to Jack Talbot-Ponsonby, when he was still in the Pytchley country. I only ever had one other and he really died on you. I got him in Ireland and sold him into the Cottesmore country. He's still there today — but I never told the owner that he was German.'

From the dealers I went to Colonel Neil Foster, then Senior Joint Master of the Grafton. 'The German horses are all right for 15 minutes on a good day; then they fade. I daresay they are quite adequate, too, for a below-average day with a lot of starting and stopping. But if you want to stay with hounds on a good day, you've got to have a horse with fire in his belly!'

Major-General Sir Evelyn Fanshawe added: 'I believe, the older I get, that the majority of our "real good hunters" stem from our wonderful indigenous pony stock. Look at the number of ponies you see going top of a hunt carrying a lady or a thrusting child. Has anyone ever seen a carthorse of any breed going with the leaders in any field? — I never have! A pony can gallop and jump — a Thoroughbred and a pony mare can produce anything!'

The versatility of the stock bred by HIS premium stallions is in no way short of miraculous, including as it does Grand National winners (1960 Merryman II by Carnival Boy, 1969 Highland Wedding by Question, 1971 Specify, by Specific, 1981 Aldaniti, by Derek H); Olympic gold medallists (1952 Foxhunter, by Erehwemos, 1968 and 1972 Cornishman V, by Golden Surprise, and 1972 Laurieston, by Happy Monarch); World Championships (1970 Cornishman V); European Championships (1967 Cornishman V, 1977 Severn Valley, by Iron Ore, 1968 Merely-a-Monarch, by Happy Monarch, 1977 George, by St Georg, 1961 Sunsalve, by Skoiter); and countless lesser awards such as the King George V Cup (Foxhunter 1948, 1950 and 1953), Badminton (1979 Killaire, by Carnactic) etc., almost *ad infinitum*.

While it is excellent that competitive riders can turn the British hunting/riding horse into a top-level competition horse (Sheila Willcox's Law and Order helped Canada to win the World 3-Day Event Championship in Lexington, Kentucky, in 1978, while Power Game (by Game Rights) helped

West Germany to win the silver medals) it is sad that there are those who are constantly belittling the work of the HIS, denigrating the premium stallions, praising Dutch and German horses at the expense of the British, casting covetous eyes at the annual Levy Board Grant and clamouring for Continental efficiency. If ever the breeding of British horses ceased to be a matter of private enterprise and became the perogative of salaried officials, the warmblood supporters would pull off a bloodless coup, to gallop into the ground forever in such suburban fields as remain unoccupied by housing estates.

But it is inconceivable that the Society will, in its second century, set at naught the work of the first by bastardising the breed with Dutch or German blood, though obviously individuals are free to import whatever blood they choose. Those whose wish is to go across country will not look beyond the Irish Draught, the Cleveland Bay (Britain's equivalent of the warm-blood) or the larger indigenous breeds of pony such as the Connemara or the Highland or the Welsh cob, which has produced horses like Merely-a-Monarch, who won both Badminton and Burghley, and High and Mighty, who won Badminton with Sheila Willcox in 1957 and 1958.

Appendices

APPENDIX I

Presidents of the Society

1886 The Earl of Coventry

1887 Colonel Sir Nigel Kingscote, KCB, GCVO

1888 The Duke of Portland

1889 Walter Gilbey

1890 Lord Tredegar, MFH

1891 Lord Middleton, MFH

1892 The Hon. T. W. Fitzwilliam, MFH

1893 Major W. H. Fife

1894 Colonel J. F. Hornby

1895 J. P. Cross

1896 Lt.-Col. the Hon. W. H. Allsopp

1897 The Earl of Yarborough

1898 Lord Wenlock

1899 Lt.-Col. G. C. Ricardo

1900 J. C. Straker, MFH

1901 Colonel Sir Nigel Kingscote, KCG, GCVO

1902 Capt. H. Heywood-Lonsdale

1903 Sir Walter Gilbey, Bart.

1904 The Hon. E. S. Douglas-Pennant

1905 Colonel Victor Van De Weyer

1906 HRH Prince Christian of Schleswig-Holstein, KG

1907 Romer Williams

1908 Col. the Hon. Charles Byng

1909 W. Hew Dunn

1910 R. G. Carden

1911 The Hon. Alexander Parker, MFH

1912 Lord Middleton, MFH

1913 Lt.-Col. the Earl of Feversham

1914 Sir Merrik R. Burrell, Bart.

1915 Sir Gilbert Greenall, Bart., CVO (later Lord Daresbury)

1916 Lt.-Col. David Davies, MP, MFH

1917 Lt.Col. Sir John Gilmour, Bart., DSO, MP

1918 Lord Penrhyn

1919 Sir Walter Gilbey, Bart.

1920 Capt. T. L. Wickham-Boynton

1921 Lord Wyfold

1922 HRH The Prince of Wales, KG

1923 Lord Mildmay of Flete, PC

1924 Lord Saltoun, CMG

1925 The Hon. Alexander Parker, OBE

1926 Major Denis St. G. Daly, MFH

1927 Lord Daresbury, CVO

1928 HRH The Duke of York, KG

1929 Lt.-Col. the Earl of Harewood, KG

1930 Col. C. Spence-Colby, CMG, DSO

1931 Sir Walter Gilbey, Bart.

1932 Major Gordon B. Foster

1933 Col. Lord Digby, DSO, MC

1934 Col. Earl Fortescue, KG, CB, OBE, MC

1935 HRH the Duke of Gloucester, KG

1936 Lord Middleton, MC

1937 Sir Robert Spencer-Nairn, Bart.

1938 Lord Mildmay of Flete, PC

1939 1945 Cecil G. Angles

1946–47 The Duke of Norfolk, KG

1948 Col. C. Spence-Colby, CMG, DSO

1949 Hon. Alexander Parker, OBE

1950 Major Sir Reginald Macdonald-Buchanan, KCVO, MBE, MC

1952 The Earl of Halifax, MFH

1953 The Lord Margadale of Islay, MFH

1954 The Duke of Northumberland, KG, MFH

1955 HRH The Duke of Gloucester, KG

1956 Colonel The Lord Digby, KG, DSO, MC

1957 The Lord Willoughby de Broke, MC

1959 The Marquess of Abergavenny, OBE

1960 Colonel Sir Ian Walker-Okeover, Bart., DSO

1961 HM Queen Elizabeth The Queen Mother

1962 Thurstan Holland-Martin

1963 J. R. Hugh Sumner, CBE, DL

1964 HRH The Duchess of Gloucester

1965 Major-General Sir Evelyn Fanshawe, CBE, CB, DL

1966 Major Sir Reginald Macdonald Buchanan, KCVO, MBE, MC

1967 E. G. E. Griffith

1968 The Duke of Beaufort, KG, GCVO, MFH

1969 The Viscount Knutsford

1970 Lt-Col. R. Myddelton, MVO, DL

1971 The Lord Margadale of Islay, TD

1972 Colonel Sir Thomas F. Meynick, Bart., TD, DL

1973 The Earl of Stradbroke

1974 Colonel G. T. Hurrell, OBE

1975 Major-General Sir Evelyn Fanshawe, CB, CBE, DL

1976 HRH The Princess Anne, Mrs Mark Phillips

1977 Lt.-Col. G. A. Murray Smith, DL, MFH

1978 John Cory, DL

1979 Lt.-Col. J. E. S. Chamberlayne, DL

1980 Lt.-Col. N. P. Foster, DL

1981 J. B. Sumner

1982 Lt.-Col. Sir John Miller, KCVO, DSO, MC

1983 The Countess of Feversham, MFH

1984 Her Majesty The Queen

1985 Lt.-Col. Sir Watkin Williams-Wynn, Bart., CBE, MFH

1986 Captain John Macdonald-Buchanan, MC

APPENDIX II

———◆❋◆———

Winners of the King George V Champion Challenge Cup

1911   Berrill, by Rouge Dragon, owned by H. A. Cholmondeley
       Reserve: Drummond's Pride, by Drummond, owned by John Drage

1912   King's Courtship, by Matchmaker, owned by Donald Fraser
       Reserve: Wales, by Belgrave, owned by Lord Middleton

1913   King's Courtship, by Matchmaker, owned by Capt. T. A. Wickham-Boynton
       Reserve: Birk Gill, by Marcion, owned by Eustace Barlow

1914   Birk Gill, by Marcion, owned by Eustace Barlow
       Reserve: Gilgandra, by Gallinule, owned by the Compton Stud

1915   Birk Gill, owned by Capt. T. L. Wickham-Boynton and H. A. Cholmondeley
       Reserve: Himan, by King's Messenger, owned by the Compton Stud

1916   Birk Gill
       Reserve: Gilgandra

1917   Rathurde, by Tredennis, owned by Capt. T. L. Wickham-Boynton
       Reserve: Gilgandra

1918   Rathurde
       Reserve: Gay Lally, by Lally, owned by the Compton Stud

1919   Rathurde
       Reserve: Gay Lally

1920   Gay Lally
       Reserve: Scarlet Rambler, by William Rufus, owned by Capt. T. L. Wickham-Boynton

1921   Gay Lally
       Reserve Scarlet Rambler

1922   Gay Lally
       Reserve: Scarlet Rambler

1923   Gay Lally
       Reserve: Scarlet Rambler

1924   Scarlet Rambler
       Reserve: Gay Lally

1925   Ardavon, by Ardoon, owned by Capt. T. L. Wickham-Boynton and H. A. Cholmondeley.

1926 Ardavon
   Reserve: London Cry, by Call of the Wild, owned by His Majesty The King

1927 Hector, by St. Amant, owned by Capt. T. L. Wickham-Boynton
   Reserve: Ardavon

1928 Brigand, by Lemburg, owned by Stephen Mumford Jnr. and Capt. D. Blew-Jones
   Reserve: Hector

1929 Brigand
   Reserve: Orthos, by Orby, owned by H. C. Callaby

1930 Brigand
   Reserve: Spearwort, by Spearmint, owned by H. C. Callaby

1931 Monkford, by Swynford, owned by Joseph Staien and Sons

1932 Ballynahinch, by Captivation, owned by Joseph Staien and Sons
   Reserve: Monksford

1933 Pal o' Mine, by Captain Cuttle, owned by Stephen Mumford
   Reserve: Double Bed, by Feather Bed, owned by Stephen Mumford

1934 Mankato, by Tredennis, owned by Southwold Hunt Sire Association
   Reserve: Ardavon

1935 Mankato
   Reserve: Warrington, by Theo Bold, owned by Miss D. M. Grayson

1936 Silver Fox C, by Courtesan II. owned by C. Roy Parsons
   Reserve: Jean's Dream, by Planet, owned by Capt. T. L. Wickham-Boynton, MFH

1937 Dick Swiveller, by Captain Cuttle, owned by Capt. R. Macdonald-Buchanan, MC MFH
   Reserve: Haine, by Hainault, owned by C. R. Parsons

1938 Jean's Dream, by Planet, owned by Captain. T. L. Wickham-Boynton, MFH
   Reserve: Haine

1947 Timur, exhibited by C. E. Edwards

1948 Henry Tudor, exhibited by W. J. Manning

1949 Henry Tudor

1950 War Star, exhibited by A. C. Mumford

1951 Court Nez, exhibited by A. C. Mumford

1952 Cul-de-Sac, exhibited by A. C. Mumford

1953 Erin's Pride, exhibited by W. J. Manning

1954 Inchydoney, exhibited by A. C. Mumford

1955 Court Nez, exhibited by A. C. Mumford

1956 Your Fancy, exhibited by Wm. Mumford & Sons

1957 Starlata, exhibited by A. C. Mumford

1958	Parting Shot, exhibited by A. C. Mumford
1959	Border Legend, exhibited by W. J. Manning
1960	Border Legend, exhibited by W. J. Manning
1961	Parlehay, exhibited by The Buccleuch Hunter Breeding Society
1962	Solon Morn, exhibited by L. B. Bloomfield
1963 1964 1965	Bleep, exhibited by A. C. Mumford
1966	Quality Fair, exhibited by A. C. Mumford
1967	Regent, exhibited by W. Powell
1968	Brother, exhibited by J. T. Q. Snell
1969 1970 1971 1972	Quality Fair, exhibited by A. C. Mumford
1973	Armagnac Monarch, exhibited by Mrs G. R. Maundrell
1974	Arthur Sullivan, exhibited by A. L. Masters
1975	Right Flare, exhibited by W. J. Lock
1976	Royal Clipper, exhibited by A. C. Mumford
1977	Major Sol, exhibited by Mrs B. A. Roberts
1978	Saunter, exhibited by J. T. Q. Snell
1979	Current Magic, exhibited by G. H. Lloyd
1980	Osiris, exhibited by L. S. Ivens
1981	Saunter, exhibited by J. T. Q. Snell
1982	Current Magic, exhibited by T. M. Abram
1983	Current Magic, exhibited by T. M. Abram
1984	Barley Hill, exhibited by L. P. Massarelra
1985	Shaab, exhibited by T. Le Grice
1986	Shaab, exhibited by T. Le Grice

APPENDIX III

Winners of the Edward, Prince of Wales's Cup for Champion Young Stock

1922 McMorran Bros's Golden Crest

1923 Major and Mrs E. A. Dodd's Elsenham Dawn

1924 Philip Burnett's Artful

1925 Major W. H. Rawnsley's Tarpaulin

1926 Major W. H. Rawnsley's Tarpaulin

1927 Miss Violet Wellesley's Eiffel

1928 Mrs L. M. Smith-Ryland's Snail III

1929 Mrs Harry Frank's Gorse Bush

1930 T. G. Phelps' Cresselly

1931 T. G. Phelps' Cresselly

1932 Mrs Howard Mander's Dunkirk II

1933 Mrs J. D. Paton's Rocket

1934 The Lord Digby's Easter Vision

1935 Major H. C. Meredith's Broadward

1936 H. L. Cotterill's Lucky Hand

1937 Major Gordon B. Foster's Firefly II

1938 Mrs Howard Mander's Demas

1939 Major Gordon B. Foster's Gadfly

1947 Mrs E. M. Vaughan's Crackle

1948 F. A. Cheyney's Twitch

1949 T. W. Jones' Son of Sieg

1950 J. R. Hindley's Prospero

1951 J. R. Hindley's Guardsman II

1952 N. Crow's Prenotion

1953 B. Selby's State Fair

1954 N. Crow's Devotion

1955 Messrs. J. E. Bennion & Sons Ballyhoo

1956 Messrs. J. E. Bennion & Sons Ballyhoo

1957 F. W. Furness' Arch Guard

1958 N. Crow's Mic Mac

1959 J. G. Henson's Boothby

1960 Mrs M. H. Tollit's Colprin

1961 N. Crow's Berkeley

1962 N. Crow's Charmaine III

1963 N. Crow's Goldsmith

1964 N. Crow's Goldsmith

1965 Mrs M. Latham's Sunset Strip

1966 J. Griffin's Blue Lane

1967 Mrs B. N. Morton's Hill Guide

1968 Lt.-Col. and Mrs A. B. Coote's Budget

1969 Lt.-Col. and Mrs A. B. Coote's Budget

1970 Mrs N. Arrowsmith-Brown's The Likely Lad

1971 A. Crow's Master Nulli

1972 N. Crow's Fresco

1973 Mrs M. F. Cail's Lucky Strike

1974 L. S. Ivens's and Mrs P. Jackson's Sammy Dasher

1975 Mrs B. A. Roberts' Highfield Diplomat

1976 N. Crow's Solgar

1977 Messrs. I. Thomas and S. Jeffries's Fair Sport

1978 Miss S. Willcox's Henry James

1979 P. Hobbs's Hilly Leys

1980 Creative Television Workshops' Keyston Kelly

1981 Mrs H. S. Jeffs's Son of Rouge

1982 W. D. Kellow's Manor Court

1983 Mrs H. H. Hindle and Miss A. Riddiough's Bright and Fair

1984 W. D. Kellow's Fairfield Manor

1985 W. D. Kellow's Fairfield Manor

APPENDIX IV

The responsibilities of judges and stewards

A FEW YEARS ago Mr E. G. E. Griffith made some extremely cogent and pertinent notes for the HIS on the responsibilities of judges and stewards. They were published for the guidance of newcomers, and His Grace the Duke of Beaufort wrote a foreword in which he warmly commended them, saying, 'How I wish that when I first accepted to judge, I had been able to study something of the sort, instead of relying on a few words of advice from a more experienced friend. Never was it more important than it is today to observe the suggestions and rules in this pamphlet, both in and out of the ring. We live in an age of ever-increasing competition and criticism; much of the latter is often unjustified, because the man in the centre must see more than the spectator outside. But if shows are to continue in a happy atmosphere, there must be confidence among competitors that the judges are doing the right thing in the right way.'

Some notes for judges

The ladies and gentlemen whose names figure on the HIS Judges list enjoy the confidence of the Council, and there can be no question of dictating to them how they should carry out their duties. It may be helpful, however, to outline some of the problems that can arise in the showring and to suggest how these problems may be solved. Certainly it is of the first importance to give to the general public a clear picture of the Judges' duties and responsibilities, and thereby to encourage an atmosphere of informed and intelligent understanding in place of the fog of criticism, all too often uninformed, foolish and ill-natured, which seems to be the current fashion. With these ends in view, the following notes are presented.

Showing differs from most other forms of competition. On the race course the horses pass the post in a definite order and thus give a definite result. In the showring, the order is merely a matter of opinion, and the result might be equally 'correct' if the first 3 or 4 animals were placed in as many different ways. Different judges will have different ideas of value and different preferences as to type, but provided that they do not depart from sound basic principles, and provided that they can give good reason for their decisions, these differences of emphasis are a potent factor in breed improvement.

Exhibitors have the right to know the names of the judges under whom they are to show. It follows therefore and if, as must occasionally happen, Judges other than those advertised have to officiate, the exhibitors concerned should be informed of the change by the show authorities.

The suggestion has been made — and occasionally put into practice — that after each class the judge should explain the placings to the public. (There must be occasions when he would love to say exactly what he thought of exhibits — and exhibitors!) Whatever may be the merits or demerits of such a plan, a judge should always be prepared to tell an exhibitor (who approaches him politely) why he placed his exhibit as he did. Nowadays he must also be prepared to give some information to the Press, but he should confine his remarks to a general description of the classes and avoid individual criticism of animals. Further than this, he will obviously discuss the classes — *after* judging — with friends and acquaintances. *But* he must be very careful what he says and how he says it. Commonsense and common courtesy demand that he should refrain from criticism, remembering that it is just as easy to say pleasant things as to condemn. Nothing can be more undignified and nothing can give greater offence than loud reference to some 'awful animal' — inevitably heard by, or repeated to, the owner of that animal.

Before and during judging, the judge will be wise to show clearly that he is entirely independent of outside influence. This is really a matter of public relations and the judges' public image. Thus he will not even look at a catalogue before he enters the ring; once in the ring, he will be at pains to avoid giving the slightest impression that he may be obtaining information from his steward, or that his steward is influencing his judgement; if he wishes to talk to friends at the ringside, it 'looks better' to do so after a class is finished rather than while it is being judged. It is a convention, too, that the judge should avoid tête-a-tête conversations with exhibitors in the ring, and it should be a rule that he should not enquire how an animal is bred until judging is completed.

It is generally accepted that (apart from some special cases) the judge should approach his task with an entirely fresh and open mind, and that he should be given no information as to the identity of the animals before him. It is probable, of course, that some of these animals, their histories and their previous performances may be familiar to him, but this in no way prevents him from weighing their merits against those which he sees for the first time. Much nonsense is talked about 'form', but it is equally unreasonable to 'follow the form' slavishly as it is to take a mischievous delight in upsetting it. It should not be forgotten, however, that a 'form horse' which has won at several leading shows under different judges is probably a pretty good one that wins on merit.

It is, very properly, taken for granted that nobody should judge an animal in which he has an interest. The problem remains to judge the word 'interest', and to draw a line between what is permissible and what is not. Clearly one cannot judge an animal in which one has any share of ownership or of monetary interest; surely one should not judge an animal which one has bred or that one has owned or sold. Beyond this, the matter must be left to the judge's conscience and commonsense. He must decide whether he can (and whether he wishes to) judge the stock of an exhibitor with whom he may have family or business connections; he cannot avoid judging the stock of friends and acquaintances. The stallion owner presents a special case, quite different from that of the breeder, and it would seem altogether unreasonable that he should be forbidden to judge the stock of one of his stallions. He will often be unaware of their identity, and in any case, if he is on the judges' list at all, he should be trusted to 'play fair', while his knowledge and experience is too valuable to lose.

What then should a judge do when an animal in which he 'has an interest' comes before him? (The words 'has an interest' may be interpreted on the lines of the previous paragraph.) It has been suggested that he should stand down altogether for that particular class, but since such action would affect all the other exhibitors, who have the right to expect to be judged by him, it is obviously preferable that he should only refuse to judge that one animal which has caused him concern. The following procedure is therefore proposed: As soon as the judge recognises, or thinks he recognises, an animal in which he has an interest, he should say to his steward: 'Is that number X such and such an animal, because if so, I bred it (or once owned it), and therefore I cannot judge it. I will place the rest of the class, and you must then get someone else to place number X. I shall leave the ring while he does so.' In actual fact it may not be necessary for the judge to leave the ring, but it is essential to show the public that he is not taking any part in judging the animal in which he may have had an interest. It may be objected that there will be no qualified person available to perform this duty, but in fact, somebody can usually be found, even if the steward has to call in a senior official to find him. Whether the 'new' judge comes into the ring for the whole judging of the class (which will certainly help him to form an opinion) or whether he comes in at the end to place number X would seem to be immaterial. Where there are two judges, of course, there is no difficulty. The one judge concerned takes no part in placing number X. The most difficult case occurs in a riding class for which there is only one judge. Here the 'new' judge called in must ride all the horses which require to be ridden; the original judge will not ride number X.

And what alternative is there? It would be a welcome reform if this procedure (or a better one if it can be found) were recommended as 'standard practice'.

Yet another problem: must the judge ride every animal in a ridden class or 'run out' every animal in and 'in-hand' class? The answer must depend on the time available.

Clearly the judge must fully test and examine all those animals that are 'in the running' for a prize; clearly too he must satisfy himself that those which he does not test so fully are definitely not in the running for a prize. It is, of course, desirable that the judge should ride or 'run up' as many animals as possible — all of them if time allows — particularly at local and smaller shows. Where there are 2 riding judges, it may be convenient for both to ride 'the tops' and each to ride half of the remainder. If unexpected quality is found among the remainder, both of the judges can ride 'the discovery'. In any case the judge must have a good look (and that means more than a cursory glance) at every exhibit, so that no disgruntled exhibitor can say 'he never even looked at mine'. The final answer is 'ride as many as you think necessary, and as many more as you have time for'. You are *not* bound to ride them all, nor are you bound to run up every exhibit in the in-hand classes. Indeed if the classes are large it is impossible to do so and keep within the time-table. Obviously if judges disrupt the time-table by taking an unreasonably long time over their task, show societies will be tempted to reduce their classification.

It is well-known that some judges seem to get through their work more quickly and in a more businesslike fashion than others, not necessarily because they are more knowledgeable than their fellows, but because they insist on proper order and method in the ring and have evolved an efficient time-saving technique, the objects of which are:

(1) To keep the judge's mind clear.
(2) To give exhibitors and the general public a clear idea of what the judge is trying to do.
(3) To save every moment in time — without hurry and without fuss.
(4) To spare exhibitors from unnecessary walking round the ring.
(5) Most important of all — to maintain a happy and cheerful atmosphere.

'Imagine yourself, then, Mr Would-be-Judge, standing in the ring waiting for an in-hand class.

'Here they come: time to put your principles into practice, and to realise that you must work hard, concentrating all your faculties on your job. And that job begins as soon as the first animal enters the ring. Please, please don't let them walk round and round while you have a nice talk to your steward. If you are told that there are some more to come, fill in your time by a preliminary inspection of those already there. Normally, of course, your class should file in without delay, and as each exhibit passes before you, you must make up your mind what you think of it — an instant impression of the whole animal. This art of rapid, almost instantaneous judgement is something akin to the action of a camera — it can be acquired with study and practice; it must be acquired by the would-be judge.

'By the time the whole class has walked past once, you should have a rough idea of how they will finally be placed: it is surprising how often one's first impressions turn out to be correct. Let them walk around again while you watch closely, but for goodness' sake do not keep them walking round and round the ring till the exhibitors droop with weariness and exasperation, and you yourself grow dizzy from their circling. If, after a reasonable amount of walking round, you can see your way to 'pull in' the exhibits roughly in order of merit, you should do so without delay. If you require more time, halt the class, take your time, and pull them in from their standing positions. Before the pull-in you may like to have the exhibits trotted past you, but remember that not all the leaders will be youthful athletes, so do not ask them to run too far.

'Such, then, is the procedure for a normal class. With a very large class one may need to adopt a plan to avoid being swamped by sheer weight of numbers. In short, one must divide the sheep from the goats — the good from the less good — as a first step. Either one may bring in 'the sheep' in the usual way, leaving the residue or 'goats' to form a second line, or, if the class is exceptionally large and appears to contain few outstanding animals, one may start at the other end, bring in the 'goats' first and line them up, thus enabling one to see the 'sheep' clearly. In either case, these 'goats' — or 'second line troops', as one might more politely call them — though out of sight must not be out of mind. Have a good look at them and make sure that none of them is worthy of promotion.

'Your first line is now drawn up in a rough order of expected merit. No undue haste now, but certainly no time to waste. Do you really want to walk down the line and look at each animal? You have already seen them and you are just going to have them out for detailed examination. Save time and have the first one out straight away, and go on saving time by seeing that your steward has each animal ready in turn to take his predecessor's place.

'Now comes the time when your first general inspection must be confirmed or corrected by due attention to details. Each horse is brought out to stand 'broadside on' before you; run your eyes all over him, walk round and see him from both sides and both ends. You must decide whether you want to put a hand on his legs or pick a foot up. You are responsible for seeing that the prizes are not given to obviously unsound horses, and, though final responsibility for soundness should lie with the official veterinary surgeon, he will only be called at your request. The ringside crowd will always spot a curb, but your examination is needed to disclose such things as spavins (how seldom they are looked for), and those ringbones and sidebones which occasionally occur. Don't forget the feet, and in a brood mare class at least have some idea as to whether a mare is 14 or 40 years old. Suggestions for dealing with unsoundness are given in the final paragraph of these judges' notes.

Your inspection finished (your trained eye should have told you a lot in a very short time), have the horse walked away from you, then trotted back to you and past you. Walking away, you can see whether he goes straight (if in doubt have him walked towards you at the conclusion of his trot past) and what sort of hind leg he has, (look carefully for the weak thigh and crooked hind leg); trotting back, you will judge the straightness or otherwise of his movement till, as he passes you, you have his complete picture in your mind.

'You have now seen all your selected front line, and you may have decided on some alterations in the order. Perhaps you have already promoted some that pleased you as they gave their show. One more walk round, you can compare them better now that they are almost in order of merit. Are you satisfied? Let them stand still, nose to tail, one behind the other, and you stand back a bit to see them better. Very little between the first three. Change over the second and third? Stand them in line one behind the other. A last keen look. Make up your mind and then call them in.'

With obvious modifications, this method of procedure can be applied to the ridden classes. The horses enter the ring at the walk, and continue to walk until the judge has seen them all and 'got them in his eye'. Without undue delay they then trot, canter and gallop, a signal for each increase of pace being given by the steward at the judge's direction. When the judge is satisfied that he has seen all he wants, he will instruct the steward to signal 'walk' and to direct the class to walk in a conveniently small circle, from which they will be called in and drawn up in approximate order of merit. Now, (as opposed to in-hand classes, where it has been suggested that the practice is a waste of time) the judge will be well advised to walk down the line and have a quick look at the horses before deciding which ones of them to ride. (Some judges think that, as in the in-hand classes, this *is* a waste of time and can be dispensed with.) After the judge has finished riding, the saddles are removed and the horses brought out before the judge fox examination and 'run-up' as in the in-hand classes. Finally, remounted, the class can walk round in a convenient circle, whence they are called in for placing and awards.

How much time should a judge devote to riding each horse? The answer is — sufficient time to form a just opinion of 'the ride' in all paces, mouth, manners and no more. The judge who appears to be going for a long hack in the ring will bore the spectators and play havoc with the time-table. In a big ring it has been suggested that it may be sufficient to walk from the centre to the side of the ring, trot down the long side, canter round the end, and stride on once round the whole ring. The judge must decide whether, and how much, he wishes to test his mount on both reins; many judges think it is essential to do so. Needless to say, a display that might become a hack is not required in a hunter class.

Mention of movement 'on both reins' raises the point that it is customary for all classes to be shown on the right rein — i.e., right-handed round the ring. This is an obvious advantage in-hand, since the leader is on the side away from the judge and does not hide the horse. For riding classes, the reason may lie in long-standing custom, based perhaps on an almost forgotten tradition.

The judge is responsible for ensuring as far as possible that prizes are not given to unsound horses. In the in-hand classes, unsoundness will be confined to actual lameness or to defects such as curbs, spavins etc., defects of the eye and parrot mouth. In the riding classes there is the further complication of unsoundness in wind. The judge has a heavy responsibility as he must come to the right decision, and, at the same time, avoid the danger of unjustifiably condemning any particular exhibit. He has therefore certain alternatives. He can decide for himself whether the animal is unsound and, having done so, can leave it out of the awards, or he can tell the exhibitor of his suspicions and give him the choice of withdrawing or standing down, or else of having his animal examined by the veterinary surgeon, whose decision, once he has been called in, must be final. It is often extremely difficult to detect unsoundness of wind unless the horse is actually ridden, and the official veterinary surgeon may not always be prepared to ride. It will be seen, therefore, how very difficult is the task of the judge.

Index

Note: Names listed in the Appendices are not indexed.

Abram, Max 188, 189, 248
Adye, Capt. M. S. 76, 92
Ainsworth, Sir Thomas 220
Aldin, Cecil 108
Alexander, Lt. Col. F. D. 138, 169
Alexandra, Queen 62, 84, 87
Allen, Miss Diana Russell 138
Allenby, Lord 247
Anderson, Thomas 37
Angus, Maxwell 22
Annaly, Lord 85
Ansell, Mike 153
Anstruther, A. W. 59, 60, 61, 62, 65, 112
Anthony, Jack 167
Appleyard, Mr 180, 243
Archer-Houblon, Mrs Doreen 208
Arkwright, J. P. 107, 130
Armstrong, Charles 2, 4, 5, 6, 7, 11 ff.
Atkins, Jock 171 ff.

Badge, F. H. (Freddie) 228
Bailward, Capt. J. 134
Bainbridge, Mrs R. C. 61
Baird, James 154
Baird, Hon. Mrs James 168, 208, 246
Balfe, Maj. M. J. 31
Balfour, Doug 162
Balfour, Frank 167
Ball, Patrick 240
Ballard, Jean 180
Bamber, Jack 184
Bankart, S. Nevins 39
Banks, Trevor 250
Barclay, M. E. 145
Barker, David 186, 192, 206, 207, 243, 251
Barker, George 220
Barker, Stanley 158
Barkley, R. A. 30
Barlow, E. H. 26, 31, 33, 84, 85, 87
Barratt, Maj. Stanley 151
Barratt, Mrs 151
Barrett, John 33
Barry, Edmund G. 25
Barry, J. Harold 22
Bathurst, 7th Earl 145

Beaufort, Duke of 145, 160, 198, 255
Beaumont, Maj. Michael 242
Beaumont, Mrs Michael 228
Beckwith-Smith, Mrs Peter 232, 242
Behrens, Maj. Clive 134
Bell, Ikey 167
Bellaney, Ernest 124, 129, 133, 134
Bennett, T. L. 42
Beresford, Lord Marcus 10
Bevan, Geoffrey 215
Biddlecombe, Walter 237
Birdwood, Lt. Col. G. C. 137
Birkbeck, Maj. Gen, Sir W. H. 88
Bishop, B. Giles 131
Bishop, Vivian 189
Blenkiron, Mr 106
Bletsoe, Jack 161
Blew-Jones Capt. D. 137, 182
Bloomfield. L. B. 184
Boden, Henry 22
Bolton, Duke of 22
Bolton, Brig. Lyndon 176
Bonner, Harry 131, 161, 176, 184, 199, 230 ff.,
    233, 242, 246
Bonnet, R. A. 244
Bourne, Mrs David 163, 211
Bowden-Smith, Brig. 'Bogey' 163, 226
Bowen, Harry 179
Bowlby, A. S. 108, 131
Bowrick, Col. Malcolm 'Peach' 163, 175, 215
Bowrick, Maj. Peter 175 ff.
Bowser, F. E. 85
Bradley, Caroline 219
Bradley, Percy 209, 210
Bradley, Thomas 26
Bradney, Frank 167
Brake, Arthur 164
Brassey, Harold 34
Brenchley, H. S. 130
Brocklebank, Maj. Gen. 66
Brocklehurst, Maj. Gen. 60, 66, 67, 79, 82
Brooke, Geoffrey 158
Brown, Denis 219
Brown, John 107
Brown, Reg 228

Brown, W. 87
Browne, Capt. Glen 244
Browne, Mrs Glen 245
Bryan, Bill 246
Buckenham, Frank 134
Bullard, R. 134, 137
Bullen, Sarah 211
Bunn, Douglas 233, 245
Burn, Clive 146
Burnett, Philip 133
Burrell, Sir Merrick R. 46, 61, 67, 85, 87, 92, 108ff., 124, 129, 137, 138
Byng, Col. the Hon. Charles 38, 43, 84, 108, 118

Cail, Mrs Molly 192
Callaby, H. C. 137
Campbell, Alec 183
Campbell, Mrs D. 211
Campbell, J. R. 66, 67, 76, 78
Cant, Derek 248
Cantrell-Hubbersty, Maj. W. P. 134
Carden, R. G. 33, 34, 37, 46, 53, 78, 85, 108
Cardiff, Hon. Mrs Stella 203, 233, 250
Cardwell, Ronnie 234
Carson, S. W. 42
Carter, F. W. 64
Carter, Len 234
Carty, Paddy 192
Cash, Mrs Ned 253
Cawsey, R. P. 134
Cazalet, Maj. Peter 235
Cecil, Lord Arthur 63, 73, 76
Cecil, Capt. Lionel 215
Chambers, A. 29
Chaplin, Rt. Hon. M. 92, 106, 127
Chappell, Rex 195, 249
Charlton, A. B. 28, 36, 39, 228
Cheyney, Mr 79
Cholmondley, H. A. 61, 84, 88, 125, 134, 137, 182
Church, Brig. Sir Geoffrey 245
Clarke, Mr Jimmy and Lady Eileen 210
Cleghorn, Col. J. R. 237
Cleminson, Bert 174, 199, 218, 232
Clonchy, George 22
Coates, W. 33
Codd, John 185, 242
Collier, John 200
Combermere, Lord 4, 10
Connaught, Duke of 10
Connors, Dr Tom 233
Cooke, Capt. C. 224
Cooke, Mrs Rosemary 237, 252
Cooke, Sir William 107
Cookson, J. Sawrey 1
Cooper, W. Horace 168, 240, 245, 249
Cooper, John 37
Coote, Col. Tony 218

Cory, Herbert C. 33
Cory, John 228
Cotterill, Harry 150
Cottrell-Dormer, J. 29
Coventry, Earl of 1
Cox-Cox, Col. Gordon 164
Croft, E. H. 240, 246
Crofts, Mr & Mrs Andy 253
Crossley, E. R. 33
Crossley, Hon. Mrs R. N. 196
Crossman, Derek 237
Crossman, Douglas 173
Crow, Norman 204ff., 244, 247, 250
Cuff, Bartholomew 249
Cumberland, Duke of (Lord Barnard) 206
Cunard, Gordon 61
Curre, Sir Edward 166, 167
Curtis, Robert 61

Daly, Major Denis St. G. 130, 134, 137
Daly, Major Dermot 233
Daly, Jim 240, 241, 249
Darby, Cyril 232, 233
Darby, John 134
Daresbury, Lord see Greenall, Sir Gilbert
Daresbury, Lady 161
Darling, Fred 166
Darling, Willie 244
Darrell, James S. 28
Davies, Bert 156, 199
Davies, Ted 228
Dary, Edmund 134
de Fonblanque see Fonblanque, Brig. 'Dolly' de
de Trafford see Trafford, Sir Humphrey de
Dean, Col. and Mrs Frank 202, 247
Dennis, Lady 137
Derby, Earl of 108ff.
Dickinson, George 107, 124, 130
Digby, Lord 225
d'Inzeo, Capt. Piero 218
Dixon, Howard 184
Dixon, Oliver 134, 156, 183, 198, 215
Dodd, Mrs E. A. 131
Donaldson, Willie 202, 247
Dorman, A. J. 85, 88
Douglas-Pennant, Hon. E. S. 29
Dowley, Mrs Molly 203, 234
Downes, John 252
Drabble, Maj. Cecil 198, 232, 242
Drage, Bert 26, 232
Drage, John 26, 33, 37, 42, 62, 85, 86, 87, 137, 215, 232
Drummond, Capt. George 177
Dudgeon, Col. Joe 148, 157, 174
Dunn, Brig. Keith 163
Dunraven, Earl of 6
Durno, Bruce 220, 221

Eckley, Mr and Mrs Vivian 227
Edgdale, William 220
Edward VII, King 30
Elizabeth II, Queen 168, 177, 208, 217, 244
Ellerby, Thomas 10
Emmanuel, Victor 165
Enderby, Maj. Bill 223
Evans, Ernie 237
Evans, George 29, 177
Evans, Gerald 202, 221, 229
Ewart, Prof. 59, 64

Falmouth, Lord 19
Fanshawe, Maj. Gen. Sir Evelyn 180, 221,
    222ff., 255
Farquhar, Col. Peter 223
Farrell, David 30
Fellowes, Rt. Hon. Sir Ailwyn 92
Fenwick, Guy 39, 130
Fenwick, R. L. 42, 85
Fetherstonhaugh, Capt. C. H. D. 31, 42, 65,
    72, 78, 84, 85, 124, 126
Feversham, Lord 109
Field, Harold 234
Fife, Maj. W. H. 39, 40
Fife-Cookson, Maj. 76
Fitzgerald, Matt 134
Fitzgerald, P. 85
Fitzroy, Hon. E. A. 108
Fitzwilliam, Hon. T. W. 4
Fitzwilliam, Lord 13
Fleming, Mrs Philip 151, 230
Fonblanque, Brig. 'Dolly' de 163
Forestier-Walker, Lt. Col. R. S. 108, 130
Fortescue, Lady 168
Foster, F. W (Fred) 34
Foster, Maj. Gordon B. 137, 138
Foster, John 176
Foster, Col. Neil 176ff., 199, 247, 255
Fowler, Jack 200
Francis, C. R. 33
Francis, Dick 244
Frank, Mrs Harry 138, 184, 205
Frank, Miss Judy 250
Franks, Maj. G. 61
Fraser, Donald 84, 85, 182
Fullerton, J. S. H. 42
Furlong, C. J. 41
Furness, Mr and Mrs Frank 202, 248,250

Gale, Harry 217
Gale, William 33
Galway-Greer, Nat 176, 177, 195, 199, 201,
    204, 205, 219, 227, 231, 232, 233, 240, 244,
    245, 249
Garrard, Linda 193
Garth, Flossie 157
George V, King 62, 84, 87, 129, 141 (see also
    Wales, George Prince of)

Gibbon, Major Geoffrey 233
Gibbs, Martin 200
Gibson, Mrs George 209, 210, 233, 252
Gibson, Michael 160
Gilbey, Sir Walter 2, 3, 6, 17, 20, 85, 108
Gilbey, Mrs Oliver 211, 231
Gilmour, Major 81
Gingell, Mrs Hugh 242, 243, 244
Gittins, Harry 201
Gittins, Jack 168, 192, 200, 201, 203, 206, 232,
    243, 245, 246, 247
Glencross, Tommy 149, 158
Glencross, Mrs 149
Gloucester, Duke of 202, 219
Gold, Mrs 205
Goldman, Capt. Edy 236
Goldsworthy, E. W. 85
Goldsworthy, Maj. Gen. W. T. 61
Gosling, R. H. 108
Graham, Col. Malise 174
Granard, Lord 76
Grant-Lawson, Miss 176
Green, G. H. 38
Greenall, Sir Gilbert (Lord Daresbury) 22, 37,
    72, 84, 85, 87, 92, 107, 108, 113, 124, 128,
    134, 137, 138, 161, 201
Greene, Col. W. Raymond 108
Green-Pike, Sir Robert 145
Greer, Capt. Sir H. 119, 122, 126, 129, 137
Gretton, Nikki 211
Griffith, Eddie 150, 160, 161ff., 203
Griffith, Col. Edward Wynne 161
Griffith, Maj. Humphrey 161
Grimthorpe, Lord 175
Gupwell, Walter 220

Haggas, Mrs Bea 246
Haggie, Miss Mary 245
Haig, Field-Marshal Earl 121
Haldin, Hugh 231, 246
Halifax, Lord 217
Hallwalker, Col. 119
Hamilton, Duke of 4
Hanbury, Maj. James 192, 233
Hanbury, Mrs James 202
Hance, Capt. Jack 159, 211, 251
Handel, Tim 193
Hanley, W. P. 85, 137
Hanson, Bill 245
Hanson, Robert 245
Hardy, Gerald H. 27
Hardy, John 215
Hardy, Col. Sir Rupert 165, 208
Hardy, Hon. Lady 208
Harford, W. A. 31, 108
Harman, Col. James 214
Harris, J. W. A. 42, 108, 122, 125, 134
Harrison, J. Simons 41
Harrison, Miss R. M. 137

Harrison, Dr 200
Harwood, Guy 218
Hastings, Mrs Aubrey 159
Hastings, Lord 2
Hatfield-Harter, J. F. 30
Hayes, Seamus 236
Helme, Maj. 237
Helmsley, Viscount 46, 53, 54, 60, 66, 69, 76, 84
Henson, 'Gino' 246
Hermon-Hodge, Sir R. T. 108
Heys, James 85
Heywood-Lonsdale, Col. A. 178
Heywood-Lonsdale, Capt. H. 29
Hickey, Michael 201, 250
Hill, Frank 215
Hill, John 29, 59, 76
Hillingdon, Lord 231
Hillman, Fred 184
Hillman, T. J. 34
Hindley, Reg 240
Hoare, Maj. Bob 203
Hoare, Mrs Bob 178
Hoare, Sir Henry 42, 61, 108, 112
Hobbs, Bruce 209
Hobbs, Reg 209
Hoboken, J. 131
Hodgson, Edward 61, 86
Holden, Mrs 151
Holderness-Roddam, Jane 211, 253
Holloday, R. 242
Holmes, William 87
Hope, Willie 243, 244
Horn, Col. Trevor 163
Howie, Maj. J. N. 180ff., 243
Hudson, Thomas 107, 133
Hunloke, Lady 230
Hurrell, Col. G. T. 'Handy' 172ff., 244
Hurrell, William 244
Hurst, Maj. C. C. 64
Hurst, Mr 59
Hutchinson, T. O. 85
Hutton, Sir E. 128
Hyde, Tim 241

Ingledew, James 28
Ionides, C. P. J. 172
Ivens, 'Tub' 206

Jackson, George 168
Jackson, Mrs Olive 218
Jaffray, Bill 156
Jarrett, Gordon 204
Jarrett, Henry 204
Jeffcock, Capt. 230
Jeffs, Mrs H. F. 193
Jenkins, W. W. 37
John, T. D. 27
Johnson, Ernie 218

Johnson, Hope 156
Johnson, Noble 126
Jones, Maxie 205, 251
Jordison, William 61

Kelly, Col. 163
Kenmare, Earl of 61
Kenny, H. Davis 249
Kenny, John 42
Kent, Mrs Dinah 211
Kenyon, Geoffrey 85
Kenyon, Miles 85
Kimball, Mrs John 211
King, Col. Alexander 163
Kitchener, Lord 101
Knutsford, Viscount 145ff.

Lambarde, Maj. W. G. 61, 137, 156
Langford, Gerry 234
L'Anson, William 29
Lascelles, Lt. Col. Viscount 142
Latta, Roy 199, 242
Laurie, Lt. Col. Sir Percy 134
Lawrey, Melville 252
Leahy, Jerimiah 42
Legard, Rev. Cecil 22, 26, 208
Le Marchant, Sir Denis 233
Lester, Ray 241
Lethbridge, Dorothy 164
Lethbridge, Jack 162
Lethbridge, Capt. James 161, 162ff.
Lett, John 29
Lewis, Harry 194
Linlithgow, Lord 217
Little, Col. 86
Littledale, St. George 42
Littleworth, Jack 220
Llewellyn, Col. Harry 233
Lloyd, Graham 189
Londesbourgh, Countess of 206
Lonsdale, Earl of 33, 127, 150
Loriston-Clarke, Jennie 211
Lowe, G. S. 20
Lowther, Col. Jack 165, 176, 226
Lowther, Hon. Lancelot 210, 217
Lucas, General 163, 232
Lucas, Guy 153, 156, 157, 161
Lucas, Mrs R. 193
Lucas, Maj. 'Tiddly' 171, 199
Luttrell, Col. 1

McAldin, Willie 169
MacAndrew, E. G. 204
McCalmont, Lady Helen 150, 151, 199
McCalmont, Maj. Victor 220
McCanlis, Sally 211
McCowan, Mr and Mrs Andrew 194, 253
Macdonald-Buchanan, Capt. John 164

Macdonald-Buchanan, Maj. Sir Reginald 225, 226
McHugh, Jane 206, 247
MacIlwaine, Andrew 168, 195, 213, 216, 217, 231
McKie, Lt. Col. J. 108, 122, 125, 127, 128, 137
Mackintosh, Mrs Christopher 218
McMahon, Capt. Ronnie 253
McMorran Bros. 130, 133
McMullen, Ruth 235, 250
MacTaggart, Col. 158
Maher, James J. 124, 127
Mahony, N. D. 245
Makin, Joe 235
Mander, Mrs Howard 204
Manning, Charlie 183
Manning, Richard 186
Manning, W. J. (Bill) 183, 184, 185, 192
Mansfield, Mrs Eustace 130
Margadale, Lord 167, 225
Margolin, Ronnie 218
Marler, Mr and Mrs Christopher 180, 249
Marmont, Ronnie 245, 246, 249, 252
Marshall, Binty 199
Marshall, Bryan 199
Matson, Bob 177ff.
Matson, Richard 177, 228, 252
Matson, Mrs Rosemary 178
Maude, Anthony 37, 61
Maundrell, Mrs Beryl 187
Maundrell, George 187, 205
Maunsell Richardson, J. See Richardson, J. Maunsell
Maxwell, W. G. 85
Mellon, Dick 198
Mellon, Norah 235
Mellon, Paul 235
Meredith, Maj. Chase 161, 184, 202
Mewburn, W. Guy 61
Middleton, Capt. Bay 183
Middleton, Lord 5, 53, 54, 57, 59, 78, 84, 92, 102, 109, 110, 114, 132
Mildmay, Sir Gerald (later Lord) 108, 132
Miller, Edward Christie 167
Miller, Col. Sir John 208
Minto, Earl of 208
Moore, John 218
Moore, Tom 244
Morgan, Laurie, 195, 249
Morgan, Mrs Tom 167
Morris, Mrs P. 246
Morrison, Maj. John See Margedale, Lord
Moss, John 231
Moss, Mrs John 250
Mumford, Charlie 186, 236, 253
Mumford, Stephen 137, 182, 183, 184
Münster, Count 102
Murless, Sir Noel 227
Murphy, Dan 169

Murray, Rev. E. T. 131
Murray, Hugh 86
Murray Smith, Col. G. A. (Tony) 220ff.
Murray Smith, Peregrine 242
Mynors, C. 107

Nell, H. W. (Herbert) 131, 155
Newborough, Lord 203
Nickisson, J. L. 33, 37, 46, 61, 66, 69, 70
Nightingale, Walter 229
Norfolk, Duchess of 216, 131, 235
North, Dudley W. J. 138
Northumberland, Duke of 184, 251
Norton, Col. C. E. G. 133
Nutting, Sir Harold 151, 152, 220

O'Brien, Sir Edward 22
O'Brien, Michael 27
O'Brien, Terry 133
Oliver, Gill 237
Oliver, Mr and Mrs Leonard 237
Oliver, Robert 207, 236, 237, 245, 248, 251, 253
O'Neill, P. 138
Onslow, Lord 69
Orkney, Earl of 27, 37, 108, 124, 126
Orkney, Lady 146
Orssich, Count Robert 206, 246
Osbourne, Joe 205
Ossington, Lord 106
Owen, Donald 247

Palmer, Geoffrey 191
Parke, Tom L. 204
Parker, Hon. Alexander 37, 46, 54, 57, 60, 61, 66, 82, 92, 108, 111, 122, 130, 133, 136, 227
Parker, Sidney 202, 227
Parker, Hon. T. Cecil 85
Parkhill, Marshall 169
Parry, Capt. Brian 187, 218, 254
Parsons, Charles 20
Part, Capt. Dealtry C. 64, 65, 167
Pascoe, Sir John 205
Peake, Dick 219
Pearce, Mrs Stella 158
Peareth, W. G. 31
Pease, Mrs Nigel 211
Penberthy, Prof. 60, 82
Penrhyn, Lord 42, 108, 118
Perry, J. W. 133
Phillips, Maj. Faudel 122
Phillips, Lort 82, 84
Phillips, Capt. Mark 253
Phillpotts-Williams, Mr 59
Phipps-Hornby, Capt. Geoffrey 107, 108
Plunket, T. L. 131
Pollock, John 220
Pollock, Lady Zinnia 206, 207, 248, 250, 251
Portland, Duke of 60

Portman, Hon. Claud B. 108
Powell, Bill 195
Powell, Jim 241
Preston, N. 131
Pretyman, Hon. Mrs G. 246
Price, Sir Richard Green 38
Price, Ryan 218, 235
Prothero, Rt. Hon. R. E. 108, 118

Rackham, Paul 250
Radcliffe, G. B. 178
Rank, J. V. 230, 231
Ransom, Mrs Bill 177, 236, 246, 251
Rawding, John 250, 251
Rawnsley, E. P. 65, 72, 84
Rawnsley, Maj. W. H. 108, 134
Rea, Mr 80, 83
Rees, J. F. 85
Reid, J. 137
Reiss, Lady 233
Renton, Maj. Leslie 37
Reynard, Charles 215
Ribblesdale, Lord 6
Ricardo, Lt. Col. G. C. 29
Rich, Maj. George 218, 255
Richards, Sir Gordon 227
Richardson, Charles 86
Richardson, J. 42
Richardson, J. Maunsell 26, 37, 208, 209
Rickaby, Frank 37, 61
Ridehalgh, W. S. 61
Rigg, Sewell 78, 81, 82, 83, 84
Rob, Mr and Mrs Guy 205, 247
Roberts, Bill 188
Robinson, Col. Brian 161, 171
Robinson, E. N. 146
Robinson, Henry 145
Rohan, Eamonn 249
Rohan, Jerry 249
Rosebery, Lord 223
Rothschild, Baron 4
Rothschild, Leopold de 10, 27, 208
Rouch, W. A. 87
Ryan, John 237
Ryan, Thady 222, 248, 250

Saltoun, Lord 67, 108
Samuelson, Francis 37
Scarborough, Lord 4
Schleswig-Holstein, Prince Christian of 46
Schofield, Maj. H. N. 46
Scott, Ian 194
Scott, Mrs Hope 215
Scott, Leslie 189, 193
Scott-Hopkins, Capt. C. 134
Selbourne, Earl of 92, 109, 119
Selby, Bernard 241
Shanahan, Rog 169

Shaw, Rev. Ronald 233
Shaw, Vero 2
Shedden, John 247
Shelly, P. 33
Sheppard, Dick 177
Shine, E. B. 135
Simpson, Sir Henry 8, 26
Simpson-Hinchliffe, W. A. 43, 61
Skelton, Mrs F. C. 184
Skinner, Sally and Norman 193, 194, 195
Smallwood, Mrs Richard 250
Smith, Eph 216
Smith, Harvey 219
Smith, Horace 158, 199, 209
Smith-Bingham, Mrs 'Iso' 208
Smith-Ryland, Mrs L M. 137
Snell, Jimmy 190
Somers, Peter 245
Southampton, Lord 137
Spence-Colby, Col. C. 142
Spencer, Herbert 19
Spencer, Lord 4
Stalbridge, Lord 108
Stanier, Lady 208
Starling, F. G. 242
Stern, Sir Edward D. 124, 130
Stevenson, Arthur 218
Stevenson, J. Kennith 131, 230
Stewart, Col. Duggie 176, 233
Stewart, Plankety 217
Stillwell, Dick 236
Stokes, J. H. 28, 30, 37, 42, 43, 85, 215
Stokes, W. E. 133
Straker, A. H. 108
Straker, J. C. 22
Strawbridge, Rob 199
Studdert, Maj. C. M. 10
Sugden, Mrs Nancy 246
Sumner, Hugh 168, 195, 199, 201, 233, 242, 243, 245, 246, 249
Sumner, Joan 228
Sutton, Herbert 161, 164ff., 176
Swire, John 150, 163
Sykes, Sir Tatton 42

Taaffe, Toss 202
Talbot-Ponsonby, Col. Jack 177, 236, 255
Tatham-Warter, Miss Kit 195
Tatlow, David 235, 244, 248
Tatlow, Harry 240
Tattersall, E. Somerville 123
Taylor, Sidney 215
Thomas, Ian 192
Thomas, W. V. Howell 85
Thomlinson, Archie 196, 205, 218, 254
Thomlinson, Willie 218
Thornhill, General 4
Threlfall, Dick 192
Tindall, C. W. 41, 46, 69, 107

Tollitt, Mrs Maurice 184, 194, 195, 208, 231, 233, 249, 250
Toone, Percy 201
Toulson, Vin 206, 207, 235, 248, 250, 253
Townsend, Mrs Bettie 226
Townsend, Col. 'Mouse' 232
Trafford, Sir Humphrey de 33
Tredegar, Lord 2, 166, 231
Trench, W. T. 54
Trevithick, Wendy and Nigel 253
Trigg, Roy 203, 206, 218, 234, 244, 250, 253
Trocke, Maj. W. 31, 42
Turnor, Algernon 40, 46, 54, 59
Tweedie, Reg 203, 234

Unwin, Fred 137
Upton, Jackie 215

Valencia, Viscount 46
Vaughan, Gen. John 124
Vaughan, Miss Philippa 187
Vaughan, Mrs 231
Vernon, Lady Violet 208, 211, 235
Vicary, Col. 161, 162
Victoria, Queen 20

Wales, Edward Prince of (later King Edward VII) 10, 20
Wales, Edward Prince of (later King Edward VIII) 132, 177
Wales, George Prince of (later King George V) 30
Walker, J. B. 163, 186
Walker-Okeover, Sir Ian 164
Wallis, Maj. K. P. 155, 161, 166ff., 171, 202
Wallis, Owen C. 31
Ward, T. and H. 126, 129, 138
Warren, Mrs Peter 250
Watt, Al 167
Watts, Billy 237
Waugh, Jack 209
Weaver, Leslie 215, 217, 232

Webster, Charlie 169, 170
Weigall, Sir Archibald 158
Wellburn, T. H. 'Gunner' 34
Wellesley, Miss Violet 137
Wertheimer, Charles 33
West, A. E. 37
Westminster, Duke of 198, 215, 232
Whitburn, Mrs C. W. Sofer 137
Whitley, W. and H. 85
Wickham-Boynton, Marcus 182
Wickham-Boynton, T. L. 34, 38, 84, 85, 88, 107, 108, 122, 125, 128, 134, 137, 156, 157, 161, 162, 182, 183, 231
Widdall, G. 250
Wilkinson, Frank B. 33, 85
Williams, Dorian 250
Williams, Capt. G. Percival 178
Williams, John 42
Williams, Romer 31, 41, 43, 46, 108, 129, 130, 133, 134, 136
Williams-Wynn, Sir Watkin 177
Willoughby de Bruce, Lord 85, 131
Wilson, Clive 108
Wilson, G. M. 85
Wilson, Gerry 147
Wilson, R. W. 137
Winser, Brig. 183
Wise, Maj. F. H. 61
Wood, Col. 167
Wood, Mrs A. L. 194, 195, 201, 249, 250
Wood, Field Marshal Sir Evelyn 222
Woolvington, Lord 226
Worrall, Howard 137
Wright, C. L. 202
Wright, George 228, 229
Wright, Reggie 216
Wylie, Hon. Justice (later Judge) 134, 197, 252
Wynne Eyton, Sandy 162

York, Elizabeth Duchess of (later Queen Elizabeth) 134, 202, 235
York, George Duke of (later King George VI) 134, 138, 140, 141, 177